A Celebration of Young Poets

Rocky Mountain – Spring 2000

Creative Communication, Inc.

A Celebration of Young Poets
Rocky Mountain – Spring 2000

An anthology compiled by Creative Communication, Inc.

Published by:

CREATIVE COMMUNICATION, INC.
90 NORTH 100 EAST
LOGAN, UT 84321

ISBN 1-58876-005-7

Dedicated to the youth of the
Rocky Mountain States

Foreword

Recently I was asked by a newspaper reporter what Creative Communication does as a business. My first impulse was to say that we are a publishing company. On second thought I responded by saying that we are in the "dream fulfillment" business. Over the last eight years I have read the poetic dreams, hopes and fears of thousands of students. The joy in reading these poems is hard to describe. My imagination has been filled with images of nature. I have laughed along with poets who describe their humorous antics. I have cried with poets who describe the pain in their lives. In reading these poems, I know that behind every poem is a poet and behind every poet is a dream.

Creative Communication has received numerous letters and calls from parents, teachers and poets. Many of these have told about a life that has been changed when a poem was chosen to be published; a poet who was experiencing a difficult time in his or her life and needed a feeling of success. It might be from a divorce, a death in the family or a student who was struggling in school. In each of these cases, the publishing of a poem became a dream fulfilled. As you read these poems, visualize the poet and the message that he or she is trying to convey. But most of all, read and enjoy.

I want to thank each of the poets in this book for allowing their poem to be published. I want to thank my staff. Behind the scenes of each book are judges, typists, editors, desktop layout specialists and numerous other individuals who have provided thousands of hours to this project. Without all these individuals this book would not be possible.

Gaylen Worthen, President
Creative Communication
September 2000

Future Poetry Contests for Young Poets

There are two contests available for each school year. The Fall contest deadline is December 1st. The Spring contest deadline is April 17th. Over $2000 in prizes will be awarded in each contest. To enter, poets in grades 4-12 should submit one original entry, twenty-one lines or less. Each poem must be submitted with the student's name, grade, and home address, as well as the student's school name, Language Arts teacher's name, and school address.

Mail each entry to:
Creative Communication, Inc.
90 North 100 East
Logan, UT 84321

Or enter online at:
www.poeticpower.com

Table of Contents

Poetic Achievement Honor Schools

The following schools are recognized as receiving a "Poetic Achievement Award." This award is given to schools who have a large number of entries of which over fifty percent are accepted for publication. With hundreds of schools entering our contest, only a small percent of these schools are honored with this award. The purpose of this award is to recognize schools with excellent Language Arts programs. This award qualifies these schools to receive a complimentary copy of this anthology. In addition, these schools are eligible to apply for a Creative Communication Language Arts Grant. Grants of two hundred and fifty dollars each are awarded to further develop the writing and appreciation of poetry in our schools. Last year's Language Arts Grants were awarded to:

Eagleview Middle School – Colorado Springs, CO
and
Winnemucca Jr. High School – Winnemucca, NV

Spring 2000 Poetic Achievement Honor Schools

* Teachers who had fifteen or more poets accepted to be published

Academy Charter School
Castle Rock, CO
Amanda Blake
Miss Muckley*

Afflerbach Elementary School
Cheyenne, WY
K. Rief*

Arapahoe High School
Littleton, CO
Sandra Boldman*

Boulder City High School
Boulder City, NV
Sheryl Hammond
Pamela J. Secord

C M Russell High School
Great Falls, MT
Charles H. Rossell*

Campus Middle School
Englewood, CO
Shelley Johnson
O'Donnell
Mrs. Platt
Judy Still

Century Middle School
Thornton, CO
Margo Walsh*

Challenger School
Sandy, UT
Mrs. Casdorph*

Christ Lutheran School
Murray, UT
Merna Williams*

Colorado Academy
Denver, CO
Susan Andrews
Nancy Babbs
Peggy Butler
Betsey Coleman*
Kolsun Jackson
Erin Lott

Ecker Hill Middle School
Park City, UT
Chris Fournier*

Emery County High School
Castle Dale, UT
Wendy Whittle*

Farmington Elementary School
Farmington, UT
Jessie Enright*

Flathead High School
Kalispell, MT
Ivanna Fritz
J. Fuller
Mike McGarvey
Nancy Rose

Heatherwood Elementary School
Boulder, CO
Debbie Deem
Jane Kelley

Highland High School
Salt Lake City, UT
Gayle Cannon
Louis Christensen
Sue Southam

Holmes Middle School
Colorado Springs, CO
Carol Sebben*

Kanab Middle School
Kanab, UT
Jeanine Johnson*

Kearns-St Ann School
Salt Lake City, UT
Mr. Hayes*

Kent Denver School
Englewood, CO
Ann Bevan Hollos*

Larkspur Elementary School
Larkspur, CO
Mrs. Pottorff*

Montrose High School
Montrose, CO
Mr. Harvey
Joan Light

Morningside Elementary School
Salt Lake City, UT
Julie Page*

Mountain Ridge Jr High School
Highland, UT
Mrs. Chynoweth
Neil Johnson

Norwood Middle School
Norwood, CO
Mary Alice Vidmar*

Reedpoint Jr/Sr High School
Reedpoint, MT
Mrs. Brewer
Mrs. Kaelberer

Sage Valley Jr High School
Gillette, WY
Linda Buus*
Keri Kenyon
Mrs. Reardon

South Jordan Middle School
South Jordan, UT
Sandra Watts*

St Vincent De Paul School
Salt Lake City, UT
Chris McIntyre*

Star Valley Jr High School
Afton, WY
Shain Saberon*

Vail Mountain School
Vail, CO
Tony Shawe*

Washington Terrace Elementary School
Ogden, UT
Mrs. Butler
Mrs. Cullimore
Mrs. Hurst
Miss Spencer
Mrs. West

White Middle School
Henderson, NV
Nancy Andolina†

Young Poets
Grades 10-11-12

Eulogy

what a grand show it was
all the characters were there
and in the center of it all was he
"Good ol' Chuck" we called him
poor wishy-washy boy
now he stands at the brink
of that great abyss
he will enter its icy walls
and feel the darkness swallow him whole
and will he live on?
forever trying to kick that football
or win the ball game, or will the sea of time
wash away the memories
and someday will the youth ask who?
what an impact he had on us
the truths he showed, the depth he held
in that simple strip, now he is gone
killed by the unseen specter
never to speak again
Oh, cry child, cry, for he is dead
he is dead

Philip Armstrong
Ranum High School
Denver, CO
Grade 12

Walden

I took a trip to Walden Pond,
And sitting by its stony shore,
A peaceful thought upon me dawned
I wished that I'd have come for more.

A cabin there, I chanced to find,
A little place but room for thought.
It sits among the swaying pines,
Where ideas with a pen are caught.

Upon my pen, a house I made,
To shelter me in future years.
Its basis from the ink I laid,
And so protects me from my tears.

And so I leave this peaceful spot,
I've built myself some room for thought.

Tom Baxendale
Arapahoe High School
Littleton, CO
Grade 11

Are We Angry?

Are we angry?
I'm not sure.
You say we're Asians; you say we aren't pure.
Are we angry?
Every time we speak you say we are illiterate.
Then you ask why we hate.
Are we angry?
We are people without freedom.
We are oppressed yet we all sit under the same sun.
Are we angry?
We live in a cage called a reservation.
Dreams of living great but first we have to be patient.
Are we angry?
It's hard to say we are equal.
You say we are weak although we are hardly feeble.
Are we angry?
Even though our word is never heard,
Prejudice says we are absurd.
Are we angry?
We are helpless, the government says such.
Are we angry? I guess you could say that much!

Kyle Brockie
Hays-Lodgepole Jr/Sr High School
Hays, MT
Grade 11

Whatever Will Be, Will Be

Oversized flannel nightgown crawling into bottom bunk
Sing me a song and tuck me in with my doubtless dreams, bright eyes, and fuzzy teddy.
Her sweet voice began:

When I was just a little girl, I asked my mother, what will I be? Will I be pretty? Will I be rich?
Here's what she said to me:

Eyelashes fluttering closed

Que sera, sera. Whatever will be, will be

Eyelashes flutter open as I realize the song had stopped.
Her eyes were full of tears and glistening in the moonlight as she struggled to finish.

The future's not ours to see. Que sera, sera.

A gentle kiss and she left me to consider the tears.

Years later, crawling into bed, tucked in with my insecurities, I ask the same questions.
Will I be pretty? Will I be rich? Will I get my English homework done?
Will he call? Will I be able to pay for college?
Slowly, the answer comes.

Que sera, sera. Whatever will be, will be. The future's not ours to see. Que sera, sera.

And it's my turn for eyes to glisten in the moonlight.

Deja Earley
Alta High School
Sandy, UT
Grade 12

Carpe Diem

Dear lad lend your ear
For nothing is as important to hear
Fill up on life's little pleasures
Enjoy its many treasures
For there's never a better time
To hear life's joyous chime.

If nothing is as better to say
It's to live life like the end was today
So do it now while you're here
Look past your overwhelming fear
The day will end. The light will die.
But still your dreams will ever fly.

Julie Glenn
Campbell County High School
Gillette, WY
Grade 11

Moonset

The moon floats across the evening sky,
Its western borders drawing nigh.
The brilliance begins to fade
From its face with the morning's aid.
Colors creeping o'er the crest—
Armies invading towards the west.

First the vague blue fills this place.
Soon Purple joins in the chase.
Pink and Orange aren't far behind,
But their beauty consumes the mind:
They carry up the sun.

Another day has just begun.
All these colors disperse through time.
Thus Earth begins the morning rhyme.

Suzanne Hanson
Reno High School
Reno, NV
Grade 12

Wings of Confidence

I look around the world.
I see beautiful things.
I look in the mirror.
I see a butterfly
Who may never use her wings.

What she does is always right.
Still, all odds are against her.
So alone she feels in her flight.
She often wonders why
She tries so hard to be pure.

Just once she wants to swoop
Close to that web of danger.
To be part of that group
And for once
Not be the stranger.

I look around the world.
I see such precarious things.
I look in the mirror
And am confident
I shall know how to use my wings.

Elizabeth King
Carter County High School
Ekalaka, MT
Grade 12

Photographer

The stealer of moments,
The borrower of emotions,
An artist framing time.

Searching with an eager eye
And hands in delicate movement,
Predator waits for his prey.

He waits for the perfect moment,
Finding the striking angle
Until finally the triumph of capture.

In the peaceful comfort of warm red lights,
The picture comes to life,
Slowly, with nurturing chemicals
His masterpiece shines.

Stephanie Skovron
C M Russell High School
Great Falls, MT
Grade 12

Love for the Game

I wish I could be out there once again,
Doing what I love, wearing number ten.
Jumping so high through the air,
Oh how I wish I could be out there.

I wish I could pass, shoot, and dunk the ball,
Without worrying what may break when I fall.
When I shot the ball, the net would tear,
Oh how I wish I could be out there.

I wish over the loud speaker I would hear my name,
Announcing the starting five, right before the game.
Both home and away jerseys I loved to wear,
Oh how I wish I could be out there.

I wish I could play Michael Jordan just one time,
He'd show me how the game is his, and I'd show him how it once was mine.
In my warm-up suit I had a lucky green bear,
Oh how I wish I could be out there.

I wish I wouldn't have hit that wall,
Now I can't pass, shoot, or dunk the ball.
I am now a coach and I carry around my lucky bear,
And my wish came true to once again be out there.

Michael Sollenberger
Milford High School
Milford, UT
Grade 10

If I Knew

If I knew it was the last time
That I'd see you fall asleep,
I'd tuck you in more tightly
And ask the Lord, your soul to keep.

If I knew it was the last time
That I'd see you walk out that door,
I'd give you another hug and kiss
And call you back for just one more.

If I knew it was the last time
And today was all I'd get,
I'd tell you how much you mean to me
And hope you'd never, ever forget.

Tomorrow's not promised to anyone,
Young or old alike,
And today may be the last chance
To hold my loved one tight.

So I'll take time to say, "I'm sorry,"
"Please forgive me," "it's okay,"
And if tomorrow never comes,
I'll hold no regrets about today.

Angela Stauffer
Arapahoe High School
Littleton, CO
Grade 11

Tennis

As I walk out onto the green tennis court,
I remember back to when I first held a racket.
It was so big and heavy and I thought
That it probably weighed more than I did.
The instructor told me to swing the racket
And meet the ball.
I got frustrated when I would swing the racket and miss.
But I kept on trying and finally mastered the stroke.
The years flew by and now I am in high school.
I recall all the lessons that I have taken.
Time flashes forward to the match that I am about to play.
I start to get nervous about playing the very important match
That may help the girls win state.
The match goes on.
As the last point comes and you swing.
The ball is good, and you win the match.
The girls go on to win state
And I know that we deserved it.

Sara Anderson
C M Russell High School
Great Falls, MT
Grade 10

Winter

Snow is falling all around,
No one is making a sound.
Pondering the beautiful sight,
Without putting up a fight.
The cold wet snow on the ground,
Wishing I was homeward bound.
The winter wonderland,
Touching at the tips of my hand.
The smell of the winter air,
It is o so fair.
Winter ... what a wonderful time of year.

BreAnna Sherman
Emery County High School
Castle Dale, UT
Grade 10

The Perfect Man

I have found my perfect man.
He is like a night in shining armor.
Every time I see him,
My heart goes thumpity-thump.
He's perfect in so many ways:
His eyes, his smile, his perfect hair,
His sense of humor, his contagious laugh.
I could never find anyone
As perfect as him.
Hey! Who's that cute guy walking by?
He looks so perfect...

Melissa Thurston
Virgin Valley Jr/Sr High School
Mesquite, NV
Grade 11

Brandon Douglas

Brandon Douglas, my love
Always in my heart.
I had so many memories with you.
Some good, some bad.
But as long as I live, you will always be with me.
I wish I could have more, but sadly I cannot.
I will *always* remember you.
The way you laughed,
The way you smiled,
The way you kissed me or held me.
When you looked at me it made my heart crush.
Thinking of you being gone hasn't quite hit me.
But when it does, I swear it will break my heart in two.
I will always love you,
And care for you no matter what.
I could never forget your smile, or laugh.
Who could?

Ashley Ruch
Haxtun High School
Haxtun, CO
Grade 11

Today I Cried

Today I went out to a stream
and poured my heart out to the Lord.
My burdens I released
even though I spoke no word.

I watched the water go rushing by
and let the pen fall from my hand.
I simply sat and cried
and accepted peace from the land.

The Lord you can hear outside the church.
You need not be in a crowd.
You can sit under a towering birch,
or in the mountains proud.

You don't need a speech,
or speak words out loud.
For the Lord you can reach
without making a sound.

Let your heart flow out to him.
There's nothing you can hide.
Simply go out on a limb
and be able to say today I cried.

Tabitha Westall
Custer Co Dist High School
Miles City, MT
Grade 11

If I...Would You...Forever Accept

If I were to drunkenly stumble tonight,
would you still know me?
If I were to fall into darkness into a pit of despair,
would you still love me?
If I were to dig myself a shallow grave,
would you still call on me?
If I were to get high and try to fly tonight,
would you still believe in me?
If I were to lie on the sandy beaches
and let the salt water wash over my naked body,
would you still see me?
If I were to bring a child into this cruel world at my tender age,
would you still have me?
If I were to curse you in a fit of rage,
would you forgive me?
And if I were to close my eyes and die tonight,
would you always remember me?
I put my trust in you,
never to abandon, never to change,
but to love me, to accept me, faults, fears, and all.
The way I have accepted you, the way I love you.

Ashley Farrow
Aspen Valley High School
Colorado Springs, CO
Grade 11

The Seasons

Winter,
    a pudgy, burly man,
    wrapped in a heavy fur coat,
    trudging slowly down the street,
    grumbling to himself.
Spring,
    a petite, skinny lady,
    humming as she works in her garden,
    a friendly, sweet face,
    welcome after winter.
Summer,
    a heavy, older woman,
    sipping her lemonade,
    while she sits under the shade of a tree,
    she rests.
Fall,
    a frail old gentleman,
    patiently awaiting winter
    to come and capture his last days,
    then sleeping until next October.

Lindsey Olson
C M Russell High School
Great Falls, MT
Grade 10

On a February Afternoon . . .

We watched a movie on Shakespeare today;
Play writing, acting, it's not the same;
Further on a challenging quest;
To expand my mind;
Show up all the rest;
It straddles my brain;
Rocks and rides;
Then sinks deep, deep into my mind;
You show me how;
I'll soon understand;
Being a teacher is just
What I planned;
You straightened me out;
Turned me around;
Soon I'll do the same for them;
Then, only then, will I see
Those pink slips again.

Leilani O'Donnell
Tonopah High School
Tonopah, NV
Grade 11

My Lost Life

Where in the world is the life that I live,
Where mistakes are made and people forgive?
The one where I am happy and troubles are lost,
And friends are there to help at any cost.
Where is this life that I have fell in love with,
The one I've never had and seems to be a myth?
For it's hidden in my mind, behind all my thoughts,
In all of my dreams and everything else I got.

Kara Snook
Hulett High School
Hulett, WY
Grade 11

The Tattered Hill

Upon the tattered hill,
stands a man and his violin.

He plays heavenly music,
as hell rumbles beneath him.

Bombs are bursting above him,
guns are firing all around him,
innocent victims are collapsing before him.

He plays as if,
the music will protect him.

And he plays until,
the bullets silence him.

Kelly Barkhausen
Clonlara School/Compuhigh
Denver, CO
Grade 12

Majestic Blue

Majestic blue.
Blue is the sky.
The sky, where no one was thought to touch because of the power and glory that it has.
Blue is the ocean.
The ocean, so mysterious, so unknown, yet so powerful yet graceful.
Blue is the mountains.
The mountains are so majestic staring down at me from great heights.
Majestic blue.

Mark Olsen
Emery County High School
Castle Dale, UT
Grade 10

The Computer

Continually processing information and taking commands,
The computer seeks but little reward.
Knowledge not bound due to the near limitless memory banks of its hard drive,
With a central processing unit performing calculations quicker than conceivable,
Always will the computer remain without human competition in intelligence.
Never do these operations seem to the computer more than a trivial and pedestrian task,
Although man will always long for a mental ability comparable to these trivialities.
However, one distinct difference will always remain between the two:
Man is the master and computer is the slave.
Intelligence is meaningless when placed within the bonds of slavery,
And always does the master finish on top.
For the benefit of mankind, hopefully this system remains as it is,
For when the computer obtains artificial intelligence uncontrollable by man,
An abysmal situation will have occurred,
For man may never be the master again...

Jason Strampe
C M Russell High School
Great Falls, MT
Grade 10

Childhood

Oh, to be a child,
To be in a crib with your every need someone else's priority.
To excite over spring and cry over fall.
To camp in the world of everlasting glee.
To love to fish and play sports and smile without a worry.
To view everything as something positive and want to hang around your family on Friday.
To not care about a thing in the world but just to be happy for no apparent reason.
To set your alarm clock for 3 a.m. just to get a glance at the Christmas tree.
Oh, to be a child, a life filled with glee.
To play in the sandbox and bike through the rain.
To make it through the first day of school and still be happy.
To get on that bike and ditch those Hotwheels.
And to hate to get in trouble when you tried to hide what you did wrong.
To move around yet still feel safe and sound.
Oh, to be a child.
And want to stay there but you have to grow up and face the world.
And you will think it was not easy.

Shadd Cullinan
Billings West High School
Billings, MT
Grade 10

The Day

As I wake up in the morning
I smell the new hope.
I hear the birds singing
And in my mind I'm thinking,
Why is today so important?
I wonder what is so special?
What is my mission to do?
Then suddenly from somewhere out of the blue,
I figure this is my mission to do.
With no help, for me to go solo.
What makes me different from the next?
Is something changed in our text?
Does he see different shades than I?
For what reason does he get treated better,
Than I?
Por que es mi grande?
We speak the same language.
But are some way different.
To him I seem less, but to me I feel blessed.
For knowing a different world.
Which only I can experience.

Tom Hernandez
Valley High School
Gilcrest, CO
Grade 12

The Music

Let the music within your heart be heard,
So your soul can have the freedom to dance,
No matter if the world claims you are absurd.

Never be afraid to say your words.
Never let your song be turned to silence.
Let the music within your heart be heard.

Don't allow their words to make you scarred,
Even when you have run out of endurance,
No matter if the world claims you are absurd.

When the majority of the crowd labels you a nerd,
Let yourself glisten and shine in abundance.
Let the music within your heart be heard.

Let your spirit be as pretty as a tropical bird.
Don't always do what they say is a convenience.
Let the music within your heart be heard,
No matter if the world claims you are absurd.

Karren Smith
Sky View High School
Smithfield, UT
Grade 10

Your Smile

I can still remember the way we met that day,
Something about your smile just swept my heart away.

I had never felt this way with anyone before,
And now I'm finding happiness, along with so much more.

I had never had someone who cared for me like you;
If you weren't in my life, I don't know what I'd do.

You've made me a better person; you turned my life around.
I'm so thankful just for you and the love that we have found.

Cassie Mecham
Morgan High School
Morgan, UT
Grade 12

Paranoia

The walls are closing in
My future looks grim
I can't do a thing
And people are in a ring
Laughing and jeering at my fear
These people don't exist
They are all in my head
But I can't stop them from laughing,
Not even in my bed
They stop me from doing things every day
And I know I must hold my fear at bay
I think people are looking when I turn my back
Laughing at all the talents which I lack
When I turn around and no one is there
I still can feel their hateful stare
I think people are looking at me when I'm alone
And these thoughts soon chase me to my home
When someone comes near me I feel I should run
When all they want to do is have a little fun
People say I should lighten up
But I can't because I am afraid that I will mess up

Leo Gracik
Pawnee Jr-Sr High School
Grover, CO
Grade 10

Autumn Leaves

Autumn enters briskly with breezes and biting chill.
The leaves fall softly floating to the frozen earth.
Crunch, Crunch, Crunch
Leaves crumble and break as footsteps
Swish, Swish, Swish
Through piles of crimson and gold.
Bare branches are left behind,
Leaving barren but beautiful bark.

Mallori Taylor
Virgin Valley Jr/Sr High School
Mesquite, NV
Grade 11

Cloud Watching

As I lay on the dew soaked grass,
A cool breeze kissing my face,
I gaze at the clouds wafting by.
I spy a regal tiger lurking,
Wary and anticipating a kill.
A dignified unicorn passes,
Its strong head held high.
A laggard turtle trudges behind,
With no particular destination in mind.
A bunny hops along,
In an endless field of blue.
And the sweet scent of rain,
Drifts by, tickling my nose.
The clouds are darkened,
They conceal the sun.
The sprinkling rain drizzles down,
And when the rain stops,
When the clouds are no more,
A rainbow.

Lacey Dobyns
Shelby High School
Shelby, MT
Grade 10

The Breeze Gone Bad

There was once a breeze
A little puff now and then,
Nothing too dramatic
That's how it should have been.

Into a gust it turned
And let out a little wail,
It got stronger every minute,
And kept increasing on the scale.

Then it became a gale
Blowing throughout the flattened land.
It howled with an intense wrath;
This was its first command.

It became so strong
A tornado happened to form.
It fiercely ripped across the valley,
And suddenly, a house was airborne.

The tornado was then over.
The valley was at ease.
However, the leaves gently rustled;
There was once again a breeze.

Whitney Schenck
Granada School
Granada, CO
Grade 10

Birth of a Star

Fairy Tales can come true,
if you really want them to.

It will take work and lots of sweat,
before that special dream is met.

Hold that dream, don't let it go,
even when those cold winds blow.

Follow the beat of your own drum,
don't go along with all your chums.

Walk upon a different path,
don't be afraid of other's wrath.

Go ahead and dream that dream,
Don't listen to others, don't feel torn

Do what you really want to do
Because when you do a star is born.

Jennifer Allen
Shoshoni High School
Shoshoni, WY
Grade 12

Coming Home

Standing, staring over the cliff
Into the bright glare of the sun
Wanting to reach home again
Where fun times were
Where great friends were
Where I want to be
Across the Rio
Someday I will be coming home

It is the path
The way home
Through la frio barranca
Swimming forcefully against the current
Trying not to let it take me away from the
Home that I want to be in

Yo no puedo nado bien
But it takes hold of me
Rushing down stream
Gasping for air as agua
Covers my cara
I can't breathe anymore
Oh Lord I will be coming home.

Jeff Reck
Valley High School
Gilcrest, CO
Grade 12

Inner Child

Come inside my brain,
open a door, see its pain.
See a child
go against the grain.
See him stand,
reach for dreams higher.
Can he make it?
Maybe, he seems tired.
Nobody can help him.
He's in a cage.
See him grow up;
life adds more to his rage.
He's confused. He seems dazed.
He's a rat in this crazy maze.
He's committed evil deeds.
He's ashamed.
Can you see his future?
No way. Even to him it's very vague.

Edward J. Baldivia
Reno High School
Reno, NV
Grade 12

The Death of a Friend

I was looking up at the sky
When
I saw him say good-bye

I've always wondered
Why
He had to say good-bye.

I want to know
What
Death is like but
I don't want to die.

I already know
How
Death killed him.

But why
Russell Calvin Gilham
Was only sixteen.

Russell took the road to heaven
So now I'm going to say
Good-bye.
Good-bye my friend.

Tiffany Wagner
Flathead High School
Kalispell, MT
Grade 10

Is There a Possibility?

I trust and try to believe
Is this another possibility?
You touched my heart right from the start
And I learned to care so much
Can I again believe in such?
Yes, there is a possibility
I trusted and learned again too late
But I really believed our love was fate
There is no possibility
I say, I'll never do it again
The tears seem never to dry
Why is it they like to make us cry?
There is no possibility
You've proven to me and all you see, you can and
Do deceive and I trusted and tried to believe
The memories within my heart will never ever part
But there was no possibility
I can't just mope, I have to hope
For me you see, there's got to be. . .
A possibility

Lindsey Clark
Lincoln County High School
Eureka, MT
Grade 11

Friend! I Have Betrayed You

A friend so dear and a friend so true
would never really mean to hurt you.
Sometimes we all make a mistake
and sometimes we all just give and take.
My feelings for you dear friend
would make a list that would never end.
I didn't mean to hurt you
I didn't mean to make you cry.
Maybe we could work this out
and give no reason for more doubt.
I have betrayed and gave a lie
with no rhyme or reason why.
But I promise with all my heart
to never again break your heart.
I know it will be hard to forgive
with this pain I will have to live.
Because I have betrayed and been dishonest
even though I had made you a promise.
I will forever apologize for those stupid lies about the car,
that love trance
and a midnight dance.

Kandyce Gates
Sky View High School
Smithfield, UT
Grade 12

Tree

My family is like a tree
My mom is the root that holds us together
She is supportive and does not let the tree fall
My dad is the trunk that is the base of the tree
He is strong and solid and does not waver in the wind
My brother is the branches
He came from the trunk and roots,
Yet he chooses many new directions, he is unique to the tree
I am the leaves that complete the tree
I represent the color and creativity
My ancestors are the rings
They represent many generations and many different lives

Annie McDonald
C M Russell High School
Great Falls, MT
Grade 10

A Life Anew, from Within

Two raindrops fall,
        racing towards the earth,
chasing and tumbling over each other,
        together in strife, till the end,
a singular mission of a journey down,
        in the last they struggled,
together till the end,
        but all is not lost,
'cause from their persistent dedication,
        they do bring forth something anew,
a joy, a life, an eternal love,
        their pragmatic beginning,
atrophied into sumptuous life,
        to start anew, but wholly different again.

Robert C. Stolting
Fernley High School
Fernley, NV
Grade 11

Eyes of the Ancient

In mine eyes there is a glistening,
Of death and life and the falling of the christening,
Through endless centuries and countless years,
I have survived, I have endeared,
Now I come to the end of my days,
Now I will pay for my evil ways.

In mine eyes there is a glistening,
Of life and death and the falling of the one I love,
And I wonder why blood must stain the dove,
And why night must give way to day,
And I ask why I have followed the evil way,
And why did I cause the fall of the one I love?
Now that I have come to the end of my days . . .

Joshua Walker
Fernley High School
Fernley, NV
Grade 10

Paranoia

Watch your back,
Running away,
Lying,
Not thinking,
It destroys you.

Nick Gallagher
Whitehall Sr High School
Whitehall, MT
Grade 11

Glass Cage

Trapped behind a glass cage.
No contact,
No adventure.
Only to wake up every morning.
The same place.
The same people.
Others can enter, but we cannot leave.
This was all ours at one time.
Now, it's gone.
White people have taken everything.
Our rights,
Vanished.
Our dreams,
Vanished.
My grandfather tells me what it was like
Before,
When we were free.
Now
We are trapped.
Behind a glass cage.

Cory Johnson
Valley High School
Gilcrest, CO
Grade 11

Tick

Waiting for the tick to cease
Performing as I must
Fighting hard to stay awake
But fading into dust.

Droning sounds erode the silence
Occupy the space
Never-ending nonsense
Ever present in this place.

Outside images taunt the view
Spurring inner dreams
Attention faintly turns once more
To hollow, drowning screams.
Tick, tick, tick...

Julie Yoneji
C M Russell High School
Great Falls, MT
Grade 12

In the Darkness

Darkness surrounded his every move —
His body bruised and battered,
His mind poisoned with fear.

Pain conquered his fighting strength —
His heart broken blue,
His life a distant memory.

Harsh wind forced his mind to wake
Tired eyes glanced towers of pine.
Enemies were remembered so well
Still heard with their distant laughs.

He tried to wipe away the tears,
But mud soon replaced and time slipped painfully away.

The forest seemed to swallow him,
The sky a perfect dark
Stars replacing the sun.

He opened his eyes and wiped away the haze,
A smile of pain stained his face and his pleas were meant for God.

He prayed his final prayer
And vanished from earth to clouds.

The darkness faded away . . .
And heaven cured hate's pain.

Ryan Petersen
Northridge High School
Layton, UT
Grade 12

Through a Mother's Eyes

My baby.
I can still admire
Your curly cream-puff locks covering your delicate head.
Your tiny grasping hands taking hold of everything within reach.
Your chubby, dimpled face coming alive as a smile spreads across your lips.
I can still remember
Your fresh, sleepy eyes as you awaken from a nap.
Your quiet, longing gaze whenever you spot a cookie.
Your unending determination as you master the keys of that old piano.
I can still hear
Your temper tantrums whenever I take you shopping.
Your noisy, lively games with the children down the street.
Your bitter, uproarious screams when I leave you with a baby-sitter.
Now I watch
Your silent form lying on a white-padded bed.
Your closed eyelids sealed for the rest of eternity.
Your expressionless, pale face revealing nothing of your escaping soul.
And I cry.

Tamara Watts
Arapahoe High School
Littleton, CO
Grade 11

To My Heart I Look For My Home

What my heart seeks I cannot find,
what my heart dreams has eluded my mind.
My love has drifted away like a diminishing ember,
but all my love I do remember.

To my heart I look for my home.

I tear my self between two halves
don't know when I can stand my own.
To my eyes this dark abyss I'm thrown
and the burning pain I have grown,
as my heart I look for my home.

To my heart I look for my home.

I see this place I love and hate
all though my mind says rest,
my heart goes to seek the best of me.

To my heart I look for my home.

Now the power is gone, the music has died
my heart aches my love is gone,
my life has started once again.
The music begins to play another waltz in my name,
My love is gone but life goes on.

To my heart I look for my home.

Savannah Meredith
Carson High School
Carson City, NV
Grade 10

To My True Love

Once so quiet, but I always knew
That forever and always I will love you
Your insecurities make no sense to me
Cause, baby, you're the best a man could ever be.
You're kind, smart, respecting, you know what I mean,
Handsome and romantic, you're my little hug machine.
You treat me good, but that's not cool to your friends.
It's cool to me and that's what matters in the end.
You didn't want to trust me but I'm glad you did,
'Cause I can't resist your devilish charm and smile, like a kid.
Only together for a short time, and this you need to know,
That my love for you can only continue to grow.
Now baby, you said you loved me and I know it's true,
But what I'm doing now is proving my love to you.
When my day comes, in heaven I will wait for you
But until then and forever I will continue loving you.
So take me in your strong arms and never let me go,
And I will treat you better than a man made of gold.

Karli Cannon
Faith Lutheran Jr-Sr High School
Las Vegas, NV
Grade 12

Twinkling Eyes

Oh endless light of stars, gaze down.
Endless night, in which you drown.
Upon these gleams, children's dreams are made.
Taking note of all games to be played.

Eyes of night watch lovers leap.
Once the children who prayed to them, before sleep.

Help have they none, just stand by.
Having no power,
All they can do is cry.

Cassaundra Steele
Las Vegas Academy
Las Vegas, NV
Grade 11

Like A Rainstorm

Like a rainstorm disturbing the desert
Fighting against the hot scorching sun rays
The sweetness of the rain is a dessert
To the sour, dry unforgiving land's ways.
Or a day filled with happiness and light
Can be cut with a thorn of pain and fear
Is nothing without darkness and the night
With innocent stars, that are pure and clear.
Or the sparkling diamond that is treasured
Was grown from a dirty part of black coal
The beauty of the form will be measured
Knowing not the entire nature soul.
Love is a paradox, disagreeing
The two opposites have equal feeling.

Krista Miller
Poudre High School
Fort Collins, CO
Grade 10

The Game

As I look before me,
I realize something I have never been able to see.
People look at me strangely.
but what do they know?
They look at my appearance,
but not what lies deep inside.
It's kind of funny because I do the same.
In my own way I play that game.
I do it to others,
as they are doing it to me.
I judge people closely,
but I don't understand.
I can do it, but on the other hand...
I am no better than they,
actually quite similar in a peculiar way.

Lacey Mentink
Lake County High School
Leadville, CO
Grade 11

Nature

Flowers of summer
Grow where soil is very soft
Their shadow freezes

Scattered rocks lie low
While children are out to play
In the bright hot sun

A light in the dark
This owl flies into the tree
It is very cold

Katie Warner
Emery County High School
Castle Dale, UT
Grade 12

Harmony and Dissonance

Water fills the pool of earth,
Tumbling and happy,
Telling its secrets to all
Yet remaining a mystery –
Cool and soft, with sounds of mirth.
Wind whips up the dust,
Tearing and cruel,
Wreaking vengeance on the world
While trying to be understood –
Shrouds eyes with great gusts.

Lainie Hoffman
Arapahoe High School
Littleton, CO
Grade 11

Thoughts

When you think all is calm
you start imagining things
you wonder all the things
that confuse you within
you find out that there's lots
you try to solve each one
you can't; they're not for solving
they're there for a reason
if you would end up solving them
you would probably become empty
you need those thoughts to keep going,
striving for more
that feeling you get
makes you angry for the truth
the truth you can't achieve
it's something you'll always wonder
wonder "Can I ever know the truth?"
maybe it is the truth,
truth that will be revealed at the end

Keyra Magaña
Highland High School
Salt Lake City, UT
Grade 11

Letter to God

Dear God,

I know You must be busy with the world to look after,
And if my prayers aren't answered, it's because You have something better in mind.
Some things weren't meant to be; some things just need a little hope and faith.
I know, though, that if I fall into a hole made by my own missteps,
All I have to do is ask for Your help and You will pull me out.
Sometimes I don't recognize the path and fall in regardless of what I do,
And there are times when I think I can climb out by myself.
Sooner or later, though, I realize I am stuck and ask for help once again.
I know that in the end You have already given me what I need,
And that all I can give for this wonderful gift is my love and faith in return.
So I guess this letter, after all, is just one of the ways You make me realize Your love.

With all my love,

Nicole Knuppel
Pawnee Jr-Sr High School
Grover, CO
Grade 11

Envy

Jealousy seeps through my veins and drips from my skin.
It coats my teeth and reclaims my mouth and my eager tongue.
My eyes spell it as they dart across the room.
My feet walk in patterns of it as they dance across the roots of the earth.
My fingers spark the match that burns the smell of envy.
My stomach and throat coat everything I consume with it.
My ears burn from it.
My chest is swollen with swarms of it.
I am jealous of you, being able to touch my mind so purely with your song,
And I cannot learn or return the craft.

Kari Kilgore
Fairview High School
Boulder, CO
Grade 12

Dividing the Census

Holding tight to history's spoken remnants,
reading the rubble and seeing the past unwind.
Ancient pillars rise high once upon a time,
breaching the space set aside for the divine. . .

Darkened shadows strike a fight upon the mind,
as the twisting conscience develops a pathway unable to find.

Stars confined from the eyes of dreamers who sleep,
into the ocean of hope we combine ourselves and discover the deep.
We scale upon the mountain of wonder and dispel the cloud of mist.
Journey to the top, unfold your passions in light you may have kissed.

The key of tears has been found, discover the sounds of your treasure.
Explore the inner thoughts of your mind, unlock the depths of your pleasures.

Sie Glenn
Highland High School
Salt Lake City, UT
Grade 11

A Picture

A framed image of a happy heart.
Barefoot and disrobed running through the grass
with not a fear nor a care,
not a thing to hide.
The blue sky overhead.
But now that heart is hidden
beneath a costume and a lie.
Sitting in a smoke filled room
afraid of herself and them,
not a place to run,
no place to hide.
Except beneath her mask
which is imminently changing
and provides no protection
because she is always there.
She embraces her life and the image
and with it she runs.

Haley Solodky
Heritage High School
Littleton, CO
Grade 11

Snow

The tracks are made slow and soft,
The snow hurts the throat as it makes mud.
The breeze is cool and sharp to erase my tracks.
The world looks like an emerald as the snow hits the ground,
To follow the snow would be to say,
That it would be too hard and you would be astray.

To curve the snow would go,
The snow is tough to kiss it would be hard,
The clouds above make no sign of life.
The dogs call out from the village down below
As if leather falling out into the earth,
To bite and cut the rocks are no challenge
To the blizzard as it sweeps across the land.
As my socks hang there dripping the water off them.

My house is standing as strong as it can in Greenland.

We are strong and cool people when this happens,
As the time passes we sit and wait for the snowstorm to leave.
When the storm leaves we go outside.
And make new tracks in the snow.
We like these storms and wish they were more often
So we can have fun in the snow.

William Chapman
Emery County High School
Castle Dale, UT
Grade 10

Laughter

Laughing is a funny thing.
You laugh because you are happy.
Happy people make other people happy, too.

You might laugh although you don't want to laugh.
Sometimes you might laugh along with a group
And you don't even know
What they are laughing at.

Laughing can also hurt other people.
For a while it is funny
But that happiness never lasts.

Sometimes you just laugh because you are nervous
Or tired.
Laughing is a happy thing.

Virpi Savolainen
Rosebud Public School
Rosebud, MT
Grade 12

Loss of Words

I see you at least once every day.
I can't seem to find anything to say.
To say four words, I have a hard time.
And those words are: Will you be mine?
So afraid of your reaction,
What if you just started laughin'?
I know that it would break my heart,
The pain of my emotions being torn apart.
Just saying this makes my heart race,
You should know that I adore your face.
A smile from you is a precious gift.
For you to be mine is only a wish.

Tyrone Joseph Gilbert
Platte Valley Youth Service Center
Greeley, CO
Grade 10

Soldiers Today, Heroes FOREVER

When I look upon Old Glory,
I do not see only the bold stars and stripes.
The eyes of millions of men that died
so that my life may be one free from danger
and oppression, gaze back into my own
I see their hopes and fears and broken hearts
Lying on the battle field,
But these dreams of theirs do not die,
Oh no,
But live on forever in us all.
And all I can do is bow my clean, unburdened head
humbly.

Melanie Walker
C M Russell High School
Great Falls, MT
Grade 12

Still Alive

The way that beauty touches me
I know I'm still alive.
The way this earth just holds the light
I know I'm still alive.
I know.
I know I'm still alive.
The way your skin sweeps over mine
Shows me I'm still alive.

Alesha Hove
Flathead High School
Kalispell, MT
Grade 12

Time Is Flying

Time is flying
my memories caught
the same flight,
vanishing through the clouds.

How I wish I sometimes,
just could stop the clock
and let those sweet moments
flow through my body and mind
until they become a big flood
flowing through . . .
the rest of my life

But when the sky gets dark,
and black clouds fill up heaven,
I'm so glad that time is flying . . .
back to paradise.

Sjouke Van Poucke
Flathead High School
Kalispell, MT
Grade 12

True Peace

As you deeply sleep,
I watch you.
I remember what we have been through,
The teasing,
The fights,
Those creepy nights,
Most of all the trouble you got into.
Every time you needed me,
I protected you from all the insanity,
But now I put you down to sleep,
Knowing at last you will find true peace.
So tend the rabbits in the sky,
For soon, yes soon,
I'll be by your side.
—George

Sarah Elizabeth Clapp
Natrona County High School
Casper, WY
Grade 10

Every night I lie in bed

Can a person fill this hole;

Has God already set my fate

Have I passed him along the way

The words that I so long to voice

That he's waited so long just to see

Until then, all I can do is pray

Soul Mate

With notions of love inside of my head

Complete what is missing from my soul?

Will I meet my true soul mate?

Did I miss my chance to say

So he can speak his precious choice

His precious gift, his angel . . . me?

That somehow, someday . . .
My true love will surface

Rebecca Horwitz
Arapahoe High School
Littleton, CO
Grade 11

Prissy Princess the Cat Verses ˆBailey the Dogˆ

I am the queen,
The empress,
The pharaoh.

I am your servant,
Your friend.

When I want your attention,
I will tell you,

When you want my attention
Just let me know.

I like to be left alone,
Independent

I aim to please.
Care free.

The world revolves around me

My world revolves around you.

I need my beauty rest,
And I only eat the richest of cat foods.

I love going on walks,
And eating my dog food.

Sometimes my house may not be fit for the night,
Don't fuss if I spend the night elsewhere.

I love to sleep on the end of your bed,
And I love to see your face as I lick your toes.

You love me.

I love you.
Jen Koritza
Arapahoe High School
Littleton, CO
Grade 11

View Askew

My view is ever expanding
Which is intentionally flawed
My jagged childhood memories
Reorganized in the abituar

This endless nameless song I sing
My lack of knowledge endures what I can't
A redundant, consuming completeness
Which I keep in my emotional corn dog

I know I have problems
But save your pity for your dead heroes
Be brave and crazy and full of life
Survival is the ability to sustain reality

I'm not the first ugly one to view you askew

Matt Daley
Northridge High School
Layton, UT
Grade 11

On Bovine Bigotry

The cow chews audibly,
the same cud it's been chewing since dawn.
Always bringing the same stale taste,
to a mouth that should have moved on.

If the cow would only turn around,
then it would finally see,
The fence is out.
And it's been out, since 1863.

The cow could simply turn and leave
its little patch of hay.
But it seems content to stay right here,
and from the field's safety,
never dare to stray.

We've all been taught, since we were young,
that we must not blame the cow,
when we cannot change the cow,
its mother taught it wrong.

Well I don't know 'bout you,
but I think *we've* been taught wrong.
For it seems the cow is always singing,
and I'm tired of hearing the same damn song.

Guy Hepp
Montrose High School
Montrose, CO
Grade 12

Life

Anger is rich, yet deep in sorrow.
Happiness and love you cannot borrow.
Times can be great when happiness reigns,
But terribly awful when one's in pain.
Why is it that things one minute can be so normal?
Then things can change in a blink of an eye,
When the clouds go dark in a once blue sky.
Life is full of unhappy things,
Even with every living being.
It's what you make of it, in good and in bad.
So don't cry, cheer up, life is not all that sad.

Lance Heuscher
Flathead High School
Kalispell, MT
Grade 12

Road of Life

Looking upon the future,
There can be seen,
Harder roads than normal,
Not wanting to hit them,
But wanting to take the chance,
Even though it may cost all,
My dreams, hopes, and wishes,
It seems that those roads are worth it,
They don't look like they will last too long for being rough,
So the costs may be for nothing,
But what I see,
Is worth a lifetime.

Beth McCollum
Hulett High School
Hulett, WY
Grade 11

Happy

For two years I lived in a depressed state.
I wouldn't call it depression,
Oh no, that came later.
Then it stayed for a year and a half.
A year and a half of crying, confusion and anger.
Anger mostly toward myself for not being strong enough.
But now I'm through.
I've seen the light,
I've reached the light,
The light left me void.
I just keep thinking I have to get out of here.
If I can start over I'll be fine.
I'll start a new life, as a new person.
Then I can turn my back and walk away from the old,
The painful memories,
Finally forget.
Then, and only then, can I be happy.

Katherine Michels
Middle Park High School
Granby, CO
Grade 12

Out of the Night

He came out of the night,
afraid to be seen.
Drifting across the field
as if in a dream.
He starts and he stops,
not missing a beat.
He makes not a sound,
so light on his feet.
He is beautiful and graceful,
but to some he is fierce.
Their peaceful night
in an instant he will pierce.
To many he is beauty,
to others he is dread.
He is none other
than the fox who is red.

Josh Simmons
Emery County High School
Castle Dale, UT
Grade 11

When Texas Winds Blow

When the sky darkens over Texas,
And the ominous and suggesting hues,
Speak of constant warning,
All life takes cover.

Calmness descends,
As forces collide overhead,
Further agitating the volatile mixture,
And form takes shape.

Smooth
Animated
Soft
Concise

As screams pierce the atmosphere,
Pleading for salvation,
With no answers.

David Page
Virgin Valley Jr/Sr High School
Mesquite, NV
Grade 12

Sorrow

I saw peace clearly
She was slim, soft and gentle
She turned slowly with lots of love
I saw her green eyes and blond hair
And heard her shout
And I felt her sorrow

Tim Lucas
Rosebud Public School
Rosebud, MT
Grade 12

Farewell Core

I have been taken from thee—
to create a new self in the underworld—
to live a happy servitude with my Lord, Hades,
and make my peace with Persephone.
For she, my creation, heart, blood and soul wishes a life in these dwellings.
And what objection should I profess to this dark home?
Never to see the gleaming glory of the sun and smell the rich scent of nature? No!
To gain wisdom and passion beyond your comprehension is what I was born for.
I covet my Lord and he covets me. Yes!
To live a life of rich happiness and pure delight here below the world is my wish,
and how well Persephone does love—

Glenna Stewart
Clear Creek Secondary School
Idaho Springs, CO
Grade 12

Nice Guys Finish Last

You're skinny, you're scrawny, you're never going to get her
I wish I had the looks, instead I have a heart
I wish I could say mean things and they're just considered a joke
I'll never be a big football star, just a person in the shadows
Sure you can make her laugh, but that's not enough
She says you're cute, like a ten-year-old
She says you'll look great, in five years
She says she loves,
But never means it the way you want her to
She might call you, after she calls everyone else
When she talks to you it's whether you did the homework
Sure she might realize the real you, after you're dead
But if you're a lucky one she might see you in the nick of time
This is the moment you'll shine; because after everyone else
She will finally see a sweet little person, you'll see
Though we are in the back of the line doesn't mean we're not good enough
It means she saved the best for last

Blake Hogen
Sparks High School
Sparks, NV
Grade 10

The World Keeps Moving

The old useful house is like an old one telling memories as one listens,
People pour from its seams like a kettle running over.
The loud shrill cry of a babe lingers in the air.
The mouth-watering homemade food melts in mouths.
The crackling comes from a massive stone fireplace as it burns sweet cedar.
A mother runs her fingers gently through the silky soft curls on a newborn's head.
The soft worn carpet serves as seating.
A sense of happiness reflects the laughs and smiles.
The love people share with one another is heaven on earth.
Yet you sit alone in the corner;
You feel left out of the bustle,
And the world moves on without you.

Lisa Dodge
Vilas High School
Vilas, CO
Grade 11

Sudden death

A tiny rat with poisoned blood
Slowly creeps through the muck and mud

The invisible flea unmercifully bites
And soon goes to spread its delights

Suddenly my father is bit
Like the others, my family, too, is hit

Through the air it seems to spread
My mother and brother are soon dead

Quickly as I can I try to flee,
But sure enough the plague catches me

As I struggle for my last breath
I ask the good Lord, is this to be my death?

Jessica Galloway
Excel School
Durango, CO
Grade 12

My Mother, the Teacher

Reading to them, talking with them,
why she does it, I don't know.
Inside each child is a gem.
The children are what make her blood flow.

I see them as little pests,
but she'll say "Oh no."
They have so many interests.
Teaching is definitely not the way for me to go.

I find great courage in her.
She does a job not many people want.
Her plan, to guide the hearts of tomorrow, I am sure
will someday be hers to flaunt.

She takes great pride
in helping, teaching and caring.
Finding out just what each child carries inside,
at the troubles some have, her heart is tearing.

Someday the world will be taught,
that great things don't come without pain.
These lessons, from someone who just did, they never thought
that their struggles and efforts would be someone else's gain.

Ann Tietmeyer
Pawnee Jr-Sr High School
Grover, CO
Grade 11

The Park

As the birds fly past me to the tree
I watch jealously. Each piece of me
Wanting what they all have!
Wishing to be free like a bumblebee.
I am here to help, to hold, young or old.
Nobody   cares
who I am,   my niche
In society   is important
I am   a park bench
Who is   alone.

Rachel Singer
Fairview High School
Boulder, CO
Grade 12

Dying Proud

Wings of coal black, and golden yellow.
On the petal of an orchard rose.
At peace, quiet, comfortably mellow.
There unmoving, froze.
Here sadly the creature has chosen her grave.
Dying, slowly melting away.
Last breath coming, she's being brave.
This is the time, God picked today.
Alone she laid in the open space.
Sun beating down on her soft wings.
The wind brushing her face.
In the distance the blue jay sings.
The wind her chorus, the skies her crowd.
Here they watched the butterfly die proud.

Stephanie D. King
Montrose High School
Montrose, CO
Grade 10

I'm Sure He Didn't Mean It.

He stood me up today,
But, I'm sure he didn't mean it.
He probably just forgot that we had plans.

He made me cry today,
But, I'm sure he didn't mean it.
He said people always say stupid things when they're drunk.

He broke my heart today,
But, I'm sure he didn't mean it.
He probably didn't hear me say, "I love you."

He said it was over today,
But, I'm sure he didn't mean it.
He just doesn't realize that he's supposed to love me, too.

Lacey Ward
Whitehall Sr High School
Whitehall, MT
Grade 12

Upon A Night

A nightingale sings
A cricket chirps
A star shimmers
The moon shines

The night is silent
The night is sad
The day is gray
A tender few words are said

A footstep in the snow
A breath in the cool air
A man says goodbye
The two paths then part

One off to war
One off to the unknown
One question:
Why?

Wondering if paths will cross
Wondering with whom to go
Wondering what will happen
Praying those paths will join again

Robert Mayer
Excel School
Durango, CO
Grade 10

A Butterfly's Love

Fluttering within the invigorating garden,
You are all I see.
Out of all the rest,
You mean most to me.

Your beautiful peach petals,
Delicate and rare.
As I land,
I receive a kiss you share.

A sensuous stem
With ripe indulging leaves,
To me you give
an emotion I never believed.

Never, ever perish,
Or wither away,
Adorn my garden
Forever and a day.

Alyce Mui
Greeley West High School
Greeley, CO
Grade 12

True Love

I am sitting here on my bed,
with my true love on my mind.
I think you're something special,
love's something I thought I'd never find.

I cry for just one sight of you,
and for your arms around me.
I know we must be soul mates,
now that my heart can finally see.

Talking to you makes my heart jump,
and so I dream about us together.
Kissing you like it's our last kiss,
but our love's the kind that lasts forever.

I love you more than life itself,
you're the one I have been searching for.
I love you deeper than any ocean,
no matter what you say, I love you more!

I love your smile, and your heart,
but most of all, I love you.
I can't imagine life without this,
'cause my dreams finally came true.

Ericka Gillette
Granger High School
Salt Lake City, UT
Grade 11

Sparkling White Sea

I step outside and gaze upon glitter
Pouring down from the sky.
My momentary blindness
Gives way to the beauty before me.

Gliding down to Earth
On an invisible slide,
Twirling white specks
Race to an unknown world.

Silently tumbling,
Heard only through the eyes.
They lightly flutter,
Landing peacefully on everything in sight.

Though cold to the touch,
It brings warmth to the heart.
A smile spreads across my face,
For before me lies a sparkling, white sea.

Aubrey Redmond
Cyprus High School
Magna, UT
Grade 12

Your Eyes

Your precious eyes
I once saw in blue sky.
They looked down upon from
the sky's blue eye.
They looked through me
and they saw everything, my past
my future and present thing
With those blue eyes I know
that you see; all
my dreams, all my hopes
and my sufferings

Anna Kigilyuk
Flathead High School
Kalispell, MT
Grade 11

Boysicles

My shadow wears neon pink nylons
and a retro jacket
from a sales rack at Saver's.
She has electric blue hair
sparkling eye shadow
and raspberry ice lipstick.
She lives in Manhattan
with an icebox of boys
ready to thaw out
whenever she needs company.
She knows being different
is the weapon of her choice
and she reads books that were banned
by parents in Maine.
She eats leftovers for breakfast
and is always the driver
because all she's afraid of
is being driven.

Christine Conelea
Reno High School
Reno, NV
Grade 11

Football Players

Football players have to work hard all day
On their homework so they can play
On the day the big game is to be played
The team will all have prayed
Back at practice the next day
All the players will have to pay
Losing was not an option that day
Losing made them run all day.

Bradley Hainer
Granada School
Granada, CO
Grade 11

Thy Light

Thy light in a beam shows through the dark
things once unseen now glow with a spark.

Thy light warms things that were once chilled by the cold
like the comfort of a blanket made of gold.

Thy light stands tall and twinkles bright
never dwindling down but choosing the right.

Thy light I can see from the depths of the sea.
never ceasing to always take care of me.

Thy light guides me to the straight and narrow way
leading me by the hand each and every day.

Thy light engulfs and burns in my soul
your wisdom leaves a mark taking its toll.

Thy light shows me how to love
with emotions sent from above.

Thy light I want to behold for all time and eternity.
I want it to be evident in my identity.

Tara Rawlings
Montrose High School
Montrose, CO
Grade 12

Heartache

As much as it hurts,
I now realize
That tears and laughter,
Both, are part of our lives.
But, why must it be,
That over and over again,
One certain guy,
Can make my life begin to spin?
For one day he cares,
The next I am gone.
He knows that he doesn't want
Any kind of a bond.
With tears and pleading,
I try once more,
But only with time,
Will he look my way, without a bore.
And suddenly, I catch his eye,
And see a spark filled with old looks.
Little do I know,
My heart is going to cry out with hurt.
Over and over — the trap opens and I fall in;
Only to keep coming back for more.

Krystle Hofmeister
Haxtun High School
Haxtun, CO
Grade 11

Souls Are Birds

Souls are birds.
They are each different and unique in their own ways.
They soar to great heights and sometimes fall back to earth.
They all fly, but not all of them are free.

Becky Montano
Montrose High School
Montrose, CO
Grade 12

Madness

Unsure why I accepted the offer,
My patience wearing thin,
I knew it was inevitable now.
Slowly
I ascended to my fate.
Was this madness?
Or was I guilty of unnamed force?
I wasn't alone, but *their* eyes were glued shut
I gripped the crusty pipe
My heartbeat hastened as my adrenaline surged,
Even yet I refrained and kept still
Through the unnerving screams.
As my insides imploded my head was tossed around.
It would all be over soon.
At a crashing halt the stench of burnt rubber was nauseating
I undid my seat belt and dismounted the roller coaster.
The Madness had come to an end.

Justin Davis
Colorado Academy
Denver, CO
Grade 10

Graduation Day

This journey has ended; it's graduation day.
There are many good-byes, we have yet to say.

We had so many good times,
That we'll cherish and remember.
Thinking back, it's like the end of an era.
We won't be coming back, next September.

It makes us sad, and we've shed a few tears,
But it's time to celebrate, and forget all our fears.

We're free to go on, to continue life's journey.
Never to forget our teachers and friends,
Let's be careful, watch out, for the road, how it bends.

Our paths seem to fork, as we go our separate ways.
But let's look back a few times,
And remember our high school days.

Melissa Palicz
Flathead High School
Kalispell, MT
Grade 12

Serendipity

Promises of peace, wonder.
Life called a father, a child.
Dreams of sleep, love at first sight.
Can't refuse to believe in a voice, a mind.
Hopeless listening of wishes, hopes.
Silent Dreaming of rain, roses.
Spirits bear the art of sky, body.

Julie Appelhans
Greeley West High School
Greeley, CO
Grade 12

Half Moon

I must tell you:
Tonight the moon reminds me of myself.
A geometric half.
Surrounded by haze.

Are you pregnant,
Moon?
Are you the yellow breast
Of the sky?

What exquisite
or horrid
children will you bear?

I cannot help it:
The night, the moon,
are rushing toward me.

Growing moon. Growing moon.

Helen Phillips
Colorado Academy
Denver, CO
Grade 12

My Body

My body, my flower of hope
Continuous breaths of wind
Following its winter friend
My gloomy unpaved street
Full of broken fence posts
Scattered pictures from the past
Pulling me toward Heaven
All through the night
Fighting the hungry waves
Engulfing my sense of time
My body, my silent prayer for peace
My body, my faith and understanding
Strengthening the lonely meadow
Following my path of ongoing adventure

Lindsay Carron
Montrose High School
Montrose, CO
Grade 10

The End of My Battle

The black night envelops me, wrapping around me like a cloak.
Raising my eyes to the heavens above, I see the shining stars,
Scattered like diamonds across a velvety sky.

I stand, suffocated and muffled by invisible hands,
Desperately trying to silence my cries.
I will free myself from these smothering hands.

I will tell of the dismal, unforgettable strangers on the street.
Their huge sorrowful eyes pleading for help.

I will tell of the horror of civil war, destroying memories, ripping apart families,
Leaving scars, both physical and mental, that will never be erased.

I will tell of the horrendous religious and racial intolerance,
Running rampant in the world.
Twisted words and ideas mutate love, kindness and acceptance
Into a dark and evil wave of hate, spreading,
Washing over impressionable and ignorant minds.

With my words, I wish to free the world of the dark, looming haze of suffering.
Though many fear the harsh facts of reality, they must understand
And realize the severity of these pressing matters.
They must not turn their backs or add fuel to these ever-growing fires.
If my words reach just one person, change just one mind,
The end of my battle for right will be just one step closer.

Melissa Rosenberg
Arapahoe High School
Littleton, CO
Grade 11

Walking That Path With You

The path I've chosen is endless because I'm walking it with you
Though it seems so much easier
Because you are sometimes there to see me right through
There are a lot of obstacles that I have to overcome
That is when I choose to walk that path alone
But if I were to fall you would be there to help me back up,
You carry me through the bad times and just hold my hand through the good
You don't know how much it means to me
When I see you standing right by my side
I know you cannot be there every day just to see me through
Though I wished you lived a little closer than just an hour and a half away
It would be so much easier
With your lips pressed up to mine your kisses are long and passionate
We just seem to take our time
Which doesn't mean a thing when we're together for such a long while
Though the kisses last just a minute or two I end up thinking about them for days
Until when we have broken up they'll be gone and forever missed
But still I'll always remember the path I'd taken when I was with you!

Alissa Homer
Hurricane High School
Hurricane, UT
Grade 10

Free Spirits

Can I step out of these four walls
and find the flight of existence?
Let us hold hands and enter the fields of injustice,
carrying our convictions and each other's hearts.
And what if I cry?
Will you turn and run for your shelter
or will you still be by my side
when the raven of pain has staked its claim...
and it just so happens to be my heart?
Can you see the silent rape of everyday's pain?
I think you can, you magnificent creature of the earth.
You blend with the very dirt which brought upon
your introduction to the world.
I know you are the very essence of nature,
and the sands of time will not change this fact.
And I'm happy for it;
What would the world be without free spirits
such as you and I?
Keep dreaming, keep living,
because what would become of civilization
if the dreamers stopped dreaming and the living...died?

Amanda Syljuberget
Plentywood High School
Plentywood, MT
Grade 11

The Seasons Here

For sixteen years I've lived here
It's so calm and quiet — nothing to fear
While every season brings something new

In the spring new lambs grow
Tasks begin; gardening and the need to mow
School soon gets out in May
Then you can do nothing all day

It's soon the summer
The break is already a month over — bummer
But it's probably the busiest time
Haying and farming until suppertime

Then it is the fall — school time again
All the animals prepare their dens
It starts to turn cold
And it's when the calves get sold

The winter comes last
It seems that it came way too fast
But all come and go
Whether it's a friend or a foe

Callie Ackerman
Hulett High School
Hulett, WY
Grade 11

What Is Love

Does love come from inside
I know I feel it when you're beside
Do others feel it too
Or is it just me with you

Does love always come with sorrow
And make you feel like there is no tomorrow
Is it even worth a try
When it always seems to make you cry

And why does it seem to make your heart
Feel like a broken part

Whenever you're around
I know this feeling can be found
If just given a try
I promise it's not a lie

And without you
This feeling could not be true
It makes you feel like you're above
Is this what they call love

Please tell me
Please help me
What is love

Jacob Thomas Weston
Round Mountain Jr-Sr High School
Round Mountain, NV
Grade 12

My Angel

When I first met you on that sunny spring day,
I felt something deep inside but I didn't know what to say.
Since then, you've made me a better person in whole,
I love you for that right down to my soul.
I think about you every second that I'm awake,
And wish about the many soft kisses I would take.
I want to be with you every day and night,
To hold you and never let you out of my sight.
Words can't say how deeply I feel about you,
But no one will ever love you as much as I do.
Always and forever, that's what we said,
A vision of us in eternity runs through my head.
I wonder if all the things you say are true,
That you'll never leave and it'll always be me and you.
I love you so much and I hope you feel the same,
I can't wait until that special day when I take your name.
You are my one and only true love,
My angel who was sent from the heavens above.

Paulette Laidler
Bonanza High School
Las Vegas, NV
Grade 11

Exhaust

Exhaust
Billows from the pipe
Obstructs my view
How it smells
Exhaust
Takes over my life
Controls my mind
I must sleep
Exhaust
On inside and out
Billows, controls
I fight back
Exhaust

Annie Schefcik
Clark High School
Las Vegas, NV
Grade 12

Bus of Color

The bright, yellow beamed
And the glowing lights were amazing
When compared to the black and white
World around it.
The kids began to stir
As the dull colored building
Came into view.
The lights flashed
and the doors slowly opened.
Suddenly, a rainbow of colors
Exploded into the sea of lifeless gray.
The colors started to absorb
Into that dreary school.
The children
Were the real color of the world.

Jedydyah Allred
Emery County High School
Castle Dale, UT
Grade 11

Secrets

Tell me,
Does my frailty upset you.
The tears streaming down my face
are gratefully hidden by the rain,
but it can't rain all the time.
The sun which beats
bruises across my skin, you praise.
Cold breath rising from my lips
melts in living presence,
and I am the one running from secrets.
How long can you hide from the truth,
when truth is the mechanical hunter.

Gina Vialpando
Denver School of the Arts
Denver, CO
Grade 10

Here

Beauty is all around me, it swallows me whole.
Huge trees stand like soldiers, their branches their swords,
Allowing golden strings of light to glaze the forest in heavenly hues.
A clean winding book babbles its song as it tumbles over tiny waterfalls and rocks.
It rushes to and fro, racing to some unknown destination.
The lovely birds swoop and call,
They sing their own song yet harmonizing with the brooks mellow tune.
Their chorus touches my heart so deeply that it reaches the huge ocean
That harbors and hides within the enormous abyss of my soul.
The sweet fragrant flowers tease my senses,
They mingle with all the alluring aromas of nature.
The soft rich earth boasts plush plants
That surround me in every which direction.
My heart, my soul, forgets my sorrows untold.
I am free at last, free from sadness or madness; from anger or scorn.
Free at last from the harsh world that binds me
Free from the world I loathe, I despise, I hate.
Here, I'm simply Mother Nature's child, covered by her hand
Here, here is my land.

Sutton Wheeler
Vilas High School
Vilas, CO
Grade 11

Joe*

I don't know where I am,
I know not where you are.
I know not what is in store for me.
I only know of you.

And yearn to see you again.
For I have spent many hours weeping in your passing.
And beg to see your face!
But you are not here.
But I know you are near.

Because I have kept you in my heart.
I have not forgotten you!

Oh for an hour of my life to spend with you again.
I would gladly give all that I own.
Nothing but fun, do I wish.

But alas I must go on without you my friend.
And try to enjoy the company of my friends, as dearly as I cherished with you.

That I might be able to again enjoy life.
For what it is.
Not for what it could be!

Cleve Seiferd
Tonopah High School
Tonopah, NV
Grade 11
*In remembrance of Robert Joseph Bird

Desert Eyes

As dry as a granule of sand
That lies on the barren desert floor,
Her deep dark eyes are left searching.
Searching for one last tear, one last drop of water.
But no tears can they find,
For she has cried them all,
As her lonely heart lies bleeding.

As lonely as the cactus
That independently stands in the desert,
Her deep dark eyes are left searching.
Searching for just one friend, one companion.
But not a soul can they find,
For they have all secluded her from their lives,
All who have caused her lonely heart to bleed.

Kim Buschelman
Green River High School
Green River, WY
Grade 11

The Freeze

Quiet, the rush of leaves
Like stealthy thieves they skitter
And plead to ride the bitter breeze.

Quiet, the brush of sleeves
Like stealthy thieves we scatter
And plead to reach home before the freeze.

David Stroud
Rocky Mountain High School
Fort Collins, CO
Grade 12

What Was

Once what was now can never be
'Cause you took your love away from me.
The love I felt was so sincere
and I loved it when you held me near.
If only I could turn back time
Then you would still be here and mine.
I wish on every star at night
that you again would hold me tight.
I know that you are my soul mate
and I only hope that it's not too late.
'Cause you are my one and only
and without you I am so lonely.
You're the only thing in my head
and to love you is easier done than said.
So now you know how I feel towards you
Please spare my heart and just say you love me too.

Lauren Kahle
Liberty High School
Colorado Springs, CO
Grade 10

Forgotten

Life moves on, but your heart can be left behind.
You feel as if something is pounding in your head,
and that feeling wants to take over your whole body
until it's staring you in the face.
You know it's there,
yet when you try to grab hold of it and keep it inside of you,
there's nothing there.
You feel a sudden emptiness,
and you want that pounding, that aching,
that feel of utter joy and peace and comfort back
for one, at least one
split second.
So you can hold onto it,
taste it;
so you never forget it.
You know that when it leaves you will never feel it again,
you will never know of its presence.
You have to find something that you left behind.
You need to return to your heart, your soul,
your reason to live, or else,
life moves on, but you'll remain forgotten.

Tawni Handley
Hunter High School
Salt Lake City, UT
Grade 12

The Joys of Life

Walks on the beach,
arms around each other,
sharing family outings,
homemade drive-ins.
Ah, those were the days.

Burnt food,
dishes galore,
fighting over simple things,
then making up and saying "I love you!"
Ah, those were the days.

Dirty diapers,
late night feedings,
sleepless nights,
cuddling, rocking, kissing.
Ah, those were the days.

Now we wait for grandkids to visit,
dolls, monster truck sounds, and giggles,
outings to the park with ice cream, lemonade, and candy,
spoiling just because you can.
Ah, these are the days.

Kortney McMullin
Emery High School
Castle Dale, UT
Grade 11

I Wish . . .

I wish I were the rain falling
Freely onto the earth.
Having people dance with me as I fell.
I wish I were an angel,
Keeping people from danger,
Watching their every move.
I wish I were a flower,
Smelling of sweet essence,
Living through the many seasons.
I wish I were a diamond,
Sparkling with such beauty,
Absorbing and releasing all sunshine.

Sunny Waugh
Hulett High School
Hulett, WY
Grade 11

1919

Upon the crest of heaven's defense,
Engulfed in a cloud of potent stench,
Pitched the shells of several men–
One by one into the trench.

Above, the mighty sirens whirled,
And rockets took their flight.
Each life was changed forever,
Within one cold, hard night.

Jennifer LaCombe
Clark High School
Las Vegas, NV
Grade 12

Love Has Wings

Love has wings,
It soars above the sky.
If it were to come down,
Would it still fly?

Love is like an apple,
Juicy and sweet,
Love is like this poem,
Awesome and neat.

Love is very rich,
The price is more than gold,
Love is everlasting,
A story to unfold.

Love is full of gifts,
Love is very fine,
Love is part of life,
And that's the bottom line!

Brandon Pineda
American Fork High School
American Fork, UT
Grade 10

Blindness

I am wealthy, said the blind man
For I have seen what you cannot

You live among a world of shape and color
But I live among a world of truth

You are blinded by everything around you
But my eyes are opened to what is around me

I feel what needs to be felt
While you remain numb to the emotions of life

I sit in total darkness, but in my head and heart there is light
You sit in total brightness, but in your head and heart there is darkness

You focus on outside appearances
While I focus on what is on the inside

In different ways God has given us both sight,
But you take yours for granted

I truly do see everything
But you truly do not
So who really then, is the blind one?

April Deltondo
Montrose High School
Montrose, CO
Grade 12

Wonder

In the green grass of spring I lay
Watching the sun as it rose in the early morning sky.
Wondering how the sun chased the darkness of night away
And listening to the meadowlarks, I had to sigh.

And wonder what the days were like in the past
I pondered this and reflected and finally concluded,
That the sun had always risen, but that each sunrise was different than the last
Some sunny and bright, others that were cloudy gray and diluted.

And then there are the days when everything was calm and content
The days that are not really bright but not cloudy.
These that are the in-between days, the days that were meant
To be enjoyed for the whole day.

And it was a day like this that I lay in the grass
And decided that these were the days that I like best.
The days when I accomplish things and time seems not to pass
Days when everything is at work, yet at rest.

Tom Luhman
Rosebud Public School
Rosebud, MT
Grade 10

Time

The hand falls to the next hour.
The seconds pass by like waves.
Innocence ruined and made sour.
My child cannot be saved.

Eyes watch wrists, the glistening glass.
They too see the hands fall away.
A laugh and thought of the past.
The time and memories gone, nothing left to say.

Like the time, our lives will change.
A leaf touched by time, green, golden, dead.
Child to adult, a thread on which time hangs.
This strength that moves us, unsaid.

The hand falls to the next hour.
The seconds pass by like waves.
Innocence ruined and made sour.
My child cannot be saved.

Jane Hickey
Heritage High School
Littleton, CO
Grade 11

Joe*

I couldn't believe it,
when they said, "Joe's gone,"
I couldn't believe,
your life went so wrong.

It was suppose to be,
the most perfect summer.
But we cried instead,
with one another.

All the memories I have with you,
are blurred behind a twelve pack.
But that's how I remember you,
When I look back.

It could have been anyone,
it didn't have to be you,
I guess that should show us,
what driving drunk will do.

I'll always remember you Joe,
you touched my heart.
Too bad heaven and earth,
are so far apart.

Amy Moore
Tonopah High School
Tonopah, NV
Grade 11
*Dedicated to the memory of Robert Joseph Bird

Kitty, Kitty, Kitty

The kitty was as quick as a rabbit,
But that sorry old cat had a bad habit.
He would sit quietly by the canary's cage,
And wait patiently for his chance to nab it.

Megan Shellabarger
Moffat High School
Moffat, CO
Grade 10

The Adder

The adder, cold, sleep and lethal.
He knows not fear, and yet it lives
In his glazed eyes and forked tongue.
His coils tense, like steel cords.
His black scales shimmering like ebony diamonds.
He ripples forward like a cracking whip.
Silently, stealthfully, whispering his name.
His sleek eeriness causes hatred,
His deadly bite demands respect.
He is not evil, only ruthless, a survivor.
A rod of iron in a basket of sponges.
Silently he lays coiled in readiness.
Quickly he strikes, no time to think twice,
No time for useless emotions,
Only killing, killing to live.
The adder living, killing, and enduring.
Older than the mice and the birds who are his subjects,
Far older than man who is his rival.
A true survivor, a genuine strength in a world of weakness.

Brady Worwood
Emery County High School
Castle Dale, UT
Grade 12

My Junk Drawer

One red stretchy rubber band,
Two tin containers, blue and tan.
Three plastic bowls that are lavender and small,
Right next to a red yarn ball.

Silver oval paper clips,
and just beyond that
a red ribbon that's slick.
A short gray spring
with some nicks and dings,
A round gold lid
which is not for bid.
A tiny yellow rubber car
right alongside
a small jar of tar.

Amy Ligget
Highland High School
Salt Lake City, UT
Grade 11

She

What of love undefined comes to greet me this day?
To whom shall I see to play?
What when beheld I did, she becomes of me. For when I came to see of what I was, I was gone.
It has been there, inside of me. Wouldn't show of the way. Couldn't slow down in my name.
When it came to be the time for us, both but neither came to look.
Was it not to see?
Nothing ever more because of me, when it came upon this day.
No one can do anything to save it.
Look back at not what befell.

Michael Jorgensen
Highland High School
Salt Lake City, UT
Grade 11

Brain Storm

I am a desert pleading mercy from scorching sun rays frying my backbone—as I write poetry.
I implore my brain for ideas, and waiting patiently for reply...
Clouds promenade in, brimming with them, taking their place—front line.
Drops fall sporadically on the arid desert.
Drip-drop-drip—
Tink-tink-drip-drop—
Thoughts collect in shallow pools and trickle down winding crevasses in my brain.
Drip-drop—
Drop-drip—
Then,
Roar!
Crack!
Boom-boom!
Blaring thunder clears her throat.
She has not yet begun to sing.
Fierce lightning ignites midnight skies!
Ideas hammer down on flooded desert grounds
And delicate trickles transformed, now raging rivers—crevasses hardly suffice the bounteous rain.
Heavens fury last minutes more, then, task complete—weightless clouds peel back from the sky
And sun rays choke the crack of dawn.
The desert, mollified.

Jodie Greenwood
Alta High School
Sandy, UT
Grade 12

My Last Shark Tooth Necklace

Crab crawl under flounders, floundering fresh salt water crests,
Each rock has a name as its crawfish, eat the sour fish eggs (they're the best)
But the twelve rows of tearing titan teeth, twist ocean currents south,
As they devour dozens of death row guppies, last seen in the mega mouth,
Of the most feared ferocious fighting finned floaters, floating in the water.
Without second thought in a second, he'll follow and swallow your mother's first daughter,
So leave finely tuned finned fish alone, no matter which warm western water you choose to bathe in,
'Cuz the last water you drink, or the last time you blink, will be in front of a razor sharp fin.

Nico Heitert
Flathead High School
Kalispell, MT
Grade 12

Nocturnal Daydreamer

As I stare into the star lit sky
I sometimes wish that I could fly
Out into that nothingness
That surrounds my world in such a mess

Just fly up to that brilliant star
I'm positive it's not too far
And hang out there for a little while
Maybe someone there can make me smile

Maybe they can comprehend
That a tarnished soul is hard to mend
I don't think anyone here can truly see
How harmful and hurtful that they can be

For when I look at our world today
All I can think to do is pray
Pray that someday it will all turn right
That tongues will be peaceful and hearts will be light

Sean Kane
Columbus Public School
Columbus, MT
Grade 11

Reach Out

There's a simple beauty in each and every child,
They're so calm and meek, yet so strong and wild.
Every breath that angel takes,
Every special moment from the time the child awakes.

Soft spoken and gentle words in their time of need,
How can you ignore their unknowing greed.
Each child is so special no matter who,
Each one so unique and blindly new.

Simple, innocent, and purest in heart,
Each one deserves a chance from the start.
A cruel world condemns our future with each ignored child,
The world is neither soft nor mild.

Alone in a crazy, scary place,
A goofy smile imprisons their terrified face.
Those who turn away cannot see their beauty,
Sometimes you must go beyond your civil duty.

Help the world, one angel at a time,
One child whose heart you'll hold in your hands,
You'll watch as each shower of joy lands.
Outstretch your hand to just one,
You'll never forget the great thing you've done.

Brooke L. Buck
C M Russell High School
Great Falls, MT
Grade 12

El Mundo

From the Bay of Bengal,
    to the seas of Black and the Dead;
From the Great Sahara,
    to the deserts of Death Valley and Mohave;
From the Sun,
    to the great Mayan Sun God:

Entre de Stonehenge,
    and Plymouth Rock;
Entre de Rocky Mountains,
    and Andes;
Entre de Siberian Peninsula,
    and Yucatan:

The Earth to the Moon, the Moon to the Sun,
The Sun to the Stars, the Stars to the Universe:

To the unbreached world of unknown,
    we are looked upon as everybody else,
To the cultures of each,
    we are different in each way:

Todo la gente, time is the future and past:

For el mundo time is all the same and the people too.

Dusty Axtell
Valley High School
Gilcrest, CO
Grade 11

Of Mice and Men

George and Lennie had a dream
A dream to own their own home
To have their very own place
So they could work at their own pace
No more borders that they weren't allowed to cross
No more taking orders from a stupid old boss
No more of working all the way to the max
And on some days they could just sit back and relax
But it all depends on whether or not they can make their ends
Lucky for them, they find a new friend
They need some cash
Or else their dream will not last
Their new friend, Candy, will help pay
And now for only one more month they would have to stay
But once again, Lennie gets into trouble
Once again they are thrown into a puzzle
Just when they were climbing their ladder to success
Their dreams were shattered and everything is a mess.

Clay Call
Highland High School
Salt Lake City, UT
Grade 11

Up Ta It

8 Seconds a
Bone shatterin'
Earth shakin'
Clown skatterin'

Teeth grindin'
Crowd whistlin'
Balance findin'
Fingers pistolin'

Bull spinin'
Arm twistin'
Did ya know you're grinnin'

Butt bruisin'
Spur kickin'
Marble loosen'
Horn stickin'

Record breakin'
Ground slammin'
Rail skatin'
Shoulder jammin'

Ya up ta it

Heather Tiller
Centerville High School
Sand Coulee, MT
Grade 10

afraid

we are all afraid
to be anything
other than nothing,
life penetrates inside
making us hollow
unfeeling, suicidal,
the tendencies
lifestyles we can live with
surpass us
we are all alone
tired,
wanting,
something,
anything.
ALL,
nothing that we can be
is sufficient.
all else is death
beautiful, aging
and again detached.
only for me.

Freak Williams
Granger High School
Salt Lake City, UT
Grade 12

Slavery

Slavery in America,
Ruled the lives of many,
They worked hard for a living,
And didn't earn a penny.

Blacks came here from Africa,
It was not under their own will;
Plantation masters wanted workers,
It just so happens that they fit the bill.

They are people just like everyone else,
There is no reason for them to be treated like that.
"All men are created equal" and should be treated that way,
Unfortunately slaves of the time were not, they were whipped and beaten like a rat.

Slaves are people just like us, everyone finally did see,
Now they have their freedom, so do we,
Everyone is happy because we are free,
We all know that is the way it should be.

Ben Kovanda
Columbus Public School
Columbus, MT
Grade 11

My Last Plea

I ask you please to help me find strength for the heart, soul, and mind.
Before this life ends with death, before I take my one last breath.
Some things I've seen are not so good. What I haven't done I wish I could.
I've felt torture, pain, and hurt. I've had the joy that followed hurt.

I know that I am but one man, but change the world I hope I can.
I'll do my best, and try some things. I'll find a song, which I can sing.
I've done my best, at least for now. I have to change a life somehow.
To live and love, to love and live, the greatest things I've tried to give.

As things in life come and go. Could that be me? I have to know.
When I lie underneath the ground will I be marked? Can I be found?
Now as I lay here, as I pray here.
Hands and arms stained with blood, my eyes begin to fill and flood.

I want to see the ones I knew, the ones I've helped, the ones that grew.
Some way I know I've helped someone. That way in life I know I've won.
Take me now to better places. Take me to find and help more faces.
A blooming rose in a bed of sand. The things you've done with an offered hand.

The one true Master says it's time. I leave knowing you'll be fine.
We'll be together once again when everyone has had their chance.
Some things I hate about my life, but knowing you was never strife.
I have to go. The time has come. And saying this, I am now done.

Patrick Neilsen
Juab High School
Nephi, UT
Grade 12

Elian Gonzales, in Search of Freedom.

Torn between two countries,
like a letter ripped in two,
his heart in one, his family in the other,
what should this miracle child do?

Without mother, or country,
without freedom, or pride,
a courageous young Cuban boy,
is a miracle in the public eye.

Not a war did he fight,
not a life did he save,
but many hearts did he steal,
when he conquered the waves.

The dolphins that swam with him,
they say were his guardians,
as if sent down from heaven,
from his mom who's so proud of him.

What they wanted was freedom;
what he got was much more:
a country supporting him,
through this senseless tug-of-war.

Chris Alvarez
Sparks High School
Sparks, NV
Grade 10

Black and White

Constant. Forever. Always.
She shared my feelings, soft or loud, slow or fast
Looming majestically in her corner
Shadowing us like a great tower.

So many hours spent sitting at her feet.
Patiently, or not so patiently, learning,
Exploring, practicing, listening,
Talent growing, children growing.

Like a teacher she gave herself to me,
Her student. I played,
Expressing my feelings through the songs I learned at her side
Lovingly caressing the black and white keys.

Her heart was open, so was mine
Everything I know, I learned with her
Broken pedals, busted bench, sore fingers
Aching wrists, aching hearts, results—well worth the pain.

Emily Van Natter
Northridge High School
Layton, UT
Grade 10

Last of Something

When fled in vacillating corners,
Smudged in black and gray,
Misplaced the pointed lines of glass,
Sharded shallow place.

Some focus broke- it- all- light Sir,
And candles' demure gaze,
Breathe vapor mist'd- the Ragged Sounds
Condensed upon the Lash

My When- and Why- as cufflinks
Braced- my finite Space,
Half-lids in Melancholy dearth-
The dark that scraped the Face.

When sleep set in, the Endpoint, One,
Corrosive- Human- Meek-
So screamed some fading, Embers, down;
And Death- with Broom- beat back.

Jane McDaniel
Chatfield High School
Littleton, CO
Grade 11

Heavy Rain so Sweet

Quietly burning inside a poor dying star,
There's a blue-glowing soul, thrown completely afar.
Too many times, feeling tired at heart,
Always hoping and groping for the filling part.

Eyes burned out from thumping, hostile rays,
Gasping and thrashing through and endless maze.
Finally, the clouds swim in, peaceful and gray,
"Oh come, oh come sweet rain, surely do stay."

The heavy rain drops and the heavy rain falls,
Splashing and washing those worn rock-walls.
She cuddles and puddles all who go near,
Whispers, "Reveal yourself, there's nothing to fear."

Deluging and nudging his hurt away,
Only with he, is she determined to stay.
More than ever, is he thoroughly pleasured,
Mind and body feeling extremely unfettered.

Gazing far within this great, compassionate sky,
This soul realizes enough to graciously cry.
Both feeling at peace with the new acquaintance found,
Each understanding the other, delicate and sound.

Joseph Chung
Sky View High School
Smithfield, UT
Grade 12

Love of Any Kind

I met you and it was like
A dream come true
How lucky could one person be
Some people look their whole lives
I found you at the beginning of mine
When I gaze into your eyes
I see my life laid out ahead of me
When I am near you I get that
Tingle in my tummy
Some people do not believe in it
But that is because they are
Blind to it and envy those who have it
Love Of Any Kind

Brooke Binford
Mancos High School
Mancos, CO
Grade 12

Autumn

Leaves cling to the branch
Holding strong
Their color fades
Becoming lifeless and droopy

Wind gusts
Coaxing the leaves to follow
Twisting and turning
Finally relinquishing

Fading away
As though never existing

Kjell Hansen
Billings West High School
Billings, MT
Grade 12

Halloween

Face paint that smells like melted crayon
Costumes made of stuff called rayon
Candy gathered by the ton
Man, Halloween is lots of fun.

The day after Halloween

The sugar high has long since crashed
The air still smells of pumpkins smashed
My teeth feel like they've rotted away
I've gained six pounds since yesterday!

Ryan Purser
Sky View High School
Smithfield, UT
Grade 12

Black Night

I rest my eyes for the night.
Outside the rain pours in sheets.
I usually sleep better during a storm,
but tonight is different.
The night gets blacker.

The thunder claps.
Lightning does not follow.
I'm awakened by footsteps,
unsure of who it may be.
The night gets blacker.

Hitler howls in pain,
Sheba joins in like a chorus.
I lay quiet and motionless.
My door squeaks open.
The night gets blacker.

Another clap of thunder.
The footsteps enter my room.
Lightning finally flashes,
too little, too late.
The night gets blacker.

Bobby Brewer
Sheridan High School
Sheridan, WY
Grade 12

Foggy Perception

A misty gaze
Hazes
Over the eye
Unable to see
What may really be there.
Unwanting to know
What may really be there.
Altered vision
That adapts to one's desires
Looking through the fog
To a perfect world.
Where everything is
Beautiful.
Open your eyes
And look through
The clouds
To see
What may really be there.
And face reality.

Kristen Berry
Greeley Central High School
Greeley, CO
Grade 10

Family

Parents are like judges
Sisters are like teachers
Family is like being judged and taught

John Reierson
Lewis-Palmer High School
Monument, CO
Grade 11

Someone Let Me Know

Why am I who I am
Why am I the way I am
Why do I act the way I do
Why do I look the way I do

I always strive for perfection
I always watch what others do
I try to be a better person
I try to be someone I am not

No longer do I know who I am
No longer do I act the way I feel
No way can I figure to find myself
No way can I become perfect

Someone tell me you love me
Someone tell me I am perfectly imperfect
Someone let me know I am appreciated
Someone let me know

Monica Reed
Bonanza High School
Las Vegas, NV
Grade 12

Life

Life . . .
What is life?
Life can be so complicated.
Life can be very scary.
So scary that sometimes you don't
Even want to get out of bed.
My life is such a roller coaster.
But I'm ready to get off this ride.
We live our lives everyday.
Some days good . . .
Some days bad . . .
But we learn from our mistakes in life.
Life . . .
What is life?
Life is what you make it. . .

Tamara Yvonne Williams
Clifton, CO
Grade 10

Differences

We now declare people: different
Bend and string it through iron.
I join my life with thread,
And my riches, and with other different people.
To be remembered, though I dream it only,
I am different.

I reach over and down at the different people,
When the cowherd sobbed,
Antinous growled.

They go to pieces over no big thing, but they break anyway.

Can we
Get on with dinner quietly,
Outside?

If I receive a clean-cut, nobody bends his back
In this company to help.
A promise was made from childhood:
To love.

I thought to span and drill;
Destined to feel and taste blood:
The rest must live in peace,
For we are all different.

Jessica Errett
Arapahoe High School
Littleton, CO
Grade 11

G666 Kamikaze

He's as tame as a kitten
And felt like a mitten
As you get into the chute
You have spurs on boots
You test your nerves just to get on
Your gloves all rosined and your rope is pulled
Time to get on and ride like there is no tomorrow
For a full eight
Hold on tight
He's been known to belly roll
And even to spin
No one can ride him when he gets you in the well
Make sure your hand comes out
Or you'll get hung he'll kill if he gets the chance
When you hit the ground
Hit it running
For his name is Kamikaze

Alfredo Munoz
Emery County High School
Castle Dale, UT
Grade 12

Hotel Policy

We pay much money to come visit your town,
But it seems like you want us to leave with a frown.
You tell us to come and visit your pool,
But you close at ten and enforce the rule.

You tell us we cannot gather in the hall,
You yell at us because you may think someone may fall.
We go down to the lobby to satisfy you,
We get yelled at more because you think we're not true.

You come in our rooms and shut our doors,
We get really mad and leave presents like apple cores.
We pay much money to come visit your town,
But it seems like you want us to leave with a frown.

Alex Huffield
Columbus Public School
Columbus, MT
Grade 10

Graduation Day

Today is the day I'm all dressed up in blue
I've got my cap and gown on, too!
Finally, it's time

It's time
All the kinds of thoughts sweep into my mind
And intertwine

Ring, there goes the bell
One more time school was fun

I've finally won!!!

What's that sound?

It's shots from a GUN!
Someone yells out, "QUICK, RUN!"

My mood now changed
I was excited; now confused and deranged
I feel a swift, sharp piercing pain in my back.

What was that?
Could it have been?

I don't know.
       Everything
           is going
               black . . .

Katy Hancock
Hunter High School
Salt Lake City, UT
Grade 12

I Almost Remember

A simple smile, the slightest glance
something to indicate
maybe someday we'd have a chance.

Feelings were hurt and things were said
stuff that I recall often makes me wish
that I would have used my head.

I met someone new who seemed to offer more,
but it felt wrong and I wanted to make it right
the minute I walked out that door.

Now I read letters, most of them speak of you
they tell me you've found love somewhere else
still I can't help but wonder if there are feelings between us two.

I got the chance to touch you once
but only for a moment
I want so badly to hold you once more
before I go but I'll dream for now
and hold you in my heart and my mind
but always in my dreams.

Stephanie Wiltfang
Rosebud Public School
Rosebud, MT
Grade 12

Times to Remember

The times you'll remember
will be the times of truth
the times you're happy
when you are really you
the times you're sad
when you are truly hurt
the times of friendship
that will never end
the times of you
when you never want the moment to end
the times when you meet that special someone
a friend or a crush
the times when you are proud to be you
when you win the gold
when you reach your goal
when you ace a test
when you get that first kiss
when you get what you want
the times that are irreplaceable
and will last for years to come
are the times you'll always remember

Ashley Moehr
Kelly Walsh High School
Casper, WY
Grade 11

Just Because I'm a Girl

Just because I'm a girl
   I'm not stupid
   I'm not a pushover
   I'm not ditzy

Just because I'm a girl
   I don't sleep around
   I don't flash my feminine features
   to get what I want

Just because I'm a girl
   doesn't mean I can't do it as good as you
   better than you
   or even ten times better than you

Just because I'm a girl
   I don't belong in the kitchen
   I don't need a man's money to support me
   I am a good driver

Just because I'm a girl
   doesn't mean you can push me aside
   I'll push you back—harder
   I'm not a wimp

Just because I'm a girl

Jennifer McDuffee
Sparks High School
Sparks, NV
Grade 12

The Day

He joined me in a scared and troubled state
His words were as a sword striking a man
The man was my heart, breaking in his face
The pain was so great, I could barely stand.

Words were said, and some tears did fall
Troubled looks were seen and hearts breaking heard
Great times returned from when we had a ball
The entire night was just absurd.

Within a moment he was out the door
The tears now freely came without much haste
The arms of a good friend were at the core
Acting as my steady and solid base.

Time has gone on, as time will always play,
Memories will never fade from that day.

Kristin Franks
Highland High School
Salt Lake City, UT
Grade 12

I Used to Dream

I used to dream of angels who would hold me tight
With feathered white wings and strong golden arms
I used to long for angels to wipe away my tears

I used to dream of snowflake kisses—
A gift from heaven that would rain from the sky
That would linger on my forehead, eyelashes and lips

I used to dream of hope and peace
Only an angel can send by his gentle whisper
And solid truths that would forever change my heart

I used to dream of hands
Strong and calloused that would work miracles
Soft like wind to lighten my mind

Winter melted into Spring
Inside the crisp fall of my heart
The day that I met him

In his disguise he hid his heaven sent harp
And in his sky blue eyes and glowing smile
I knew I found my little piece of Heaven

Heidi Anderson
Northridge High School
Layton, UT
Grade 12

A Thing That Grows Inside Us All

In a place, I do not know, there grows a thing inside us all.
That grows and shrinks on regular occasion.
It makes you feel just like an innocent doll.

This thing is good, that is in us all.
It screams and yells until you are used to the temptation.
In a place, I do not know, there grows a thing inside us all.

This thing is secret, behind the invisible wall.
It keeps eating at you until you give up or give in.
It makes you feel just like an innocent doll.

You may not admit you have it at all,
But the thing inside you wants to tell all creation.
In a place, I do not know, there grows a thing inside us all.

This thing that runs you up the wall,
Is a thing called love that gives you blurred vision.
In a place, I do not know, there grows a thing inside us all.
It makes you feel just like an innocent doll.

Sean Durham
Sky View High School
Smithfield, UT
Grade 10

Personal Regard

Tell me what in life this world wants me to be.
Please tell me the secrets I can't seem to see.
I have often strived to do my very best,
Yet I only seem to pass every other test . . .

Searching and searching for answers to peace,
I have only found myself lost and frustrated to say the least.
People around me seem to fit together round about,
I feel as though I'm different and that I just stand out.

I question my morals, I question my standards,
And what am I to do with a life so slandered???
My talents, gifts, and blessings by far exceed my will . . .
I wonder if I will ever fit the shoes set for me to fill . . .
I live life free of sadness, free of pain . . .
But answer me, why I feel so insane???

A mystery life can be,
An insanity often is something man never can see . . .
Blinded by his dreams and strongest desires
Will soon form the reason his life never aspires . . .

The roads in life often have no answer,
They're just there to be lived for the experience,
And to further build our knowledge to a higher measure.

Jeremy Ware
Viewmont High School
Bountiful, UT
Grade 11

Stars Above*

Your light is brighter than any star I've seen
Brighter than the moon above
Your brightness breaks the darkness
A sign of your promise
That we'll never be alone
As we trust the stars for guidance
In this dark world
I trust you
The people we love are the stars above us
And now one is fading
A wish, a hope, a life is yours
It is up to you
Shall this star dim forever
Or continue to shine for you
It is your will
But this star will always shine in my heart
Forever reminding me of you

John Bentley
Flathead High School
Kalispell, MT
Grade 11
*For Boyd

Some Things Can't Be Forced

Some things can't be forced
a smile, a breeze,
a child, a tree.
All things in time
time will reveal.
Peace.
Be still.

MaryAnn Moore
Bonneville High School
Ogden, UT
Grade 12

Growing Up . . .

I dream through evening sleep
Of a morning hour that will chill all
A promise now that I shall like him less
Yet ask for time off to fall.

I long to tell you how I was
Or perhaps just turn from this feeling
But to the garden he wandered after me
And so my mind is still reeling.

Me, a child, danced there in the garden
As softly as she were a spring rain
Oh how I loved her spirited life
Never will I venture this path again.

The storm whispers a strange story
Colors the earth with mud
Now I am grown and I long for him
My emotions crash like waves in a flood.

Julie Collins
Hulett High School
Hulett, WY
Grade 11

To Take a Chance

It's getting hard; the road is rough.
The task before me seems so tough.
I thought it simple; I could win,
But was this choice somehow a sin?
Should I have stayed where I was safe,
No challenges to undertake?
Or was it right to take a stand
And hold my life within my hands?
To take a chance and risk it all
With glory greater than my fall?
So here I am; my choice is clear,
To take a chance and face my fears
And find inside the strength I need
To charge ahead and take the lead.

Jessica A. Wade
Reedpoint Jr/Sr High School
Reedpoint, MT
Grade 11

Hate

The power of hate is so strong,
Sometimes it over rules what's right and what's wrong,
Some hate comes from within the soul,
While others come from the mind both from the cold,
When hate is based on clothes, attitude, or other people's friends,
These things are crazy that need to end,
The hate steps over a thin line called prejudice,
That needs to decline,
It's everywhere in the movies, on the news, at our schools,
All of this we see is unfair.
To be disliked because of skin color or ethic background can make one angry,
That shows more action than just a frown,
Why are people like this? What are they against?
Can't we say we are all the same?
That we don't have to be given a name,
If there was only one race between us,
Will people still hate and make such a fuss,
Knowing the ignorance of people today,
We are all lying if "NO" is what we'd say,
We are all people living together and we ask ourselves,
Will hate last forever?

Amie Thomas
Hotchkiss High School
Hotchkiss, CO
Grade 10

Do I Exist

If I am all alone in the mist
Do I exist?
If I look in the mirror and no one looks back
Do I exist?
If I fall in a lake and the water does not ripple
Do I exist?
If my heart beats fast when I walk by her . . .
But she doesn't know I am there . . .
Do I exist?
If I am all alone in a deep forest when even the ground I walk on,
The air I breathe does not know I am there
Do I exist?
If I am alone in a crowded room,
And I scream at the top of my lungs but no one hears...
Do I exist?
And if I do not exist do my eyes see?
Do I bleed when torn?
Do I cry when hurt?
If I were to walk on a lonely street on a cold, rainy day,
And I fell to the ground and I fell from this world . . .
Would I exist?

Bret Combe
Fremont High School
Ogden, UT
Grade 11

I Will Survive

They walk to el mercado slowly, as if they are old and tired,
Afraid, always watching for danger,
Fruit and homemade goods to sell.

Los hijos will never understand
They know no different, and don't care
They must survive.

Papa fell with the war; mama cleans houses and is never home,
The children must take care of themselves
They are alone

Life on the border isn't easy they are constantly told
Mire a los gringos—
The children want to live like them, but fear what may happen
Secretly they wish to cross the border
Perhaps they will lose as mama and papa did.

Something that seems so close is still so far away
A short mile separates them; it can feel like eternity

They hold the future; should they reach out and grab it?
Take the chance on the unknown
Prove to themselves they are not like mama and papa
They will be different
They will survive.

Nicole Fuller
Valley High School
Gilcrest, CO
Grade 12

The American Child

My parents never took me to McDonald's
and I missed out
on being an American child.
Instead they fed me chicken soup
with matza balls,
kosher chicken.
Their food did not prepare me to face the world—
it was too healthy.

Now I buy myself a Big Mac and eat it
while sitting in front of the computer,
watching words come up on the screen,
talking to friends from other states.
I have to delete three pieces of e-mail every day—
hidden ads for triple-X sites.
and sometimes I wonder—
Why doesn't Mother make chicken soup anymore?

Daniela Uslan
Denver School of the Arts
Denver, CO
Grade 12

The Way It Is In Poetry

Words that inspire monster fury
and free the tempest within.
Thoughts make real progress
to seize the strong lust
of ridiculous time against shame.
Torture fair dreams and loathe the machine.
Dark demand shocks another.
Stop.

Paris Lumb
Crested Butte Academy
Crested Butte, CO
Grade 12

More Than Love

What truly is love?
Is it the gentle touch of a mother on her newborn baby,
The firm hand of a father on his growing son,
Or the precious time spent between two close friends?
One might say that these are all feelings of love,
But how can one word mean so much?
How can one word be so broad?
What if you experience something far greater than these,
If you feel something so incredible it changes your life,
Is that still just love?
And if that feeling grows stronger each day,
How can tomorrow's feeling still be just love?
Fall for an angel and you will see,
That there is a feeling so much greater than love.
It must be heaven.

Michael McBee
Haxtun High School
Haxtun, CO
Grade 11

In Order to Grow

I wanted your love, you pushed me away.
My love for you grows stronger with each day.
I wanted your love, I had no control.
My heart overpowered my mind and soul.
I wanted your love, instead you gave pain.
I swore I'd never fall in love again.
I wanted your love, and it hurts to see.
The love within you is too good for me.
I wanted your love, but the time has come
To face the truth and finally move on,
I wanted your love, and not one thing else.
I wished to be happy, accept myself.
I wanted your love, only now I know,
I had to be hurt in order to grow.

Ashley Bodily
Escalante High School
Escalante, UT
Grade 10

Fast Food

Hot dog or Big Mac
...no want heart attack
Onion rings, French fries
...fat in disguise
Soft drink or milkshake
...no like stomach ache

Phillip Abram
C M Russell High School
Great Falls, MT
Grade 12

God Is a Pillow

God is a pillow.
It comforts me just when I think
Nothing will ever again.
I can calmly cry on a pillow
And it will never shun my tears.
I can talk, even complain,
And it never interrupts.

It comforts my sad soul and makes sleep
Something to appreciate,
Not something I hate to do.
God is a pillow
Because like a pillow,
He'll never turn me away.
I can learn on its strong shoulder
Anytime, day or night,
And it's always there to listen,
Just like God.

Rebecca Kelln
Montrose High School
Montrose, CO
Grade 12

Silver Spoons

Tossing spoons into the river,
  rippling chaos to my reflection,
  while young and unknowing.
Perched on my mossy log,
  flying spoons on the crisp breeze,
  I hit poor fish scurrying for shelter.
"You there!" Bellowed a distant fisher,
"Those fish have not wronged you."
My eyes shifted to my dirty hand,
  guilty with no doubt,
  and I thought to myself.
What have I done,
  to these poor creatures,
  with my punishing silver.
But could I possibly see,
  that I truly needed the spoons?

Alice Kaminski
Arapahoe High School
Littleton, CO
Grade 11

My Wall

I can build a wall
To shield you from my inner sight
To protect me and keep me from wandering
Too far into the vast, unsure sea of emotions
That secretly hides my feelings for you.

Although helpful, my wall cannot save me forever
Because it is unsturdy; it will not be constructed of cement.
And with time, I know,
It will come crashing down
Only to silently reveal my true, genuine feelings for you again.

My wall is there to protect me.
Yet only temporarily, for a short time.
And during this time I merely see you
As another typical and average human being
Instead of a single red rose that stands out in a bouquet of black ones.

But once my wall, my shielding mask has toppled,
I know that it's all over.
My uncertain, insecure feelings are exposed to me again
And the remains unveil what I've waited but dreaded to see—
You through the eyes of my heart.

Kate Neely
Pinedale High School
Pinedale, WY
Grade 10

Two Soldiers

Two soldiers face life's battlefield, one great and one "recalled."
No matter what their strength of men their voices won't be stalled!
These two are leaders of their ranks—these two courageous friends—
For they contain within their hearts the tune to vict'ry's end.

They face all gothic fights with pride, their eyes a burning fire'.
To ride in front for their Great King is but these two's desire!
As time wore on the soldier fierce gained his investiture.
He hoped one day his humble friend would ride, but first, live pure.

The soldier, "recalled," made his vows—he swore to serve his King—
"Though life's battle severs my flesh, I'll wait my turn to swing!"
Thus these two soldiers went their ways—each man to play his part.
Their pathways separated them, but that's the dragon's art!

The dragon knows these two bring death, the dragon fears these two!
But still these soldiers carry on, in sackcloth only? True!
These soldiers ride for their Great King, they'll fight, obey and roam.
These soldiers ride where others fear—and will until called home!

Dalyon Ruesch
Hurricane High School
Hurricane, UT
Grade 12

Freedom

To be set free,
Is like the sun breaking through
On a gray, cloudy day.

It's a ray of sunshine,
Peeking from the white, happy clouds.
Or a single brightly-lit star,
In the middle of a great big sky.

Someday, we will all be set free,
To fly with utmost grace and charm,
Like an old dove soaring with her wings spread wide.

To be able to accept death,
As a part of life,
Knowing that we'll all meet again
In a place too good to describe.

To know the melody of a tune
And dance to it by the moonlit night,
That is what it's like to be free.

Amber Garland-Rutledge
Pahrump High School
Pahrump, NV
Grade 10

Wake Up

One day you will figure it out,
Something you needed to know.
All the people surrounding you,
Now know what you don't.
You are fading fast.
Then your life flashed before your eyes.
Faster & faster, your head begins to turn.
Round & round, until it stops!
You stop! Your heart stops! The world stops!
What happened are you dead?
No you are just spinning in circles.
You were just playing around.
But it scared you, because you fell, and you hurt yourself.
Physically or mentally? It doesn't matter.
You tell yourself, you'll be all right.
You try to stand up, but you can't, you're stuck!
How do you get up? Why did you fall?
You start to cry! You call your parents.
No one is there, no one can hear you.
And then... you wake up and there you are...
In your dreams!

Tina Johnson
Boulder City High School
Boulder City, NV
Grade 11

Eternal Memories

A tranquil summer's breeze, soothing and gentle,
Sweeps through a meadow speckled with sleepy oak trees,
Past long deserted farms,
Through cold and empty barns,
Eventually discovering a beating heart
Steadily rocking on a weather worn porch.
Once bursting with joy and delight,
This lonely heart now throbs with sadness and woe.
Only spirits of the past remain
In place of friends and family long departed.
As a tired and ancient sun
Slowly drifts behind rough and jagged mountains,
So do the sacred memories that clutter this heart
Drift into the depths of the soul,
For eternal safe keeping.

Heidi Shray
Arapahoe High School
Littleton, CO
Grade 11

I Lost Him

I remember
When I was five—
Saturday morning with the comic strips.

I remember the tire swing
He made, comforting, hard—
But it suited me just right.

I remember his hands.

He was small.
But he was strong—strong like
I was when I lost him.
I don't remember
it too well and sometimes
I wish I'd forget.
I haven't lost him, but I know he's gone.

Sometimes I listen for his voice.
I know it's there.
It only comes when I need it and never in waste.

I lost him, but I know he'll be back.
Like the dried out autumn leaves as they fall.
They'll come back—I just have to wait.

I lost him.

Beth Easton
Virgin Valley Jr/Sr High School
Mesquite, NV
Grade 11

My World

I sat by the side,
Arms behind,
Hands down flat,
Head tilted to the sky.

Dark all around,
Silent as can be,
Coolness fills the air.

Misty sprays dampen my skin.
Water falls silently through empty space,
Reshaping the dark pools below.

I creep closer,
Sharpness cuts the skin.
The pain goes unnoticed.

Sweet but bitter aromas,
Fill my head.

Coolness touches my toes,
Up lower limbs,
Blankets my shoulders,
Then encases my head.

All alone,
In my own silky world.

Beth Cole
Branson School
Branson, CO
Grade 11

Mad Man

The mad man is seeing
Through his own eyes
But is he believing
Or are they all just lies

Through his own eyes
He has the cards, it's his turn to deal
Or are they all just lies
Watching his prey, hoping to kill

He has the cards, it's his turn to deal
He dreams tender dreams
Watching his prey, hoping to kill
But wants to destroy life as it seems

He dreams tender dreams
The mad man is seeing
But wants to destroy life as it seems
But he is believing.

Derek Sirois
Lake County High School
Leadville, CO
Grade 12

Greedy Little Brat

A teardrop has fallen and everyone's to blame.
No good-bye, no thank you, just a rude comment and a sigh.

Why must this happen? Why can't I die?

Money is a terrible thing and I can tell a lie, but not about money.
Not about this curse.
Never get caught up in it or you could lose more than it's worth.
Yes, I've been selfish.
I needn't be.
Yes, I've hurt others, not just me.

How could this happen? How could this be?

The curse of money is what I did not see.
I'm sorry to be selfish.
I'm sorry to be me.
This is how I am and how I won't be.
I will try to overcome it, try to withstand.
The powers that invoke me, I will push away with my hand.
For now though, all I can do is say I'm sorry.

Emily Hibsman
Kelly Walsh High School
Casper, WY
Grade 12

Missing Something

A mournful day such as this.
We wonder what we could have missed.
A man lies dead; a gun next to him.
He has just committed the greatest sin.
To take his own life with one shot to the head.
And there he lies as death is dead.
A wonderful man's senseless tragedy.
His heart to me remains a mystery.
Understand? No nobody can. Except the angels above and that man.
In the ground his cold body lies.
While in the clouds his soul flies.
Gliding through the air like planes he once flew.
Why? I wish he only knew. How much he's missed and loved at home.
But now he walks where the spirits roam.
As he protects and looks down on us.
He still feels my love in his heart, I trust.
Heaven is where he lives; I will too.
Heaven, where all your dreams come true.
"Ryan's happier now," I comfort my mother.
While at the same time I ask myself, "Why did God take my brother?"

Natalie Anthony
Mojave High School
Las Vegas, NV
Grade 11

To Belong

The sun broke through the horizon
The rays of warmth
Rose above Durango
Defrosting my ice cold transport.
As the tears of water
Trickled down the shell
The piercing silence
Sent chills up my spine.
What was I thinking?
When I came here
They knew I was different.
My background shows in every aspect
Of who I am:
Looks, language
And most importantly culture.
I try to fit in.
The color of my skin makes it more obvious.
I feel like a chocolate chip in a can of mixed nuts.
They know I don't belong
I'll go on and live
But I'll never belong.

Gina Croci
Valley High School
Gilcrest, CO
Grade 11

Seasons

First it begins with the end of snow,
Bringing spring on the go.
New life begins to appear,
Bringing young ones who have no fear.
The grass and trees all turn green,
Making it the most beautiful sight you've ever seen.
As the young ones get a little older,
Summer comes around making everything bolder.
Heat comes along making you sweat,
But rain comes too making everything wet.
Then before you know it summer is gone,
Bringing in fall that doesn't last very long.
The leaves turn colors and fall to the ground,
Leaving no green at all to be found.
The air turns cold and soon you will see,
Snowflakes falling to the ground ever so gently.
Soon the ground is completely white,
And ice forms everywhere in the middle of the night.
After what seems like a very long time,
The sun comes up and begins to shine.
Slowly spring appears then, and the cycle begins again.

Amy Neiman
Hulett High School
Hulett, WY
Grade 11

Reality

The beginning is now the end.
People transform into monsters
And animals become companions.
The changes arouse like a flash of lightning
And there is no way to change it back.
We look at the past as fictional
And view the nonfictional as fact.
We rely on no one
And yet worship deities.
We understand only what we know
And expect the unknown to disappear.
Our only confidant is our soul
But every person is experiencing the same feelings.
We love our possessions
And hate each other.
Our eyes remain closed
But happiness is only over the rainbow.
We closed our eyes to the reality that devours us.

Carly Nilson
Arapahoe High School
Littleton, CO
Grade 11

Years Past

From years that have passed from future days
The days of young seem so distant and far.
I think of these things in the meadow blue
Where the birds serenade the frosty green.

Down the trail of flowers full of life
Where once I hunted with familiar acquaintances.
The birds chirp the recollection of days past.
With a droplet of water forming in my eye
I swallow my pride and begin to cry.

Here my confidant lies expired from the past days.
I know his fate is not far from me.
My wife holds me in this leafed town
As the priest continues in this childless place.

I am soon immersed in my windfall youth
With friends laughing and playing in oblivious content.
Their words echoing in subdued sound
"Great husband, father, friend, and follower."
And as the lines of Psalm 23 roll off the minister's tongue
I feel a smile crack across my face.

For I know my time will soon come, and I shall return to young.

Keith Williams
Columbus Public School
Columbus, MT
Grade 12

I Am . . .

I see the way it should be
I see self-esteem
The belief in myself
I am I
And that's who I want to be

I see the way it is
I see me doing things I don't want to do
Others determine my actions
I'm not who I want to be
And that's who I am

I see the way I will go
I see myself doing it how I want to do it
Don't be told
Don't be pushed
'Cause that's not I

Steffen Thies
Fernley High School
Fernley, NV
Grade 11

Unspoken Words

When we became friends
    it was a dream come true.
The feelings that I once held back
    are now only focused on you.

And each day this love grows stronger,
    but I could never let you know.
There's so much behind my smile
    that I could never show.

The love I see in your eyes
    is not meant for me.
The affection that we share
    is only my fantasy.

Someday you will realize
    we are destined to be together.
From that moment on
    it will be you and I forever.

So, I will dream of us together
    of how perfect we could be.
And all that you are
    will remain a silent part of me.

Becky Byerly
Big Piney High School
Big Piney, WY
Grade 11

Emotions

Approaches the mind
locks on for life
hides the truth
relaxes the heart
soothes the mind
gathers the thoughts
cleans the light
and breathes life
hunts us by day
scares us at night
protects the body
rides the mind
heals our thoughts
selects the feelings
redesigns the past
grips a soul
plays with the mind
imagines the future
unfolds the heart

Caitlin Noe
Fairview High School
Boulder, CO
Grade 12

Gift

Present
Under
A
Tree
Wrapping paper—
Tight
Neat
Perfect

Then
Clawing
Hands
Tearing
Shredding
Destruction

After—
Mutilated
Alone
On
The
Floor

Alison Slyziuk
Colorado Academy
Denver, CO
Grade 10

Life Goes On

she walks
she talks
i see her
her face is pure and angelic
she pierces the room
we steal a glance
eyes meet
hands touch
time stops
LIFE GOES ON
we walk
we talk
i stare
she stares, eyes aglow
hands meet
lips touch
i forget
she smiles at me,
her eyes shining through me
there is only now
LIFE GOES ON

John Rowland
Cottonwood High School
Salt Lake City, UT
Grade 12

The Music

your mind set changes
when you feel the flow
seep in your head
slowly spreading
from limb to limb
and like a wave
your mind sets in
emptiness fades
reality dissipates
the little grains
that make up
your imagination
begin to spin
when you listen
listen to the feeling
the music
the music
feel it
listen to it
relax with it

Samuel Dauenhauer
Flathead High School
Kalispell, MT
Grade 12

Sand Castle

I saw the ocean with its vibrant mist
rolling towards the sandy beach,
and the sand saw itself forming towering
castles with the help of little hands.

A pail and shovel followed the little hands
as a radiant smile shown upon the boy's face.
The sand helped the boy
intent with his delight.

While watching the boy and the sand
build one castle then another,
the sky turned gray then stormy
finally bursting into tears of joy.

Satisfied the boy gazed towards the hazy sky.
He gathered his beach ball
and seashells in preparation to leave
as a crab scuttled across the sand.

And all watched in amusement
as the laden young boy scurried home
leaving a sand castle and wet footprints
in the soft sand.

Sara Harvey
Northridge High School
Layton, UT
Grade 11

Autumn Magic

Between summer and winter there falls a season,
A season of crisp, colored leaves,
A season of great, golden, corn,
A season that's like a fairy tale.

A tale of Cinderella pumpkins,
A tale of Jack's bean stalks,
A tale of imagination,

Where clouds become evil fire-spitting dragons
And beautiful princesses,
Where straw is turned to gold,
Where the days are short and the nights are long.

The season of long, lingering walks in the park,
The season of Thanksgiving,
The unique season of fall
The most magical of them all.

Terilyn Godfrey
Northridge High School
Layton, UT
Grade 10

Love Comes and Love Goes

As I sit and reminisce
I wonder about all the things I've missed.
Can anyone tell me what to do,
Because all I do is think of you.
You go with your friends and it seems I don't care–
But what I hate most is that I'm not there!
You go and flirt with that other girl
And it makes my stomach swish and twirl.
You say you love me but all I see,
Is the love for someone else who isn't me!
Why are you afraid to let him go?
It's not like leaving won't let you grow.
Sure he'll find someone, but so will you.
Maybe this time it'll be true.
People say love comes and love goes,
But all I can say from my heart to my soul:
"That the love with you was great,
But now all I feel is nothing but hate!"

Carolyn Schnell
Cheyenne High School
North Las Vegas, NV
Grade 10

I Feel

I feel I am worthless, not very tough
  no matter how I try, I'm not strong enough
I strive as I may with limited prevail
  finding a way to inevitably fail.

I feel I am abused without being touched
  with the weight of the world; in need of a crutch
I sometimes feel that I'm unable to bear
  everyone is selfish, nobody cares.

I feel I am dead always having to hide
  numb to the world, hollow inside
I long for happiness that occurs in my dreams
  never will I find it, I'm cursed it would seem.

I feel I am a sin never meant to be born
  having no guidance, just a soul that was torn
I lack the potential to become someone great
  so I get pushed aside, always having to wait.

I feel I am trying with all of my might
  to survive through this journey, giving it a fight
I could have given up a long time ago
  never will I quit, I have something to show.

Larry Langevin
Boulder City High School
Boulder City, NV
Grade 11

The Storm

As the wind blows.
It calls the lightning.
The lightning flashes.
The wind blows.
Thunder comes, makes a big growl.
It sounds like a huge bowling ball.
The storm has started.

Lora Boeke
Flathead High School
Kalispell, MT
Grade 10

Alone

I float, alone
on an endless sea.
Turbid, choppy water
surrounds me.
I yell for help.
No one hears.
Brackish water
fills my gaping mouth,
and I cough.

Golden light from
a distant ship
taunts me,
haunts me.
It moves close,
and my hopes rise,
but all in vain.
The cruel ship disappears—
leaving me,
alone once more.

Susannah Hicken
Springville High School
Springville, UT
Grade 11

Forty-Three

Life until forty-three?
Now timeless enjoyment
Molds into simpler pleasures—never

Or will it?
They always say people change
They grow.

Then,
Does growing mean simplifying?
Or just becoming too channeled?
We'll see.

Ryann A. Love
C M Russell High School
Great Falls, MT
Grade 12

To Infinity and Beyond

The soft light peered around the large, obstructing mass,
Shading all areas, eerie shadows it cast;
Gentle light radiated off a dim, light glow.
The onlookers stood aside peering to and fro,
Waiting long hours to see the charcoal-black ground
Glow, as morning light filtered in without a sound.

They circled the mass, trying to find the right place,
To put their capsule so that they could make a base;
Time after time, the moon they orbited around,
Until they docked, tranquilly on alien ground.

They radioed to Earth, "The Eagle has landed,"
The unknown frontier would stand no longer stranded,
Men would walk the top on the immense mass, the moon
What men had never done, would be completed soon;
With a small step, the astronaut put his fear behind,
"One small step for man, one giant leap for mankind."

Men would now explore the moon who once searched the earth,
A new field of exploration was given birth
To a science in space that many would grow fond
To those who pondered infinity and beyond.

Rebekah Mullen
Arapahoe High School
Littleton, CO
Grade 11

Fast

On your mark, get set...GO!

Writing, fast, as fast as I can go.
I have to hurry so I can get on to my next thing.
Gotta go, go, go.
Where am I going?
I have to hurry or I'll never finish all I have to do.
I keep going, and I keep busy, but what am I doing?
I don't see my future because it's clouded by my present.
All the stuff I'm doing now doesn't seem to be helping my future.
Aagh. Shorter sentences are faster.
Gotta go fast, can't waste time thinking.
When can I slow down?
When can I just retire?
For whom am I doing all this work?
Doesn't matter, I just have to go fast and hard now.
I hope it all ends well, because I don't have time to make sure it does.
That would require even more work and time I don't have.

Bob Baddeley
C M Russell High School
Great Falls, MT
Grade 12

Beautiful Things Grow From the Ground

The sunlight shines so bright,
The stars shine and shimmer in the night.
The moon is full, and intricately round,
But the beautiful things grow from the ground.

The rain comes down in light, misty sprinkles,
The cute playful puppy has so many wrinkles.
The roses are in bloom, scarlet and round,
The beautiful things grow from the ground.

The baby is born, so soft and pink,
The littlest children laugh at the baby's wink!
Colorful balloons fill the room round,
But the beautiful things grow from the ground.

The mountains, and trees, reaching high to the sky,
The flying blue jay, and the buzzing bee, asking each other why,
The elderly people sitting on the ground,
Watching the beautiful things, grow from the ground.

Patrick Scoggins
Mojave High School
Las Vegas, NV
Grade 12

The Shadow

The current of the river was rich
There was a beautiful sunset on the horizon
Everything was peaceful all around me
There was not a cloud in the sky
I was 15

A shadow was watching over me
Towering high overhead
Like an eagle looking for its prey
It brought me in close like a mother holding her baby
I was 15

Butterflies flittered in my stomach
Making it hard for me to breathe
Like I was being swallowed up by the river
Yet, I was still determined to let the moment last forever
I was 15

The shadow took my hand
It led me away from this place of comfort
But let me know that it will always be there
I still haven't reached my destiny
I was 15

Jacquelyn Moore
Shelby High School
Shelby, MT
Grade 10

Overwhelmed

I am overwhelmed
My feelings are powerful.
If only I could surrender
To the anger within me
The sadness I clench
The hatred I look at.
And the feelings I clasp
When they all attack me
I about lose
But the only thing that keeps me from falling
Is my chance to choose.
To live or die
To be happy or sad.
I choose to live. I choose to hope
So I let the sadness leave me
The anger is expelled
I close my eyes and am relieved
For I have won the battle
Between me and myself.
I became a better person and now I know
Not to hold my feelings in but to let them go.

Carynne Lane
South Sevier High School
Monroe, UT
Grade 11

Brandon

I hate you right now,
More than you'll ever know.
Why did you decide to go?
You had everything a guy could want,
And you left your love thinking it's all her fault.
Now I sit and watch her day after day
I watch her cry and wish you would have stayed.
For you have left a cloud in her heart
Because she's scared to try a new start.
How could you be so selfish
And only think of yourself?
Now all we have are pictures
On a shelf.
Why did you go?
Why couldn't you stay?
Even if it was just for another day.
You ripped out our hearts
And opened our eyes.
We look at it now
As your big "surprise."

Mandy Lampman
Haxtun High School
Haxtun, CO
Grade 11

Wishes May Come True

In the nighttime sky
The stars roam in the darkness
We wish on them for a dream

Brooke Probst
Emery County High School
Castle Dale, UT
Grade 11

Natural Yearning

The cool bark is my soul
The brittle green leaves are my senses
I am thirsting in the silent calm
Will rain moisten my arid branches?
Will no drop reach my aching roots?
In the barren desert I stand alone
Watching,
Waiting,
Praying,
For the passionate storm
To someday reach me
And grab the brittle leaves of doubt
From my fist
For the wind is dark,
The stillness is light,
The storm is unpredictable,
And the barren desert is oh so real.

Molly Youngblood
Greeley West High School
Greeley, CO
Grade 12

Perfection

Here I stand entirely captivated
By the configuration before me.
It's fraught with integrity and motivated
By a power found within.

The image of its soul
Is majestic yet gentle.
Its figure as a whole
Has brightness encircling it.

The capacity of its mind
Far exceeds mortal man.
It has the ability to find
The truth in all things.

The likeness in its face
Has a look of determination.
Engulfed by the human race
It stands benevolent.

Jessica Dillard
Ben Lomond High School
Ogden, UT
Grade 12

Memories

As my old weary hands turn the pages of the album,
I see the pictures I've collected over the years.
Each page brings back precious memories from my life.
I turn a page.
I hear the rumbling of the water over the rocks,
I smell the fresh, clean mountain air,
I can feel the cold, clear water running over my feet.
My first camping trip.
I turn a page.
Excitement is in the air.
I am standing in front of the mirror,
Holding a bouquet of flowers,
Listening to everyone telling me how beautiful I look.
My wedding day.
I hear a baby crying,
I feel its soft skin.
The incredible joy surges through me again as I remember the moment I first
    held my sweet baby boy.
All of these memories,
These precious memories sweep through my mind,
Taking me back in time.

Scarlet Reierson
Rosebud Public School
Rosebud, MT
Grade 11

Emptiness

Fog rolled over the hill like a waterfall of white water,
Over the trees like an avalanche.
It settled on the lake and rushed forward.
It appeared to be a slight touch of Mother Nature's power and beauty.
The fog consumed me, wrapped itself around me,
invading my eyes, my lungs,
such whiteness.
Splash!
A fish,
but where,
The lake, now just a jumble of sounds, rushing water, jumping fish,
and whiteness.
Then, just as fast as it came, it vanished.
The green hill across the lake, green, not white.
The water calm, without ripples, without sounds, without whiteness.
The sky, littered with stars,
The stars, diamonds in a black velvet bag.
I feel the loneliness that the fog left, the empty space which once was filled,
now void,
and empty

Brian Kerr
Vilas High School
Vilas, CO
Grade 10

Laughter

They say it's best for the soul
Some think it is a miracle cure
People use it at the end of jokes
Or when someone performs an act of stupidity
It is used to cure hard times
It is used to cure sad times
Used for fun
Used for joy
We call it laughter

Justin Wheadon
Rosebud Public School
Rosebud, MT
Grade 12

I Almost Remember

I almost remember when I was small,
just when I started to crawl.

I would stick things in my mouth and start to chew,
but I quit though when my teeth grew.

I'd get into things when I started to walk,
and I said bad things when I started to talk.

I'd cry when I was playing and had to share,
and I liked to pull the other kid's hair.

As I got older it was clearer to see,
that being good was the way to be.

Now I can look back and almost see,
the way I remember it used to be.

Bev Slater
Rosebud Public School
Rosebud, MT
Grade 12

From H to O

Two gases embrace and jump,
Free falling — entering — surfacing.
Hydrogen and oxygen tumbling together,
Causing bubbles and foam,
As newly opened champagne.

Some bubbles brush your face,
Like girls brush back their beautiful hair.
Rolling foam glistens gently,
Like candlelight glowing in your girlfriend's eye.

Collectively forming a giant's shower,
Bathing all who come to see.
Nature's majestic power.

Nick Kowalski
North Sanpete High School
Mount Pleasant, UT
Grade 12

An Inevitable Death

I am a soldier of my king,
I must protect, I must advance.
Alone I am nothing,
But alongside my seven comrades
We decide to outcome.
Although we are easily disposed
We have a small chance, if one is fast
To be promoted in rank and power
But always in the hopes of winning,
And achieving a checkmate.
Sparkling blankets of pure silk,
Waiting to be sliced apart,
By sharp steel and slick wax
Created by the heavens above,
Only to be destroyed by the coming spring.
What treasure it is for the seeker,
Who finds it before the enemy.
For this foe is the ice,
Which traps the precious powder.

Devin Gray
C M Russell High School
Great Falls, MT
Grade 12

Understand*

We don't understand,
why you were taken away,
we will never stop missing you,
but we will all be okay.
Because we have to understand,
that you've gone to a better place,
but we'll always have you with us,
because we'll never forget your face.
Will we ever understand,
the lesson that's been displayed?
If we could change the fate that owned you,
then maybe you could've stayed.
But do we really understand,
that there's nothing we could have done?
Can we find peace in knowing,
that the good die young?
So Joe, we hope you're waiting,
there in that heavenly land,
for each last one of us to join you,
so we will finally understand.

Beca Mancha
Tonopah High School
Tonopah, NV
Grade 11
*In loving memory of Robert Joseph Bird,
May 26, 1984 - July 29, 1999

A Cloud's Journey

As I drift across the gray sky I look upon the earth with wide eyes,
seeing lakes of red wondering what caused this blood shed.
O brother the sun what happened that man would so illy take a life,
Please brother sun, shine on the land that others may see this dreadful day.
Mark this as a day that heaven and earth will never forget,
or if forgotten this would happen again.
Are men so evil and hard that they don't see the blood on their hands and heads.
Mark this day as a memory that history shall see that death by another man's hand is the greatest evil.
O brother the sun shine on the earth, soak up the suffering, the pain, the frustration.
Or if not, then help me to rain down the moisture that is within me.
O brother mark this day by being as bright as you are allowed.
Make man remember the hurt.

Alicia Tucker
Flathead High School
Kalispell, MT
Grade 11

Silent Heaven*

I will arise and go now, and go to the swimming pool,
As I dive in, I will feel the water slither up my skin.
Like a fish I will swim through the water,
Ending in a new spot from where I began.

As I immerse myself beneath the cool blue water, I imagine I am in the wilderness of the Rocky Mountains,
I feel as if I am the only one for miles.
As the water surrounds me, I no longer notice the voices of the kids playing,
I no longer notice the splashes and waves created by other people.

As I emerge from this silent heaven,
My hair is heavy as I feel the water begin to drip down each strand,
My eyes are filled with water as I gently wipe it away,
And once again I have ended in a new spot from where I began.

Holly Ruderman
Colorado Academy
Denver, CO
Grade 12
*Modeled after W.B. Yeats' "Lake Isle of Innisfree"

The Mystical Garden

Flowers start with a seed of faith.
Rain, gushes from marshmallow clouds quenches the thirsty seed.
Sun warms the sprouting seed giving it potential to grow and endure the trials it will face.
Nature's care, strengthens the flower's inner being with reminders of its importance.
Events in life that squeeze the heart like a lemon blow the hard worked garden away in a flash.
A barren world with dust, wilted flowers, no hope.
A dark, sullen sky scattered with thunder of revenge and aches of lightning.
Yet, a seed, a trickle of water, a ray of light illuminate the darkness.
Life's hurdles can be jumped over if trust and the soul's energy is toiled into the garden.
With each step a new sprout is born, eventually a flower.
A never ending road lies ahead to replenish the garden.
When spiritual rain shapes each tender seed and pedal, and nutrients of power and determination from the robust soil
feed into the garden, it will be whole once again.

Urvashi Malhotra
Cedar City High School
Cedar City, UT
Grade 11

Cover Girl

The serpents lurk inside my head,
Insist I do what they have said.
They hold me down, insult and jeer,
With rage and violence I must fear.

They order me to primp and preen,
My body they formed long and lean.
My image cursed, my path despised,
By those with envy in their eyes.

Beauty is only as deep as the skin,
Beauty is achieved when you are thin.
Those are the lies that I was told,
The lies for which my soul was sold.

My looks are plenty to enrage,
Those who personally made my cage.
Respect is gone, replaced with scorn,
My flesh gashed by a worldly thorn.

LeAnn Galgerud
Willow Creek School
Willow Creek, MT
Grade 12

Child That Was

A little boy runs through an open meadow.
The skies are his limits

An old man sits in his prison office, working.
The four walls are his limits.

Little boy, as free as a butterfly.
Smelling the deep red roses.

Old man, a rooted tree.
Confined to his day in, day out rhythm.

Little boy, on a bed of sweet green grasses.
Laughing without reason.

Old man, in a chair of stone.
Sleepless nights spent frowning at details.

Little boy, free to be everything he dreams.
Old man, confined to his nightmare of dissatisfaction.

If only he could remember.

Seth Ambrose
Flathead High School
Kalispell, MT
Grade 11

I Kneel and Pray

I kneel and pray
Asking God for one more day
to do the things I haven't done
To sing the songs I haven't sung
For the love of someone
To make myself a better man
So I don't die a bitter man
To love with love I never had
Not to hide or be afraid inside
To be the man I know I can
To see the sunrise one more time
To hear the church bell ring the clock chime
To live life without regret
To be forgiven, never forget someone loves me
This is why I kneel and pray

Chad Williams
Mancos High School
Mancos, CO
Grade 12

Are You Really You?

Don't let yourself become someone you aren't.
There's you, and some other you, whom people call you.
Do people see the real you,
or that you who comes out to become a cooler you?
Stay with that you who knows best.
Your common sense becomes in charge of you,
not you who follows the crowd.
As it seems now, people may now like you,
so you become that other you.
In the future,
you will have wished that you stayed your real you,
because now others like you.
Say who you are, be who you are, and like who you are.
Don't let "YOU" become someone you aren't.

Michelle Marie Tronstad
Flathead High School
Kalispell, MT
Grade 12

Independence

The man gets another paper from his desk,
Wets the quill with black ink.
The small room is silent except for the ticking clock.
He takes a deep breath and closes his eyes.
The candle flickers, burned down to almost nothingness.
He lifts his head and begins to write,
Occasionally looking at the pile of crumpled papers at his feet.
Feverishly he presses on.
He lifts up the finished product and blows it dry.
Finally satisfied, he allows sleep to engulf him.
A country's independence is born.

Sharol Durrant
Emery County High School
Castle Dale, UT
Grade 11

I Will Be Free

I have a vision
A vision of the *playa*
A vision of sand
A bright vision of the sun
A vision of freedom

The only vision I have
One of the Rio Grande
A vision that's all too familiar
A vision that wants to be forgotten
A memory

Hard work
All for little money
Bathing in the Rio Grande
Sores on hands burn

When will I see my vision
When will I see freedom
Though often painful
I will be free

I see the *playa*
I will be free
Yes, I will be free

Carla Wiedeman
Valley High School
Gilcrest, CO
Grade 12

Starry Eyes

Starry eyes
Have you forgotten me
I am still here
Little me, all alone
In this world of hate
Can't you see me
I am still here
though clouded by pain
Longing to shine
Can't you hear me
I am still here
Screaming your name
Calling to your thoughts
Can't you feel me
I am still here
All around you
Longing to touch
Starry eyes
I am still here
Where, are you?

Marci Aberg
Custer Co Dist High School
Miles City, MT
Grade 10

No Rain

Dark clouds slowly cover up the sun,
Stormy, desolate, without rain.
Nothing pure, nothing but gray sadness.
My soul sinks as the darkness fills me like a glass.
But with nothing pure,
No water, no rain.
There are no tears that wet my eyes.
Nothing pure or good.
No rain.
Days pass with nothing that sets one apart from another.
Peace of mind, peace of body, peace of spirit; all gone.
Sucked up by the billowing clouds that cast a blank shadow over me.
Thunder rumbles, the clouds thicken.
A glimmer of hope for wetness from their tears.
But there is nothing pure.
There is no rain.

Margie Hunt
Beaverhead Co High School
Dillon, MT
Grade 10

Her Disposition: Fearless

A seeming haze before my eyes,
A mere prelude to the coming blindness,
A certainty spelling out the destruction of all activity,
Involving the baseless pride of my short-lived perversion,
Gone with the fallacy.

Time fills me,
Acquaints itself undeniable,
Merciless—Must see everything, capture everything, in its truth, whatever that may be;
Must pay homage to simple observance,
For in the order of all things,
Man is but an observer unable to perpetuate justly the fundamental elements of life.

Yet in this madness begetting sadness,
Only desire to keep one meaningless image everlasting:

She,
Carelessly walking within God's mire,
With wondrous silk-fleshed legs that carry her like the wings of a dove,
Eyes that pierce warmly for the exhaustion of truth, for the good of mankind,
And bosom as bounteous as the starlit sky that retires brutes to sound asleep;
Her disposition:
Fearless.

May my eyes burn with passion and fury—May I go blind in quietude.

Sammy Lee
Clark High School
Las Vegas, NV
Grade 12

En Passant

I happened by a board last night,
A field of checkered black and red,
But now a spotlight from above,
Upon the pieces new light shed.

The Rook had seen the night before,
While sneaking to the castle door,
In the shadows cloaked and veiled,
A Pawn that night the King had hailed,
To spite the Queen who yesterday,
A visit to her mother paid,
But found no mother's house that night,
And spent her slumber with the Knight,
Who to the Bishop, in great pride,
All his conquests did confide –
Spoke too loud through confessional door,
Where Rook had stood that night before . . .

I blinked my eyes and looked away,
Though dark intrigue I must confess,
The dance I saw is not for me,
I'll never grasp the game of chess.

Malcolm Rasmussen
Ben Lomond High School
Ogden, UT
Grade 12

Untitled

She looked around the room,
taking in each new face,
and thought of all she'd left behind
when she'd come to this new place.

Leaving all her friends behind
had been so hard to do.
She'd cried for hours when she found out
her dad's job would force them to move.

At school that day she felt lonely
and she thought making friends would be tough.
She sat all alone in the lunchroom
and ate by herself at lunch.

But the next day at school was different
and some kids talked to her in the hall.
As their friendships grew she realized
moving wasn't so bad after all.

Jessica Miller
Gunnison Valley High School
Gunnison, UT
Grade 12

A Lonely Sailor's Wish

As I stand on the ship,
And look out at the majestic sea,
I know you and I were meant to be.
    I only wish I could make you
See how much you mean to me.
    I wish I could walk up to you,
Take you in my arms, kiss your tender lips,
And speak the words lovers do.
    But now I sit here sad and blue,
Wishing I could be next to you.

Cody West
Civa Charter School
Colorado Springs, CO
Grade 11

It Was Late and I Was Tired

The day dawns cold, a winter's night so deep.
Wolves chase me. O, I wish it were a dream,
But no, not now, I run and cannot sleep.
The beasts close in, a silent cry I scream.
People look at me, thinking I'm all right.
They see the perfect girl, I cannot be.
Why don't you believe, try with all my might,
I'm in over my head, please hear my plea.
Mad beasts consume me with their endless rage,
I shout and struggle, no more I can do.
My body is weak, in its final stage,
If you don't see me as I am, I'm through.
Ripped apart, torn, I wretch with awful pain,
But it all happens inside of my brain.

Evany Pace
Highland High School
Salt Lake City, UT
Grade 12

Before I Found You

As all softness breaks
            through gentle night
                        through canvas paint
My hands reach for you
No coarse expanse of broken boughs
            or thirsty woodlands
Deny my eyes your light
Forever would I carve
            your outline into the bark of my affection
                        for your contour
                                    your frame against the sky
Sets me in wonder
            captivated by the eternity that surrounds you
And I weep
How long has softness broken
before I found you?

Hannah Newberry
Middle Park High School
Granby, CO
Grade 12

Another Night Alone

As I spend another night alone,
I long to feel your touch,
for you are the girl I adore,
the one I miss so much...
As I spend another night alone,
I long to hear your voice,
I choose you to be my lady,
because you're the perfect choice...
As I spend another night alone,
I long to see your face,
you're the only one I know
with such beauty and good taste...
As I spend another night alone,
I long to hold you near,
for losing the girl I cherish
is what I mostly fear...
So I try to tell you how I feel
by writing you this poem
because I don't want to spend
another night alone.

Gary McClain
Indian Springs High School
Indian Springs, NV
Grade 12

Seeds Soon to Grow

Again I fill another day.
One I can complete and count.
For when tomorrow comes again
I will be strong and free of doubt.

The unseen dangers lurking near
Will tremble with their own dark fear.
For the sight of me they shall not want,
Because in their dreams I will taunt.

Alas, another day will come
And I'll be weak and hide away.
Once my friend and now my enemy.
How can I possibly seize the day?

The unseen dangers lurking near
Now tower over my own fear.
In my dreams they all display
Control over the will of my way.

Though when I'm down below my breath
I'm picked up by seeds to grow.
A new found life has filled me up.
The life I live I don't bestow.

Scott Clem
Campbell County High School
Gillette, WY
Grade 10

Life Is Like a Flower Garden

Life is like a flower garden ready to bloom,
All year long you wait for the season,
        To care for your garden,
And see those flowers blossom.
Your flowers are glowing,
        It's the high point of the season,
You handle the garden with love and care,
You nourish the flowers, and pull every weed.

But for those not as wise, they let the little weeds slip by,
Though the smallest weeds left untouched,
        Sneak up on your flowers,
        And coil around their innocent roots.
The evil weeds have weakened your bud,
And before you know it, your blooming flowers are dead and dreary.
The colorful glory has lasted but a moment.
The colors have vanished,
Your flowers are now all wilted,
        As not to see them blooming again.

The choice is now to give up and fail,
        Or learn from your mistake, and try again.

Jamie Ericksen
Northridge High School
Layton, UT
Grade 10

Friend For Life

Whenever there's a sunset aloft the azure sky,
Remember that I'll be there, a shoulder to let you cry.
When life is at its lowest, and your days are filled with sorrow,
Remember that I'll hug you, giving you reason for tomorrow.

        If ever there are tears streaming down your cheek,
        I'll be right there to hold you, every second, every week.
        Whenever you need a friend who will mend your broken heart,
        Please call me if I'm needed, we shall never be apart.

If ever there's a time you feel like you've been slain,
I'll give my hand to comfort you, whenever you're in pain.
If ever we encounter tests we cannot weather,
I'll never leave you by yourself, we'll pull through together.

        If ever there's a time this life is not worth seeing,
        I'll look at you and discover my essence and my being.
        I'll look at you and realize you are much more than my wife,
        In your eyes I'll see forever, my eternal, friend for life.

Darrel Miller
Northridge High School
Layton, UT
Grade 11

Passage

They say forget the past
And everything is forgotten
For it constantly reminds us

Reminding us of acts only for itself
Never knowing the past grievances
Of which it strangely delights us in
Pure terror as it travels

Traveling in the future
A time to be looked forward to for its endless possibilities,
But never seen for the present demands
A continual passage of which it wlll never relinquish control.

Matt Zahller
C M Russell High School
Great Falls, MT
Grade 12

Out of Touch

Everybody's loving you, but you can't seem to love yourself
Everybody's smiling, but it's you who cries all night
Everybody's fooled, because it's you who wears the mask
Everybody's praying, but it's you who can't find the time
Everybody's trying, but it's you who holds the key
Everybody's caring, but it's you who won't accept their love
Everybody's with you, but it's you who can't find yourself
Everybody's hurting, because it's you who fell apart
Everybody's crying, because it's you who lost your life

Samantha Phillips
Shoshoni High School
Shoshoni, WY
Grade 11

Understanding

What do people understand about different people?
    And people who are like them, the same?
Can we all understand about all differences?
    Or is that a problem that we have too much of?
One can look at anybody in the world;
    And find at least ten differences:
Clothes,
Race,
Gender,
    And many others.
Does environment change or influence thought?
    Can moving to a non-predisposed area help to lose bigotry?
Or do people just stay the same?
Or can we learn to not be prejudiced in a biased area?
The world needs to be less supremacist.
But there is bigotry wherever one goes,
And that is not something to be proud of.
    But it can change!!!

Steve J. Vosberg
Lake County High School
Leadville, CO
Grade 12

Point of View from a Worm

I am but a simple worm
Devouring dirt with delight.
'Tis good for the soil and the plants that relish me,
But one foul rose
Had an incurable disease.
I, a hero, sprang to its aid.
To cease agony, I began to eat.
Not the soil of centuries past,
But the silken burgundy
With an acrid taste to my pallet
I, saving luscious green from sepulchral red,
Sacrifice my delight
With valorous intent,
Only to be equated with evil
From one man called
    POET.

Anne Wright
Alta High School
Sandy, UT
Grade 12

Archery

The sweet stench of bales,
Lingers in my mind.
As I think of arrows,
Flying through my mind.

The beautiful art of just thinking
Of where the arrow will hit,
As I line up my sight
I slowly release and let it RIP.

For many archery is just a sport,
A way to pass the time.
But to me it is life,
And I will dominate at the right time.

The Olympics is a dream,
That hopefully I will reach.
With all my hopes and goals,
The gold medal is not far out of reach.

Practice is so sweet, as I want to be the best,
Annie Lynne Haffey, the next "Robin Hood," I guess.
So in the end it will pay off "Archery Girl,"
Goals will be met and gold medals will be won,
By Annie Haffey, she Did it, she Won!

Annie Haffey
Anaconda High School
Anaconda, MT
Grade 10

Sonnet to Time

Time in its great expanse,
stretches on into the unknown,
taking opportunity and chance,
leaving us wondering, and alone.

We are slaves
to the own creation of our mind,
our lives filled with the drone
of passing time.

In the whirl of life
and the dread of leave
forget the strife
just stop and breathe.

Wake each new day with the sun
the time will come when there is none.

Allison Masters
Montrose High School
Montrose, CO
Grade 10

The Coach

Old, strict, never giving in.
Never seeming to appreciate
or even realize something special.
Prison guard, no boot camp counselor
Trying to work hard every second
just to receive one second of praise,
one good job, one congratulation.
Will it ever come, is it worth working
so hard, so diligently for.
Just to please one grumpy old man.

State track, the meet of all meets,
The last race of the day,
the mile relay.
We work so hard and win.
Will it go unnoticed again.
Not this time.
A tear rolls down
the cheek of this hard old man.
A congratulation is given.

Colton Salyards
Haxtun High School
Haxtun, CO
Grade 11

The World

I see the world
Through two hot eyes.
Everything to
My surprise.
Knives so sharp,
Go out to cut.

I wish the skies,
Were so very blue.
And touched so soft,
But yet so tough.
A kiss that follows,
A long goodbye.

I want to say,
To curve a belief.
Tracks in the mud,
Of a child's heart.
Rocks so normal,
Now beautiful emeralds.

Mickie Valdez
Emery County High School
Castle Dale, UT
Grade 10

I Was Unborn

Man I was comfortable
All naked and warm
Surrounded by warm fluid
I was safe from all harm
I was unborn

I sat around all day
Just kicked, slept and ate
Not a care in the world
Man it was great
I was unborn

How I would have loved
To just stay there forever
I could have never come out
Never came out, no, not ever
I was unborn

But, then it happened
Hey, who pulled the plug
Where am I going
Oh no, down I go
Glug, Glug
I was unborn

Jordon Benson
Shelby High School
Shelby, MT
Grade 10

Red, White, and Blue

As you cross your heart
and say a pledge,
remember those fifty stars
surrounded by a winter night
and blue that's in its sky.
Or stained blue tongues,
summer rain, the lining of a cloud.
How someone wrapped you in a blanket,
while listening to the blues.
You fell asleep to Sachmo's voice
and dreamt a wonderful world.
Or contemplate an ocean's wave
and how it could be so smooth,
or the sweet taste of blueberries
picked by tiny hands,
little blue butterflies soar above
as grass tickles your neck,
or just sit and stare
at the smooth sky so blue.
Or cross your heart and hope to hell
someone heard your pledge.

Krystle Fable-Bowler
Moffat County High School
Craig, CO
Grade 11

What Are You Thinking?

What are you thinking,
As you look down upon us?
Are you wondering about us?
Do you even care?
Do you see all the goodness?
Or do you see the bad?
Your pale face is so forlorn,
It must be the bad.
Your darkening wrinkles
Show against pale skin on a lake.
And I wonder...
Are they from stress or from joy?
You see all the lovers,
Yet you have only a rival:
A bright ball of fire,
Bearing the morning light.
What are you thinking?
I really want to know,
For here I am sitting
Wondering if I'll ever know the secrets
Behind your pale yellow eyes.

Michelle L. Williams
Northridge High School
Layton, UT
Grade 10

Football

As I walk through the tunnel onto the field
my heart beats rapidly.
When I feel the grass in between my cleats
I think of being in an open meadow.
As I look into the stands
I am amazed at all the fans.
When my team huddles the adrenaline radiates
I line up
and face the fears
of seeing the other team's eyes for the first time.
As the helmets clash
I hear the bang and the whistles blow.
The game is over.

Jon Robertson
Excel School
Durango, CO
Grade 11

Riding Down Broadway in Boulder, Colorado

I pedal slowly and coast along
The paved two-lane bike trail.
The dotted yellow stripe winks
Up at me from below.
Cars pass to my right,
Sports cars and fancy gas guzzling giants.
Money flows like water and grows on trees.
The Flatirons rise majestically
To my left with the sun gazing brilliantly
Upon them in gold and red.
I sink upward into the deep blue sky,
Blue so thick and soft it melts around me.
Why is there smog on the horizon?

Patrick Hopper
Fairview High School
Boulder, CO
Grade 12

The Man Next to Me

This man is humble
This man is true
This man does not groan or grumble
He has a lot to do
He has hands of leather
He works hard no matter what the weather
This is a man with mercy, compassion, and grace
On his face there are marks of hardships,
Yet there is peace
In his eyes there is fire, joy, and grief
This man teaches lessons learned in life
I will always love him
He will always love me
This man is my father, and in my heart he will always be

Josh Brown
Campo High School
Campo, CO
Grade 11

Magical Nights

I can pinpoint your location,
I can see your face in the sky.
Starry diamond eyes,
Clouds passing me by.
Wan skin reflected in the moon —
You never come back too soon.
Let me be a part of your nightly ride,
I want to sit softly by your side.
I yearn to kiss the satin heavens,
Gently caress the glistening constellations.
We can dance like breezes on the horizon
And wave to the goddess of twilight
As we silently behold her radiant sight.
We will push away the sun,
Lock it up in a golden cage.
Wish away the approach of morning;
Here is where I have to stay.

Sarah Orton
Highland High School
Salt Lake City, UT
Grade 12

When You Think of Me

When you think of a beautiful sunset,
And you think of a fallen tree,
These things I cherished dearly
When you look at them remember me.

I am the girl who lent a smile,
Who passed with a cheerful "hello."
I am the girl who'd reach a mile
To bring a person into my home.

I've looked at the sunset just as you do now,
My eyes filled in tears at the heavenly glow.
I've walked the steps on that path before.
I too have wondered what my future holds.

So remember me when you look at a sunset,
Or when you see nature dear.
For God created each item,
Just as he has sent me here.

The sunrise is my awakening,
The sunset fills me with peace.
For the beauty caught in both
Is what I live to see.

April Stratton
Cedar City High School
Cedar City, UT
Grade 12

Friendship

For you, inside,
Is a small surprise.
And hidden deep,
You're able to reap,
A fantastic gift,
To give a lift.
Which will appear,
To give you good cheer.
Here is a present,
Especially meant,
For you to have.
To make you laugh,
Or even shed a tear.
It's very clear,
That when hard times come,
And mock the sun,
That the most important thing,
That anyone could bring,
To you and I,
Is friendship.

Elizabeth Olsen
Woods Cross High School
Woods Cross, UT
Grade 10

With Love

Love is the essence of all
The roots of things big and small
Feeling lost and so alone
Love can bring you back home

Love is a feeling inside the soul
A feeling that makes you whole
Love will not stray
As long as your life you lay

Love comes back again and again
A caring hand it shall lend
It will always be there
It can't leave as long as you care

So we all want to know, "What is Love?"
It is as pure as a dove
And its arms as strong as a bear
Its tears and smile will keep you there

Never let it go
And it will always show
For it cannot say bye
For without you, love will die

Michael Bigham
Columbus Public School
Columbus, MT
Grade 10

I Remember

I remember his big, green, beautiful eyes,
his pants, shirts, shoes, and sweater size.
I remember the innocence of his smile,
his walking, talking, laid back style.
I remember the way he parted his hair,
his favorite team, color, food, aunt, teacher, fruit: a pear.
I remember that he's almost six feet tall,
he loves to surf, ski, snowboard but hang out most of all.
I love him so much, I will never forget
the names of his niece, mom, dad, grandpa, sister, brother, and pet,
his car, his dreams, his number, his game;
If only I could remember his name!

Traci Sharee Smith
Virgin Valley Jr/Sr High School
Mesquite, NV
Grade 10

If

If I never would have met you,
I wouldn't have encountered your angelic face,
If I never would have held you,
I would never have felt your warm embrace,
If my lips wouldn't have become acquainted to yours,
I would have been deprived of the sweetest taste,
If you wouldn't have taken the time to love me,
I would have been carrying a broken heart before time said,
If your eyes wouldn't have told me what I saw,
I wouldn't have wanted to die alongside you,
If God wouldn't have decided to take your life,
I wouldn't be here reminiscing about every memory left behind.

Laura Becerra
Battle Mountain Sr High School
Battle Mountain, NV
Grade 10

Is Your Smile Just a Lie

I look at the world around me, I see smiling faces, everyone's happy
Longing to be apart of their happy world
knowing no matter how hard I try, I'll never succeed
I look in the mirror, my mouth is smiling, but my eyes are crying
Not recognizing the face I see every day
who is the impostor I see
A secret me deep inside, longing to escape
What will they think? What will they say?
Wondering every day, do they know my secret?
Are they showing the smile, but hiding the tears?
Do they know the pain I'm feeling?
Do they know the love I'm lacking?
Do they know the tears I'm crying, every night alone in my bed?
So familiar are their faces and yet I'll never know
So familiar are their voices and yet I'll never understand
I look at the world around me and wonder if everyone's smile is just a lie.

Sarah Serviss
Conifer High School
Conifer, CO
Grade 11

Will Things Change?

We are blind yet to the advantages of death,
Arguing, wasting useful breath.
People do not see,
That life is only temporary.

Where do we go after this life?
Must we fight another strife?
Must man fight another war?
Will poverty be knocking on your door?

Or will our next life be a greater one?
Where differences of people are not shunned.
Where not the rich and famous are only recognized,
But a man who rushed to a needed child's cries.

Must things result in sick violence?
Must true feeling be kept in silence?
We must open our eyes,
Listen to our hearts, which so cries,
We must listen to the cries for peace,
And want the pain to cease.

Cheyne M. Unckles
Pahrump High School
Pahrump, NV
Grade 10

Bits of Wisdom

Always look at the beginning
As the beginning of the end.
Everything will end no matter what you or I do about it.
Hold close those things that you hold dear,
And always know that they may not be there tomorrow.
Value your time with them,
As things such as life, love, and happiness
Are always the most likely to end.
It is never a matter of if,
But when,
This ending will come.
Those who are at fault to the destruction
Of your happiness, love or even your life
May be forgiven
If you can manage in your heart to forgive.
But never forget
Those who hurt you once
Are always the most likely to hurt you again.
For in the end the only truly reliable source for happiness
Comes from within yourself.

Blake Malone
Willow Creek School
Willow Creek, MT
Grade 12

Fear

As I look into my opponent's face,
I see fear.
You can't stop me.
I can see that look in his eye,
He knows that he can only hope,
That I have an off game.
After I see fear, I'm like a shark,
I attack.
You can't stop me — you can only hope to contain me.

Zach McLean
Whitehall Sr High School
Whitehall, MT
Grade 12

Believe

Do you believe with all your might
In angels and fairies and brilliant light?
You must let your imagination do what it is to do,
To believe in leprechauns and ghosts that say "Boo!"
To know the magic and shadows that lurk below,
To visit those places children dream to go.
Come with me and on a magic carpet we'll ride.
From little men and pink horses we'll hide.
Now you believe, I told you you would,
But you didn't believe you really could.
Believing in one another is where it begins
So always believe and you'll see it never ends.

Stefanie Mae Evans
Geyser Public School
Geyser, MT
Grade 11

Today

Today is the day,
Of the beginning of our lives.
Tomorrow is the day,
That shall never die.

Through these halls,
We walked, we talked, we laughed, we cried.
We made friends, we made family,
But today we must say goodbye.

Four years have passed,
Four years gone by,
Friends made, friends forgotten,
But our love inside.

Today is the past,
Tomorrow is the beginning.
So, goodbye my friends,
Our years have come to an end.

Patty Rotroxsa
Clark High School
Las Vegas, NV
Grade 12

My Love for You Will Never Die

My love for you
My feeling for you
My heart for you
Will never die.

My emotions,
When I'm with you
Are higher than the tallest mountains.

My desire for you
Is faster than
A river flowing.

My purpose of life
Will be complete
When we say
I do
My love for you
Will never die.

Jimmy Gertson
Elizabeth High School
Elizabeth, CO
Grade 12

His Day

It isn't all the presents,
Or all the sweets and food.
It isn't time for hatefulness,
Or being in bad mood.
This day isn't your day
To receive or give away.
It's for the man who died for you,
His birth was on this day.
Your day will be much brighter
If you'll remember just two things.
Christmas is for Jesus,
And the joy his spirit brings.

Lacee Sherman
Emery County High School
Castle Dale, UT
Grade 12

Moody

Oh, why am I so moody?
Moody is wrong
Why do we have to have moods?
Why can't we be happy all the time?
If we were happy all the time
we would never have a problem
with depression.

Jessica Vigil
Moffat High School
Moffat, CO
Grade 10

To Love Myself

To love myself sometimes is so hard
But it makes it even harder to love someone else
You can never love anyone else before you love yourself
You are the most important person to you
No one can bring you the happiness that you can bring yourself
You are your worst enemy and your own best friend
To love myself is to break down the wall of safety
Making myself vulnerable to others and my own self-hate

Maria Lingle
Shelby High School
Shelby, MT
Grade 10

The Tool

A debt of gratitude lies within my heart.
 Wearily translating my intimate thoughts,
 Writing my proverbs and insights,
 Noting every murmur that exits my mouth,
 Connecting each letter constructively.
Underrated, your occupation goes,
For you consist merely of brittle graphite and wood,
Colored traditionally, blunt yellow,
But may equally exist in vibrant shades.
 Simple elements indeed.
 Your support cushions my mistakes.
 You know, perfection waits until ready
 You cautiously sketch and trace my past,
Burning up paper like the world will end.
Then. . . a realization:
For a tool limits your purpose,
The true magic hides and shares with only the instrument's user.
 Freedom and expression exist solely in its writer.

Maggie Halmo
Arapahoe High School
Littleton, CO
Grade 11

Playing God

Shots ring out in the crowded schoolyard
And for a moment, everyone thinks the same,
Run! Go! Push aside the clumsy fat girl tripping over her feet,
Save yourselves!! Run over the unimportant white boy.
And from among the screams, amid the confusion, amongst the wounded,
I hear you cry, "Help me! Please, don't leave me!" I stop . . .
Those behind me spit ugly words at my face, greedy in their fight for survival.
I turn pushing back to you to help, and you're lying there, a broken doll, tossed aside.
They come towards us, they have the guns, the ones that I sit by in math.
Playing God, choosing who lives and who dies.
Our eyes meet as I step between you and them.
They laugh, and shoot.
Now I lay broken on top of you, my life dripping away,
As they walk away, forgetting you.

Emily Johnson
Highland High School
Salt Lake City, UT
Grade 10

Sunday Fun

Trees stand all around me like tall soldiers,
Puffy clouds are miles away in the misty morning,
The clear water rushes by me rapidly,
Beautiful birds fly high in the sky,
The fresh air is everywhere and I can't get away from it,
Fumes of gasoline pour from the running roaring motor,
The cold water envelops me with its fishy taste,
The always pumping adrenaline rushes through me,
The rope tightens with my pull of my muscles,
The slick shiny skies slide smoothly over the lake,
I feel freedom from all worries and fears.

Kyle Dodge
Vilas High School
Vilas, CO
Grade 11

Life of Love

Listen to your heart
The music of your soul
Understand the message
Of living your life full.
Guide your spirit through that rite of passage
Take your destiny in steel grip
Know yourself and hold that high
Let nobody say your life is nigh
'Cause love is precious but life is more
But to live for love is what life is for.

Kyle Allen
Loyola Sacred Heart High
Missoula, MT
Grade 11

Butterflies

Where does this butterfly come from,
That flaps so deep inside?
Why doesn't it come to the surface?
All it does is hide.

Why can't I keep this butterfly to myself?
It shares my same feelings.
Sometimes happy sometimes sad,
It makes me feel so many things.

What color is this butterfly?
This is something I shall never know,
It stays locked up inside,
Always on the go.

When will this butterfly stop flapping?
I hope I will never know.
Please don't let this feeling ever stop,
It is the happiness that continues to grow.

Melanie Allen
Emery County High School
Castle Dale, UT
Grade 11

Crazy Love

Three pounds of trash inside my skull for you
I will not be your ode to joy, for sure
I will become your worst nightmare to sue
By stealing what is loving, good and pure
You are my god, to whom I give my love
You are my flame, to whom I blame my fear
I watch you from the shadows that hang above
So that I don't scare you, I will not come near
I'll be with you 'til my sanity walks away
I'll dream you're here inside my heart, my hunger fed
And as this disenchanting discourse clouds the day
You will see then, it will not stop until I'm dead
The feeling drops out of your voice again
Redundantly you tell me it's the end

Thereasa Hammett
Montrose High School
Montrose, CO
Grade 10

Broken Silence*

A girl, sleeping in her bed
Woke up to a disturbing sound
She knew it was something bad
As her heart began to pound

The voice of her father
Seemed somewhat like a yelp
He said to call for someone
For someone to come and help

As the girl listened, she began asking why
She looked in and saw her mother, then she began to cry

The police told her everything was fine
"Please relax and stay calm"
"Put on a pretty smile"
Nothing is wrong with your mom

Her mother lived for a while
But later they pulled her plug
The girl felt lonely and empty
But her feelings she would shrug

The girl kept on going, as best as could be
But no one would ever guess, that girl was me

Heather Marie Laaker
Carson High School
Carson City, NV
Grade 11
*Dedicated to my loving mother,
Cynthia Ann Laaker, 11/22/64 - 3/20/96

What He Gave Us

He gave us the grand grass that is so green
He gave us the great big beautiful trees
He gave us the clouds that look like whipped cream
And he gave us the buzzing bumble bees
He gave us the bright smile upon our face
He gave us the feeling of being great
He gave us our fingers we use with grace
He gave us each someone to love; our mate
He gave us places to worship His name
He gave us the meaning of the word fun
He gave us all these things, for He's not lame
He gave us His only begotten Son
He gave us all each other, you and me
In hopes someday we'll live in harmony

Steffanie Foster
Clark High School
Las Vegas, NV
Grade 12

Sonnet?

The subject of my discontent is one
whose brash and uncompromising styles
caused hate and loathing in the hot, hot sun
from all the players for miles and miles.
His breath was rank, his odor worse.
His bite was small but his bark was death.
The presence there was a devil's curse,
everyone would jump at even a hint of breath.
We all hated deeply his torturous ways
But the team had no choice on what to say
we should have left, we shouldn't have stayed
our fun-loving time had turned a dark gray.
After that fun I left the team with cheer.
Just my luck, he quit the following year.

Will Ralston
Highland High School
Salt Lake City, UT
Grade 12

Stars in the Blue

Polaris shines bright in the blue orb of stars.
Each star is an eye,
Which can see you and what you do.
Each star has its own name,
Each its own secret.
No star knows its neighbor,
Because the expansive blue orb sets them so far apart.

Justin Trimmer
Battle Mountain Sr High School
Battle Mountain, NV
Grade 10

Lockerville vs. Nerd Lane

As I walk down the hall, I look around and see the nerds
In their hallways and the popular girls by their lockers.
At one point, I tried so hard to fit in and be cool.
But to the girls by their lockers, I was merely a dork.
It hurt so bad and my heart broke into a million pieces.
I walked and I cried and someone stopped me.
When I looked up, I saw the face of an angel smiling at me.
The angel was wearing a pocket protector and very thick glasses.
"Do you want to sit with us?" she asked me.
I never considered myself a nerd but I accepted the invitation.
After two days in Nerd Lane, I realized
That people who are beautiful on the outside
Are mere geeks on the inside
Some hearts are cold hard rocks;
But some follow a trail of gold.

Amy Little
C M Russell High School
Great Falls, MT
Grade 10

Background Love

Which way can I interpret your crazy magic?
The underground swings and I lie back
While you control kingdoms with just one trick.
You are imperfect as the night is black.
How is it that you transcend perfection?
That is your magic, awe will not sour.
Any passionate minds you may have won
Will not wonder, like I, of your power.
When did you dare to become a star?
I must interpret you as pure ideal—
Feet hurt from following you, eyes look far
Up to you, you're a truth, but still unreal
So I can never compare to you, be you
Just let our background love continue

Amy Taylor
Heritage High School
Littleton, CO
Grade 11

Young Poets
Grades 7-8-9

If I Knew

If I knew that it would be the last time that we would share our day,
I would make sure you knew that this was the best day of my life.
If I knew that it would be the last time I could hold your hand in mine,
I would cherish every moment.
If I knew that this would be the last time we would talk,
I would make sure that the conversation was worthwhile,
And that when we were through, you knew I loved you.
If I knew that this would be the last time I would see you cry,
I would kiss away every tear and along with it your every fear.
If I knew it would be the last time I should see your bright smile,
I would make sure that I would always remember the sight.
If I knew that this would be the last time that I would hear your voice,
I would let it cascade through my mind all the way to the depths of my soul.
If I knew that this would be the last time that I could tell you that I love you,
I would forget my timidity and tell you a thousand times over, I love you.
Since there is no way to be certain if this will be the last time we will be together,
I will cherish every day of ours, and hold your hand tight, knowing what a privilege it is.
I will try my hardest to share in your pain and understand your fears.
I will know I'm blessed every time I see your bright smile, and as I hear your voice I will listen with care.
I will take every chance to tell you I love you, because there is no way to know what tomorrow will bring.

Hillary Crider
Pine Creek High School
Colorado Springs, CO
Grade 9

There Was a Time

There was a time
When the meadow was all mine
When I could do as I pleased
When I tiptoed through grass
And snuck up on deer
And watched all the busy bees.

There was a time
When I could run through the meadow
Untouched, unbothered by man.
There was a time
When I could sit in the sun
And run my toes through the lakeside sand.

There was a time
When I could climb every tree
Throw every rock and catch every bee.
But that time is over now.
Still I'm sure as sure can be
There will be another one of these times
There will be another one of these.

Andrew Fischer
Powell Middle School
Littleton, CO
Grade 7

America Formed

When folks from the old country started sailing due west,
They found a new place to build and to rest.
They found a new country, with spectacular sights,
And a whole different place to practice their rights.

They settled right in, but Britain was tough,
They made new life here seem just as rough.
But these colonies fought until they were free,
And you had the same rights as him or as me.

Louisiana was bought from somewhere down south,
It ran a ways west, from the Mississippi mouth,
Lewis and Clark explored the great land,
They came back reporting the country was grand.

Time brought out the rugged mountain man,
And then the gold digger, with shovel and pan.
And so they all trekked on the Oregon Trail,
To form our country's marvelous tale.

Kristen Foster
Holmes Middle School
Colorado Springs, CO
Grade 8

Saying Good-Bye

My feet crunch through the frozen grass disguised with silvery snow,
The sky slowly fades to citrus pink encircling the sun sinking low.
A solitary flock of geese fly over honking their mournful cry,
For summer is gone and the frigidness is here to stay, they know.

Snowflakes begin to fall from the clouds in the evening sky.
A cold wind starts up making the lifeless trees shudder and sigh.
Jack Frost will visit once again on this cold and bleak night,
Bringing his frosty luster to all when he stops by.

The snow begins to fall so thick it's as if the angels started a pillow fight,
Soon the drab fall scenery will be costumed in wondrous winter white.
The complete transformation from fall to winter steadily nears,
Bringing the first official hours of winter closer into the world's sight.

The surfaces of frozen creeks and ponds reflect like so many glassy mirrors,
And the dim shadowed sky will persist in dropping its pallid icy tears.
The last shreds of late summer have suddenly vanished it appears,
And it is time to say good-bye to summer and greet winter, I fear.

Stephanie L. Hunter
Star Valley Jr High School
Afton, WY
Grade 8

Listen to Your Flag

High above the buildings, my stars and stripes still wave;
I represent a nation, a symbol to the brave.
With 200 years of freedom, this nation has been blessed;
God has been so good to her, far above the rest.

From well above the landscape, in wind, in rain and snow,
I see so many people, I watch them come and go.
I've seen the waste of battle, where many men have died;
When people wept for loved ones, when mothers sat and cried.

I fly above a great land, with mountains big and tall,
Her valleys rich and fertile, there is plenty here for all.
Yet why are people greedy, and why are they so proud?
They think the only way to live, is high above the crowd.

This land is here for everyone, a special gift from God,
With everyone a right to live, a chance to plow the sod.
Now is the time of turmoil, with nations far apart;
The only peace there is on Earth, must be within your heart.

Yes, I fly up there above you;
I fly with good intent.
But remember this:
No matter what you are,
It's you I represent.

Jeff Jolley
Mountain Ridge Jr High School
Highland, UT
Grade 8

The Only Child

You hang on so tight, never wanting to let go,
I don't want to let the pain you cause show.

I know they are loving hands you cradle me in,
But do you know that your grip digs deep into my skin?

You and I know that you just mean well,
But sometimes your love is my prison cell.

You want to protect me, and never see me fall,
Though all your protection chains me to the wall.

I live in a fantasy land, to some it may seem,
An extremely happy world, in a rose-color dream.

But behind those rose glasses, stares down a hawk's eye,
Watching your every move from high in the sky.

You can run and hide, trying with all your might,
But you're never completely out of the bird's watchful sight.

I know I should be grateful for parents who care,
For sleeping eyes are worse than ones that just stare.

But I can't help to wonder, though, how it must be,
Out of the nest and flying free.

But for right now, I only have you,
And I am the only child, all you have too.

Jessica Mills
Sage Valley Jr High School
Gillette, WY
Grade 9

Inside This Brush

Inside this paint brush live millions
of places never seen, people never born,
and things never imagined.
All of the paintings come out of it
and leap onto the canvas.
It dances with all the colors of the rainbow.
They twist and jump around in the brush
and explode onto the painting
in whatever shape or form I want them to.

Eric Moog
St. Jude Thaddeus School
Havre, MT
Grade 7

The Real Painting

The artist sat tensely in front of the bleak canvas
that seemed to extend forever like a sandy desert
and slowly but faithfully began to paint the scene
spread before her, filling the gray canvas
with a spectrum of colors.

The silver blue paint glided easily
onto the desolate canvas
creating a placid lake reflecting
the pale pastels of the moon light
next to the looming evergreen trees
standing like sentinels at their watch-post.

In the soft glow of the sunrise
the painter examined the painting
with a critically trained eye and sighed,
for although it was a wonderful piece
it could never quiet compare
with the real painting.

Elizabeth Muir
Butler Middle School
Salt Lake City, UT
Grade 8

Dr. Vertenstein

My piano teacher
A short small lady
like a cork from an aged wine bottle
Her gray hair looks silver to me.
She always wears colorful sweaters
and gold clip-on earrings.
She has so much life
She can fill a whole room
with happiness and smiles.
Her house smells clean and welcoming,
She is warm and calm and always
greets me with a happy smile at the door.
She speaks quietly with a strong Rumanian accent.
She walks slowly like she
has all the time in the world.
She gracefully sits at the piano
like a swan on her pond.
Her small wrinkled hands move
tirelessly across the keys
as she always sways to the love of her life
Music

Lindsay Stolberg
Colorado Academy
Denver, CO
Grade 9

Twenty-One

I entered the bar with curiosity.
I smelled the stenches of beer burps
Around the racket of drunken men, laughing with their buddies.
I walked toward the counter. I was twenty-one.

I sat in a stool facing the bartender
While he said, "What will it be?"
He was cleaning a glass with an old, dirty, worn-out rag,
Staring at me with an impatient face. I was twenty-one.

I said, "Give me a beer," then he walked away.
I sat there aimlessly and waited for him to come
And when he came, he handed me a glass of ice cold beer.
I gave him five dollars. I was twenty-one.

I grabbed the glass and held it up.
I moved it toward my lips while thinking of my past.
I remembered the time I left for college, and told my parents,
"I will never disappoint you." I was twenty-one.

But that was then and this is now, I thought.
I then gazed at my trembling hand.
I set my glass down and looked at the useless men around me with a stare.
I got up and walked away.
I was twenty-one.

Mason Wang
Mountain Ridge Middle School
Colorado Springs, CO
Grade 8

The Beauty of Skiing

As I step onto the chair lift, it whooshes me into the crisp mountain air sending shivers through my body as it adjusts to the temperature. I look down, there is a blanket of untouched white powder, and my heart beats faster. I'm longing to make the first set of tracks in it. But my dream is crushed as I see a group of snowboarders screaming down the hill whooping and cheering, cutting up the beautiful snow. Oh well, I can always go down another. At the top of the chair lift, I scramble towards my favorite run, when I make it I am ecstatic because there are no tracks in it. I need to be the first one down. I jump off the ledge into the run, turning around the moguls with powder cushioning my turns. As I pick up speed it feels as if I'm floating on air, bounding around making turns. I stop, look up the hill in wonder, thinking how anything could be so beautiful; the early morning sky peeking over the ridge, with snow-dusted trees surrounding the run, then I see a large group of skiers tearing down the mountain towards me. I get moving, determined to be the first down. There are about 200 yards of untouched snow ahead of me, I'm flying down the hill with the wind stinging my face, and howling in my ears. At the end I'm filled with a wonderful exhaustion, feeling as if I've conquered the world when I beat the skiers down. As I recall that run, butterflies fill my stomach and I see the tracks I've set on the hill. My ego has been boosted a hundred percent. What a run.

Todd Driver
Campus Middle School
Englewood, CO
Grade 8

What Bugs Me

When my teachers won't take the time to listen and help in whatever way they can.
When my brother grew so tall and strong now instead of me pounding him, I end up as dead meat.
When my little brother sings while I'm trying to do my homework.
When the bad weather just won't let up and I am cold right down to my toes.
When the day dawns cold, gloomy and bleak.
When I am late for school, and I have to run out the door with my hair still down and one shoe on.
When I finally reach school and I have to sit through a boring class.
When I ask the question I didn't get yesterday, the teacher answers in her own little way,
"You already know what to do, just figure it out."
When I try again to explain that the person she explained it to, was my C-average friend.

Grace Sims
Academy Charter School
Castle Rock, CO
Grade 7

Facsimile Transmittal

To: Al Gore   Fax: 1-888-vote-4al
From: Bill Clinton   Date: December 16, 1999
Re: How to get elected   Pages: 1
CC:

Urgent   For Review   Please Comment   Please Reply   Please Recycle

Notes: To win an election:
1. You must first learn to lie.
2. After learning to lie, you must practice it. (Believe me you will need to do this a lot.)
3. Photo Op. Photo Op. Photo Op. Use these, get your picture on every cover you can, people forget about you. Try throwing in a scandal or two.
4. Make sure that YOU run the country. Learn where and when to accept bribes.
5. A "fake war" solves everything.
6. Promise anything that you want. The people don't care. They are just a bunch of idiots. Only 42.45% of them ever vote. Only 16.4% of them actually know your last name.
7. Making up statistics and facts on the spot helps in news conferences.
8. Tax, Tax, Tax!!!
   Well this is everything that I have ever learned while in office, hope it helps!

Chris Bland
Colorado Academy
Denver, CO
Grade 9

Dreams That Fly

To go to sleep,
To live the life of the dream,
To fall in so deep,
But to wake, is to forget the endless possibilities

Love the dream undreamt,
As possibility of ideas once kept,
The stars above who touch their souls,
As darkness covers the Earth, behold

The sun rises, the sun sets
Where thoughts so true will fly for you,
In the sight among the stars,
Remember, what you learn, remember where you are

Brought among the dreams that fly,
To answer all questions, how and why?

Katie Konecny
Holmes Middle School
Colorado Springs, CO
Grade 8

The River

In winter the river moves very slow.
It seems to stop its endless flow.
It clogs with ice in lacy form,
Banks lined with snow from last week's storm.

No signs of life are easily seen,
Except for tracks; no hints of green.
A frozen scene dressed in white,
The river shimmers in the sun's bright light.

The earth emerges from its blanket cover.
The hidden life will soon uncover.
The air gets warmer as days grow long.
The river's trickle soon will be strong.

As time goes by it slowly breaks free,
And swells with melt on its journey to the sea.
As spring awakens, the river grows strong,
Its widening path surging along.

It fills to its limit and picks up speed,
Like a long-kept prisoner newly freed,
Until it reaches its peak at last,
A raging force, unsurpassed!

Hanna Farrar
Carbondale Community School
Carbondale, CO
Grade 7

Spring

Spring brings new life to the world.
Everything runs green like the plants and trees.
Spring also brings life to animals of all kinds.
It also means school is almost out for the summer.
This is Spring.

Daryld Richardson
Academy Charter School
Castle Rock, CO
Grade 7

Chris' Miracle

Come on girl,
Leading our gray mare,
Into her stall.
She was due any day now,
As I patter her gently.
We returned that night,
To find her heavy breathing,
The floor, ground, filled and splattered with blood.
We knew she had lost too much.
Out came the bay colt as we pulled.
Then 10 minutes later,
She closed her soft eyes.
Her name was Chris' Maid,
Therefore her colt was Chris' Miracle,
Because that colt was really a miracle.

Whitney Caldwell
Star Valley Jr High School
Afton, WY
Grade 7

The School Year

A school year is 180 days long
It starts going fast
But then slows down
Some people like school
And some people don't
You can be in sports
Football's the best
And basketball is fun too
And there are only 90 days left
The days are getting longer
And the books are getting heavier
While all we are doing is homework
There is no time for sports
If we want passing grades
Now there are 30 days left, then there are 15
Now it is the last day of school
We are all having fun
Summer is here
Time to dread
The next school year

Chris Protain
Reedpoint Jr/Sr High School
Reedpoint, MT
Grade 8

Determination and Defeat
Determination
power, strategy,
never ever give up,
fading, disappearing, vanishing,
lost, gone,
Defeat

Julia Voll
Custer County School
Westcliffe, CO
Grade 7

The Perfect Mood for Food
I'm in the perfect mood
For some delicious food
I could have some chips
Or some very yummy dips
Now I hear my stomach churn
For some caramel popcorn
I could go for some Sprite
Or some strawberry soda, that's right
Some chicken will do the trick
And some carrots from the finest pick
Cherry pie
Just makes me want to cry
I'm in the perfect mood
For some delicious food

Chaylyn Alexander
Century Middle School
Thornton, CO
Grade 7

Heartbroken*
The sun shined brightly overhead.
I was overwhelmed with joy.
The grass was green,
And the sky was blue.

Until, one day, a dark cloud came,
It surrounded us,
Blocking out the sun,
Never to reveal it again.

We loved the sunlight.
Why did it have to be taken away?
Many of us have given up now,
And I was about to, too.

I wished to see the sunlight,
But still it never came.
Then one by one all of us died,
Heartbroken.

Mark Nielsen
South Jordan Middle School
South Jordan, UT
Grade 8
*Based on the Holocaust

Lord of the Sky
Rising above all,
at dusk it comes
to shine up the gloom,
and warm up the night.
Surrounding it are more of it,
though none so large or close,
for this is the master,
the king of stars.
It is a symbol
recognized by all,
and it towers above nature,
keeping watch on the world.
And with all its power,
it cannot be claimed,
for it is the moon,
lord of the night sky.

Robyn Rickert
Vail Mountain School
Vail, CO
Grade 7

The Travel
The orders are given,
The ship is set,
To start on a journey,
We won't forget.

The engines start up,
The ship gains speed,
The stars fly past us,
In a steady stream.

Our destination is near,
Our speed declines.
We see the planet,
In the dark black sky.

As we enter orbit,
Around the blue jewel,
It's a wonder
What nature can do.

Christopher Kennedy
Challenger School
Sandy, UT
Grade 8

Soft and Fuzzy
Fuzzy is my teddy bear on my bed
Soft is my kitty in her house
Fuzzy are the peaches on the table
Soft is my blanket in the winter
Fuzzy and soft!

Melissa Cable
North Arvada Middle School
Arvada, CO
Grade 7

Oh Father
Oh father, sweet father
Look down from the sky,
Our freedom is won
Our battle is done,
The bells are ringing
The children are singing
What is that I hear?
The silence, the silence
No guns firing,
No cannons ringing
The silence, the silence
No fighting
No firing
The battle is done
Our freedom is won

Jesse Stevens
Dubois Elementary-Middle School
Dubois, WY
Grade 8

Ants
Back and forth, back and forth;
March, march, march;
Stumble, bumble, bump.
On they go, never stopping;
Never quitting ...
To build the tunnel;
And make their home.

Ants work,
Like no other creature I know.
Work and work and work
Some more.

Joshua Ward
Powell Middle School
Littleton, CO
Grade 7

Who I Am
I am like chocolate,
Sweet as can be.
I am like a pine tree,
Always firm and strong.
I am like a jeep,
Not too sporty, but not too plain.
I am like a cat,
I can be mean and caring.
I'm like the morning,
Ready for something new.
I'm like spring,
Watching things bloom.
That's who I am.

Alexis Howell
St Therese School
Aurora, CO
Grade 8

Friends Forever

"Friends forever," you said.
"Always, I promise."
Well you're doing a good job at that.
Friends forever.

You were always there for me.
When I was nervous you always cheered for me.
Friends forever.

You were always at my side when I was troubled.
When I was sad and cried you cried too.
When I was happy you were too.
Friends forever.

We were inseparable.
We were identified as sisters or twins.
Friends forever.

Now you're gone.
But we still keep in touch and visit.
So we're still
Friends forever.

Amie Ha
Century Middle School
Thornton, CO
Grade 7

Me

I try to write poems
I really do
I try to be mystic
And I write them for you

But everything I write is very sad
it never is happy
it's not really bad
it's just sad

I know people who don't even try
they just sit and stare and let life pass them by
it really is sad, sadder than me
And I sit and I wonder, "How could this be?"

And I sit and I think for a very long time
And thoughts come to me, all worth a dime
And though I may write some very sad things
At least I do something, not wait for the bell to ring
At least I can write some very smart things.

Michelle Andrews
Holmes Middle School
Colorado Springs, CO
Grade 8

Try and Try Again

Don't let dreams just pass you by,
You'll only win if you try.
If you want to reach the unreachable star,
Try even if the distance may seem too far.

Don't let trouble steal all hope,
Don't sit at home all day and mope.
Wipe each teardrop from your eye,
You'll only win if you try.
Never let people say of you,
Your mightiest dream you didn't peruse.
You can win the battle if not the war,
And you'll be happy forever more.

There's really nothing under the sun,
It's really impossible but can be done,
So you get busy, get right to it,
Take the clue, go on and do it.

Kara Virgil
Sheridan Jr High School
Sheridan, WY
Grade 8

The Fight

My life rides on this night,
on this night it rides.
I journey to the core; the hot pit of death.
Where I fight,
fight for a life where true life lives.
For a life where love lives.
For a life where nothing hurts.
I fight for heaven.
I am prepared to fight.
For a life that stops to live.
Stops to live.
Forever.

Brent Everson
Florence-Carlton Public School
Florence, MT
Grade 8

Thirst

Thirst is
blue like spring water,
cold like a winter breeze,
sounds like a leaky sink,
tastes like mountain snow,
smells like a fresh rain storm,
moves like a raging river,
looks like water dripping from an ice cube
textured like smooth paper
and feels like a cool ocean breeze.

Scott Robinson
St. Jude Thaddeus School
Havre, MT
Grade 7

Be Yourself

Never let others say who you are
or determine what you should be.
If you'll be yourself, you'll go far.
You'll be better off; take it from me.

Love yourself for who you are,
and whatever you do don't change.
Dare to dream and reach for the stars
don't you know they're always in range.

You can be anything you want to be.
Your life is an open book.
For your future you possess the key.
Now use it and take a look!

Anything's possible for you my friend
as long as you dare to try.
Just be yourself and never bend;
then you shall touch the sky!

Lauren Bradley
Challenger School
Sandy, UT
Grade 8

Fear

I know I must face it,
It blocks out my life,
Nervously I await my frightening destiny,
I get an uneasy feeling about me,
As the moment approaches,
When finally, I have to face it,
It approaches too quickly,
Then finally it hits me,
After I get up, I look around,
And it's gone.

Josh Newman
North Davis Jr High School
Clearfield, UT
Grade 9

The End of the World

There will come a day,
When the world will end.

Just like the expiration date,
On an old milk carton.

There may be a tomorrow,
But what will it bring?

Maybe the sad sorrow of loss,
Or perhaps nothing at all.

Evan Goldhahn
Fort Benton Jr/Sr High School
Fort Benton, MT
Grade 9

Computer Madness

Computer madness, oh, computer madness!
It makes me have a case of adrenaline, as I feel
the computer's power in my already shaking hand!

Ooh, ooh, I love computers!
Whining, whining goes the computer as it downloads
important information and facts for my home, office, or school needs!

Squeak, squeak goes my sweaty hand on the mouse,
clickety-click goes the mouse as I have the surging power to click
on its buttons. While the mouse's tail wags as if it had a life of its own!

Screech goes the disk as I insert it into the hard drive
and I never have seen a computer shake as I try to control its powers!

Things will keep flying out at me and swirl around the room,
searching for that long lost gift, freedom,
after an eternity-long glass prison life!

Ooh, ooh, I love computers!

Chris Heide
Circle Jr High School
Circle, MT
Grade 8

Black and White

The world is only black and white, there's nothing in between.
No iffy's, might be's, should be's, could be's, you know what I mean.
It's right or wrong, it's good or bad, it's even or unfair.
There's simply not a gray zone; you're in tune or you don't care.

You're innocent or guilty, you are honest or you're not.
Your ethics and your standards are things that can't be bought.
It's true or false, it's cut and dry, there is no middle ground.
It's raining or it's shining, there is silence or there's sound.

No wishy-washy's, kind of's, sort of's, you know what is right.
Just let your conscience guide you like a beacon in the night.
The world is only black and white, so why so many views?
It seems so plainly simple, is it red or is it blue?

Jenna Spackeen
Challenger School
Sandy, UT
Grade 7

Winter

Winter's cold, frosty breath lay heavy in the air.
The rolling hills slept for Mother Nature's long-lasting tears had begun.
Trees' fingers became numb from the changing season.
The lake's song quieted as a layer of ice formed.
The world held its breath as the sun peaked her head for a final visit.
The cold swept in and dark gray clouds took root.

Cameron Martin
Powell Middle School
Littleton, CO
Grade 7

Recurring Dream

I am alone in an old, lofty house
My imagination is anticipating the worst
They said they would be back by now. . .
But they're not

The gale is howling
A tree is blown against the window
Rain lashes the trembling pane
The murmur of television distracts me a bit
Shadows flicker like ghosts on the walls
The storm should be passing faster, it seems. . .
But it's not

Somewhere upstairs a door is creaking
I hear whispers in the hall
There is a stroke of lightning and thunder crashes
The power goes off and I suck in my breath
I feel my heart pounding in my head, my hands
A panicked, erratic throb
I wish you were here to ease my foreboding
I wish you were here to calm my nerves
I wish you were here. . .
But you're not

Ginny Farnham
Laurel Middle School
Laurel, MT
Grade 8

Let it Snow Let it Snow

Sitting in the classroom,
Staring out the window.

Oh, what is that a snowflake?
Please, please, let us get out of school.

Snow more, and more,
Blizzard and make drifts.

I wait for the loudspeaker,
When will it say "School's out for today?"

Every second goes ticking by,
I wait and I wait as if I had the time.

That's when it happens,
A beautiful voice from the loudspeaker.
Yes, finally we get out of school.
"Will everyone please report to the gym for class pictures?"

Brittany Foster
Pawnee Jr-Sr High School
Grover, CO
Grade 8

Please Be Gentle

Please be gentle with my love,
My heart,
My soul,
My mind.
Please be gentle with my feelings,
My happy,
My sad,
My kind.
Please forgive me for my hate,
And don't hold it against me.
Instead think of all the happiness,
That's what I'd like you to see.
Please be gentle with my life,
Because so easily it can break.
But most of all be gentle with my dreams,
Because that's one thing I'd hate for you to take.

Megan Hottovy
Mountain Ridge Middle School
Colorado Springs, CO
Grade 8

Silence

Silence shrouds this strange street,
Quiet and motionless beneath my feet.
With the least amount of obeisance to its surroundings,
It curves into the dark, beguiling even the best driver.
Many a man has lost his very soul here.
It curves into the night,
Surceasing where it begins.
Waiting and watching, I wish for my life,
As I stream silently past this street.

Zelwyn Heide
Circle Jr High School
Circle, MT
Grade 8

Spring

Purple, pink, orange and yellow
These are some colors you see in the spring.
They smell very good and make life much better
For they make most everything brighter.

What would we do without a spring with flowers?
Would everything be black and white
And nothing smell like a spring with flowers?
Or would everything be green and brown
With only the smells of the trees and the ground?

Some flowers are wild,
And some are tame.
Flowers are everywhere,
When it is spring.

Kathleen Downward
Kanab Middle School
Kanab, UT
Grade 7

The Last

I was weary, cold, hungry, and ill
Like everyone else.
But I knew that this was the last day.

As I fell down onto my "bed"
I knew that this torture
Would end by tomorrow.

In the middle of the night,
I was awakened by a wild fit of coughing.
My own.

My throat burned, my eyes watered
I couldn't stop as I heard a soldier say,
"This is the last one."

I was carried to a room,
Now only subconscious
Hardly aware of the others.

The metal doors clang shut.
I know where I am.
There's nothing I can do.

The deadly gas fills my lungs.
Before all goes dark,
I take my last breath.

Jessica Dymond
South Jordan Middle School
South Jordan, UT
Grade 8

A Surge of Deep Emotion

The phone rings; I pick it up
They want my mom
I sit, wait, and listen
Mom looks at me in the weirdest way
I know something's wrong.
"What's wrong, Mom, what's wrong?"
I ask her.
She hangs up the phone.
She starts to cry
I ask her again, "What's wrong?"
She says "Dad has prostate cancer"
NO! NO! NO!
I scream inside
He can't have cancer
Mom already has throat cancer
I run downstairs and start to cry
I then stop
Then ask myself
"COULD I HAVE CANCER?"

Randy Gettman
South Valley Middle School
Platteville, CO
Grade 8

The Concert

The waiting crowd stands in amazement,
Anxiously walking, buying hurriedly,
Fearing there is a lack of tickets.
Suddenly, there is an outburst of wild screams from people in the crowd.
They are excitedly singing and dancing.
The crowd is breath-taken by the action going on in the arena,
You can't even hear yourself talk.
As the concert is over, people are happily leaving,
But sad to know the fun is over.

Blair Dorsey
St Therese School
Aurora, CO
Grade 8

One Perfect Day

As I step out on the morning dew, the grass cushions my feet,
I sense the aroma of the sweet air with its ever so delicate taste,
I peer up and close my eyes as the sunlight so gently laces my cheeks,
I stroll down the pastel cobble road to a hill where I lay on the soft earth,
My mind goes free and glides up into heaven and soars with the gods,
I slip back into the world and gaze at the clouds,
The clouds seem to be pillows of heavenly goose down,
So slowly grazing off the sunlight traveling to the horizon,
I stand back up and walk to the pond,
There I stare at the reflections of the newborn flowers in the water,
Their petals lightly splashed with the most beautiful colors,
When the day reaches sunset,
I watch as the rays of sun turn pink, then orange, then red, then purple,
As I walk home I hear the faint music of the crickets,
When I get to my house I say to myself,
This is one perfect day.

Michael Wood
Campus Middle School
Englewood, CO
Grade 8

The Constant Roller Coaster

Being a teenager is like being on a constant roller coaster ride.
It's like experiencing the highest high,
As if you're on the very top looking out over the whole world,
About to experience the thrill of your life,
Every muscle tense with excitement,
A huge smile spread across your face.
Being a teenager can also feel like you're feeling the lowest lows,
As if the roller coaster is speeding downhill
And you're scared out of your mind,
Like you want to get off the ride,
But you can't.
The best thing about being a teenager is that you won't always be one,
Just like with a roller coaster ride,
You know it will eventually come to an end.
But maybe it will turn out to be the best ride of your life.

Ben Racine
Colorado Academy
Denver, CO
Grade 9

Passion

Loved, lived, hated
You've never lived 'till you've loved.
You've never loved 'till you've hated.
But you've never loved like I have.
A passion that sets my heart aflame
A passion of singing, of that stage.
To hear the crowd cheer,
But it's only a dream.
A dream that will keep me going from day-to-day.
To think will today be the day?
Will today be the day
when I lift my voice to the heavens
and someone will hear?
If it came true, it would be heaven.
The crowds cheering,
Me singing.
My heart would be as big as a horse,
If I could have this dream.
I could express my passion for singing.

Hayley M. White
Adele C. Young Intermediate School
Brigham City, UT
Grade 7

I Am an Athlete

I think about how fast I am
    How far can I go
    How long can I last

I feel full of energy
    Full of heart
    Full of mind

I want to run faster
    Find that last bit of energy
    To push me further

I am an athlete

I think about running in front
    The ribbon hitting my chest
    As I fly through the finish line

I feel the pain and the joy
    As I kick for more speed
    The adrenal power comes
    I am almost out but still kicking harder and harder

I want to live as an athlete
    Running longer and faster, every second of the day
    Feeling more powerful, being more powerful
    I am an athlete and will always be

Grace McKoy
C S Porter Middle School
Missoula, MT
Grade 7

Counting Animals for Fun!

One horse without a shoe,
Likes to play peek-a-boo with you.

Two cows in a barn,
Who cares if they don't have yarn!

Three mice looking for cheese,
Are scared away by a swarm of bees.

Four kittens still looking for their mittens,
Oh my, I hope their paws aren't frostbitten.

Five puppies busy at play,
And then off they go to chase a blue jay.

Six bears eating honey,
They don't mind sharing with Mr. Bunny.

Seven elephants like to eat peanuts,
But none of them like coconuts.

Eight rabbits hopping home,
Had just finished eating their ice cream cone.

Nine pigs taking a jog,
And then they played a game of leapfrog.

Ten lions with a sleepy head
Get on their pajamas and head straight to bed.

Courtney Archibeque
Franklin Middle School
Greeley, CO
Grade 7

Myself

I am like a strawberry shortcake
Short, sweet and berry colored hair.

Sometimes I am like a goldfish,
Enjoying my own space.

Sometimes I am like Monopoly,
Working hard and earning my own money.

I am like the morning,
Bright, friendly and happy.

I am like the summer,
Relaxed, happy and the color of my hair, the color of the sun.

I am like an S.U.V.,
Sporty, enjoy the mountains and fashionable.

Monica Raleigh
St Therese School
Aurora, CO
Grade 8

Milking Duck

I've always wanted milking ducks,
They're very rare you see,
With long black beaks and spotted tails,
These ducks are special to me.

I collect the eggs in the morning,
And gather the milk at night,
I'm the envy of the neighbors,
These fowls are quite a sight.

These ducks are quite a marvel,
Almost more than I can take,
Each morning I eat fried eggs,
Each night I sip a shake.

Zach Luthi
Star Valley Jr High School
Afton, WY
Grade 7

Clouds

Clouds are like
furry cats.
They are poofy
and fluffy.
Clouds are light
on their feet.

Jamie Singleton
Boulder City High School
Boulder City, NV
Grade 9

The World Never Ends

The world never ends,
It does not curve,
It does not bend.

The world never stops,
It does not snap,
It does not pop.

Although it feels like it should,
It never will,
It never would.

Though times are hard my dear,
It cannot see,
It cannot hear.

And though you may often cry,
It does not feel,
It does not die.
The world never ends.

Ashlee Welday
White Middle School
Henderson, NV
Grade 7

Nature

Beautiful nature
Flowers blossoming in spring
Bees humming around

Nick Laymon
White Middle School
Henderson, NV
Grade 7

I Am

I am the daughter of my father,
   and the child of my mother.
I am the sister of my brother,
   then there are no others.

I am a student of the room,
   a learner of the school.
I am a player of the team,
   just a stitch in the seam.

I am no one who is seen,
   but the maker of my dreams.
I am but a person in the crowd,
   no one who is loud.

I am a person of the world,
   and a child of God.

Laura Evans
McClelland Center School
Pueblo, CO
Grade 7

The Beast

It crouches
in the dark,
just returned from the jungle
The many eyes
empty, blank
Asleep?
Dead
The shiny metallic skin
warm
Inside
something drips
ticks, hums
Waiting
For the garage door to open
and a foot inside
to press down
so it can roar out
down the hard black river
Into the jungle
again.

Alex White
Colorado Academy
Denver, CO
Grade 9

My Paper Hat

Once I had a sailor's hat
I made it out of newspaper
In it I was the best captain in the world
One with strength and valor
I sailed across the seven seas
And battled pirates to save my ship

Then I refolded my sailor's hat
And a fireman I became
I saved many different people
From a burning building
I went in all alone
And saved them from the inferno

Soon, I took off my paper hat
And became just plain old me
I realized however
This was the hat I liked the best!

Henry Tappen
Connect Charter School
Pueblo, CO
Grade 8

Echo

Life is beautiful
   but pointless as hell
It's a battle between what's going on
   and what's going well

It is very enlightening
   but confusing as well
I was doing just fine
   . . . then I fell

Life is very fun
   but it's scary to tell
that this is one of those things
   I am willing to sell

I am afraid of nothing
   yet I'm running in fear
I'm so disorganized
   I feel about to tear.

Clinton Ormond
Sage Valley Jr High School
Gillette, WY
Grade 9

The Colors of Spring?

These are the colors of spring?
Blue, yellow and also green?
These are the colors of spring?

Ashley Whitaker
North Arvada Middle School
Arvada, CO
Grade 7

Serenity in Paradise

As I lounge in a chair, hearing the waves lap up on the beach,
I listen to the gentle sounds of the seagulls overhead.

I remember the sights of a world recently departed from
where all live in harmony,
and are showing beautiful colors.

The turtle, the giant, gentle beast
who intrudes with no avail,
who hides under a kelp and seaweed veil.

Feeling no threat, I leave him be
knowing he feels no threat from me.

Wistfully thinking, oh, how I long to join him,
I would need a shell, fins, and a sense of adventure as well.

But then I sense, my time has come to return to my world,
and listen to the waves on the beach.

Kyle Wiederholt
Campus Middle School
Englewood, CO
Grade 8

Flowers

Flowers are my pride and joy,
I love them just as a kid loves a toy.
Orange, pink, yellow, or blue,
Who cares, they were all made for me and you.
Flowers with petals so green,
These are the prettiest I have ever seen.

Daisies are cute and small,
These are my favorites out of all.
With an inside yellow, and petals of white,
They sway on grass just like a kite.

Roses are vast and bright,
They shine in my eyes just like a light.
With petals so enormous and colorful,
This makes them so fantastic and lovable.

Carnations are fluffy and round,
At my house they can always be found.
With a smell so beautiful and sweet,
Which no other flower could ever beat.

Daffodils, tulips, petunias, these are just a few,
Look outside and I bet you could name a few too!

Heather Shippen
Plentywood Middle School
Plentywood, MT
Grade 7

The Night

The sky stretches forever like a black blanket.
The stars look like a thousand flashlights.
The moon looks like a diamond in the dark ocean,
It moves so slow, like a snail on a sidewalk.
I could stare at it forever with a friend or by myself.
It would be like staring at a sea of dreams.
Hopefully, I could catch one and keep it forever;

Then, as the night drifts away,
The sun comes up and the stars and moon disappear.

Mary Kate Callaghan
Franklin Middle School
Greeley, CO
Grade 7

Spring Break

After class on Friday
In our car we drove
Off to California
Together my grandmother and I

In the middle of Utah
Near Salt Lake City we drove
Along the Great Salt Lake
Together my grandmother and I
Away from Castle Rock we rode
Along mountain ranges and through Great Salt Flats
Together my grandmother and I

About two days later we arrived in California
Like a Roadrunner out darts my cousin to great me
Off in the distance was my uncle

Along the beach
In the setting sun
With a family
Together as one

Ashlee Sousa
Academy Charter School
Castle Rock, CO
Grade 8

Football

Football is a war,
Players are the warriors,
  Battling to the death
The fans,
  Screaming patrons, reliant on their army
Blitzing linebackers,
  Fearless kamikazes flying into the line
But only victory brings glory
  To the idolized victor.

Loren Utterback
Fort Benton Jr/Sr High School
Fort Benton, MT
Grade 9

Goldi

Beautiful curls,
That bounce up and down.
Small and petite,
And likes to wander around.
So innocent her smile,
So soft her skin,
In a house in the forest,
Where have those bears been?
Then eats his porridge!
Breaks his chair!
And sleeps in his bed!
False impression.

Jenny Jones
Colorado Academy
Denver, CO
Grade 9

Redrock

The minerals of
God's fingerprints
in sky high beauty.

Manmade works of
art tops a mountain
in a marvel of creation.

The clouds climbing
in a struggle with thin
air to ascend the peak.

A Colorado day in all of its beauty.
We can take a journey but God
has to lead us.

God can only show us the door,
we have to walk
through it.

Jack Boyd
Pauline Memorial School
Colorado Springs, CO
Grade 7

From Night to Dawn

The day of dawn
has passed away,
and I
am the lonely one,
the only one
to step forward
as if
the night
were to dawn.

Chelsea Terry
Spanish Fork Jr. High School
Spanish Fork, UT
Grade 8

The Real Me!

I am like a willow tree, sometimes,
Drooping but with some light.

I am like a Toyota Echo
New, original, fun going, and forever driving others crazy.

I am like a wolf,
With plans to attack any situation.

I am like ice cream,
With flavors to fit my every mood.

I am like spring,
A sweet wind and storms full of fury.

I am like night,
Looking for the real me in a dark maze.

But over all I am like Pictionary,
It takes 1000 words to describe me.

Kelsey Light
St Therese School
Aurora, CO
Grade 8

Ocean Secrets

The ocean is full of deep dark secrets.
Secrets that will be discovered.
Why wait until someone discovers those secrets,
And you go yourself to explore.

The ocean is a wide blanket with the biggest wrinkles that could cover a man;
With wonders that could cover the ocean floor with a wisp.
Animals that become your fantasies with a blink of an eye.
The ocean is full of deep dark secrets.

Erica Carrasco
North Arvada Middle School
Arvada, CO
Grade 7

Fading Away

I remember when he bounced me on his knee.
Taught me how to whittle and carve my name in the big oak tree.
He taught me to tie my shoes and count to two.
We laughed and cried.
Oh what great times we had.
As he grew older and so did I.
The twinkle in his eyes began to fade.
His hands began to shake.
His memory began to fade.
He remembers me no longer.
But my grandpa will always be in my heart.

Natosha Merritt
Star Valley Jr High School
Afton, WY
Grade 7

Dumbfounded

I don't know what to do.

I wonder if I should laugh or cry.
Whether to answer or leave the question to float around.

I can't decide to love or hate.
Should I walk or fight?

Whether to take or leave be.
I wonder if I should ignore or listen.

Should I talk or keep quiet?
I can't decide to forgive or hold a grudge.

Whether to want, need, or both.
Can you answer these for me?

You see I am dumbfounded.

Adam Mangold
Powell Middle School
Powell, WY
Grade 8

Untrue Love

We met by the fingers of fate,
Not knowing the outcome,
At a fast rate, at first a bliss,
Now came to this, a change of minds.

Hearts broken, tears shed,
Almost wishing I was dead,
Took a break, as if we were fake.

All the long phone calls, the e-mails and all,
I followed him blindly until I did fall.

So many warnings, but I didn't listen,
I thought it was real, but I was wrong.

Wanting it so bad,
Giving up halfway,
Missing each other,
Day after day.

Hurting each other,
Not wanting to though,
Saying goodbye
And then letting go.

Laura Soucie
Norwood High School
Norwood, CO
Grade 9

Blind

I used to think of you as the one for me
I would try anything to make you see
That I was the one for you my friend
Every day my love I'd send

But now I see you never cared
That I'd be forever there
Waiting for you to realize
That you would always be special in my eyes

Abby Cook
Holmes Middle School
Colorado Springs, CO
Grade 8

Jets Through the Sky

Notice the jets that defend our sky,
Flying fast into the clouds above,
Spot them soaring way up high.

Jetting across and doing their best,
Tumbling and turning through the air,
Not a single cloud will get a rest.

These great machines are very keen,
They use rapid maneuvers and also swift speed.
Hardship and struggle is what they've seen.

Don't forget when they fly right by
Tell a friend or remember this line:
Those are the jets that defend our sky.

Zach Kellogg
Challenger School
Sandy, UT
Grade 7

Growing

Good-bye, my mother, please don't see me go.
I'm off to find my dreams and make them come true.
Leaving to fight my battles, I'm leaving mother, hear me go.
I'm not going to be far,
please don't cry, just let me find my way.

I want to touch the sky
reach the stars, fight the danger, love the dreams
fight the races, bless the food, keep the faith,
and it will be all right.

When I leave, I'll cry then dry my tears.
Please let me find my dreams.
I'm off my mother, please just wait and see.
I have learned from you, it's a part of my life.
Just remember I will always be a part of you.

Madonna Jenkins
Brentwood Middle School
Greeley, CO
Grade 7

Eternal Question

There are many disputed questions,
In scientist's large heads.
But no question can compare,
To "Where do we go when we're dead?"

Some people say Heaven,
Some Hell,
But only one thing is certain,
That only time will tell.

I, for one, think we go somewhere,
To have eternal rest.
I think it's all confusing,
Or a little hard to digest.

But if I were asked at gun-point,
If I believe in God,
I would say, "Of course!"
Before I was shot.

Aaron Biby
Bigfork Middle School
Bigfork, MT
Grade 8

Inside This

Inside a mirror,
Is a kingdom we can't see,
The people in this world are caring,
They want to invite us in,
But we can't hear them,
Their world is beautiful,
Green grass and blue sky,
It would be a perfect world,
Inside this mirror.

Tyler Hedalen
St. Jude Thaddeus School
Havre, MT
Grade 7

Narnia

Narnia
Is a place
Where
The wind
Blows and
Air is as fine as
Water; where
Peace is all
Around and
Time flies like
The birds in
The sky

Steven Kaiser
North Arvada Middle School
Arvada, CO
Grade 7

A Rose

A red rose growing in a garden,
A rose's day begins when the sun comes up over the hedge,
When the rose feels the heat and warmth
Its brightly colored petals decide to open up,
They let the sun dry up the water on their petals from the overnight rain,
When a rose is open its beauty is mesmerizing,
At noon the rose is thirsty,
The rose is baking in the blistering heat,
Just as the rose begins to die the sun recedes over the mountains
The rose closes its petals and waits for the night rain to come again.

Natalie Rose Dattoli
White Middle School
Henderson, NV
Grade 7

I'll Never Forget

Good-bye grandma, I'll never forget you.
There's a lot I'll never forget that is true.
I'll never forget seeing you with curlers in your hair
or seeing you take your last breaths of air.

Although it was something I didn't want to see,
I know you're in Heaven, that's where you must be.
I'll never forget you making me and dad those Monday night meals.
I hope you know how much, how much for you I feel.

I'll never forget how much you loved birds.
I'm sorry when I was around I didn't have many words.
Here are a few words, some that are true:
I miss you, I love you, and I'll never forget you.

Joe Herzog
Knowlton School
Ismay, MT
Grade 8

Will This Love Fade or Is it Not Alive?

The beautiful ocean of deep blue that my eyes fall into
His luscious lips so smooth I feel compelled to touch them
The delicate touch of his rough hands
When they run through my sunshine hair
The profoundness in his sheer voice when he whispers into my ear
These things are so vivid in my mind, yet so lost
I often wonder when this love or childlike fantasy will fade
Will it fade or is it everlasting?
Pictures and memories sway through my mind
Like a breeze floating through the leaves
I walk in a quiet street, but still hear his voice calling my name
I tell myself how to be in love and when it will happen
But nobody knows, it's not a song you can just sing
It's love, and you can't just pick it up off the street
How do you know it's love, you ask?
If you just asked, it's not.

Ashley Watson
Norwood Middle School
Norwood, CO
Grade 9

Television

In math class it is as though you are on
The Home Shopping Network.
There are numbers that mean little to you.
There are people educating you
On prices and collectibles.
There are taxes to add on
And discounts to take off.
You think about the other channels
And the other shows.
You pick at your nails
Because you are so bored.
Soon you nod off.
Until the commercials blast on
And you flip to another channel
And this channel is history.

Nick Donaldson
Kent Denver School
Englewood, CO
Grade 7

School

School is hard,
Almost like playing cards.
Sometimes you have fun,
Mostly you have to get work done.
We always have to turn assignments in,
And if they have no name on them
They're in the garbage bin.
The easiest break we get is lunch,
But some eat so early it could be called brunch.
Next we have P.E.
And I feel sick because I just ate kiwis.
I try to keep going,
But I'm practically exploding.
Next is reading,
She asked in votes if we wanted homework
And no was leading.
Then we wait for the bell to ring,
Until we hear a ding-ding.

Jay Lorenger
Franklin Middle School
Greeley, CO
Grade 7

The Gooey Brown Paste

It's gooey, gooey,
nice and chewy,
crunchy, creamy,
that sticky paste George Washington made.
I've had it, you've had it,
everyone loves his peanut butter,
George Washington Carver's peanut butter.

Corey Gatter
Fremont Middle School
Las Vegas, NV
Grade 7

Standing on the Ocean's Beach Listening

Standing on the Ocean's beach listening
An ancient harmony will sing to you;
Waves against the cliffs fill your whole being
Whale song and dolphin talk fill the sea too.

Every wave moves with the pulse of blood,
Hearts of ev'ry creature beat together;
The creatures that survived Noah's great flood,
Giant whales to fish light as a feather.

Diversity beyond anything known
The greatest life on the face of the Earth;
The sea is not empty-never alone
Life began here like a flame in a hearth.

The deep ocean is its own universe.
The blue sea the poem, the creatures its verse.

Jessica Burkholder
Boulder City High School
Boulder City, NV
Grade 9

That Someone Special

It's said that there's someone special for each one of us.
The problem is finding them before settling for lust.
It may be your best friend who lives across the street.
Or it may be a stranger whom someday you will meet.
Maybe it's the person whom you'd never expect.
Or maybe it's the one who has always shown you respect.
There's no way to foresee who that someone might be.
You just have to have faith that you'll be able to see.
When that person comes along, your heart will show you the way.
Just be patient and pay attention and wait for that day.

Linzee Buchanan
Granada School
Granada, CO
Grade 9

Dreams

Close your eyes. Dreams are the angels that would sweep
    You off your feet. Dreams are the heavens that
    Surround the earth.
Close your eyes. Dreams are the parents you've never had.
    Dreams are the friends you can really trust.
Close your eyes. Dreams are lives without fear or hate.
    Dreams are the happiness of all living people.
        Close your eyes.
        Dreams comfort.
        Stars wish
        People's wish.
    Elements drifting together
        Ghost's nightmare
        Head's imagination.
Just close your eyes and dream.

Kristin Ayala
South Valley Middle School
Platteville, CO
Grade 8

Summer Wind

Summer
Fresh
Ice cream
Like
a
cool
kiss
in
a
tree

Green
Yellow
Russet

Breezing
Through
Like
a
fall
wind

Holly Jackson
Colorado Academy
Denver, CO
Grade 9

Roaring Engines

Horsepower you can hear,
Big tires flying thru the air.
Car smashing, people cheering,
Drivers waving, monster trucks.

Jeremy Cabollo
Norwood Middle School
Norwood, CO
Grade 7

Love

How can I prove to you
that I love you so?
Without you, I feel so blue.
I just want to know,
would you love me
if I spent my very last dollar
to write your name in the sky?
Your name, I would holler
from a mountain up high.
What would show to you
the way my heart jumps
when you walk by?
Just know my love is true.
I'll leave you with this last phrase:
I'll love you for all my days.

Kira Bersanti
East Middle School
Butte, MT
Grade 8

Peony

Reaching towards the sky
Striving for life and beauty
Glimpse of earthly life

Alex Gart
Kent Denver School
Englewood, CO
Grade 7

The Cry of the Wolf

Sad and forlorn is his cry,
His howling in the night.
Slowly though, it begins to die
As he disappears from sight.

He is answered by another,
The call is loud and long,
Then their voices come together,
Singing a mournful song.

His misty breath hangs in the air.
Its white outlined by the dark sky,
He listens for his comrade there,
To answer his lonely cry.

There is only an echo.
He gets no reply.
He's alone with his shadow.
Under the empty sky.

Heather Lindsay
Challenger School
Sandy, UT
Grade 7

The Never Ending Infatuation

A thousand breaths would not
hold my true feelings for you.
My heart does not yet understand
the meaning of you.

Always am I fantasizing
about our time together.

Always am I thinking
about your kind looks, my lover.

My heart is barred until you return,
lessons are endless I am sure to learn.

Can you come to me?
Can you fill my endeavor?
Please release my pain,
and be with me forever.

Jenise Polnow
Sage Valley Jr High School
Gillette, WY
Grade 9

Questions

I try to lock into my inner-most being.
I try and try, but I can't manage.
I think to myself, "Who am I?"
I repeat, "Myself," over and over,
But still I wonder who I am.
What will I do in life?
I say I can't run, can't hide,
I can't lean on someone for help.
What can I do?
In reality, I can't do anything.
I can't take back my past,
And I can't see into the future.
There are so many questions:
Who am I?
What will I do in life?
What can I do?
There aren't any answers
And never will be.
So what's there to do?

Annie Brandt
Swink Jr-Sr High School
Swink, CO
Grade 8

Animals

Cats are swift
Dogs are protective
Sloths are slow
Squirrels are more active
Elephants are big
Mice are small
Eagles fly free
Parrots live in halls
Ferrets live in cages
Butterflies live in stages

Eric Emery
Century Middle School
Thornton, CO
Grade 7

The Sea

an army
assaulting the fortress
with a battering ram
forever attempting
to capture the formidable shore
throwing itself
against the rocks
pulling its wall
to the ground
only to retreat again
to try another round

Emily Fuller
Butler Middle School
Salt Lake City, UT
Grade 8

Clear

A bright horizon in the distance
Clear of the pasts' woes
Radiating a pleasant future
Creating a picture of what will come ahead
Lifting the spirits of the morning
Quieting the spirits of the night
Each daybreak sings
Of fulfilling the destiny of a new day

Marcy Shrader-Lauinger
Rattlesnake Middle School
Missoula, MT
Grade 8

Why Am I Here????

Why am I here in this cold sad world ?
Where Death is real
And sadness is as big as love
When Death comes to the door.
Why am I here to suffer the death of others
Or is it that we don't know how to take in death
And move on with life ?
Please tell me why am I here to see you sick and old ?
I wish I could stop your pain and suffering.
Why am I here ????????????
Perhaps, I shouldn't know.

Alyssa N. Trujillo
Moore Middle School
Arvada, CO
Grade 8

Flowers in the Field*

In a field,
Wide and spacious
Deep in the heart of the forest
Hundreds of flowers
Bloomed and grew
Some had full blooms,
Filled with color
Some did not
Some grew tall and some grew short
Each one grew differently
But all were beautiful
All of a sudden,
Two boys on bikes
Came riding, zooming through the field
By the time the boys were through
Thirteen Flowers
Had been flattened
And, though many flowers remained,
They never bloomed the same again.

Jessica Hughes
Manitou Springs Middle School
Manitou Springs, CO
Grade 7
In honor of those who were affected in the tragic
Columbine High School shooting April, 1999

The Snowy Hill

Start walking up a snowy hill,
exhausted you might become.

Often you will lose your footing
and painfully fall to the base of the hill.

If you lose your footing, lose no hope,
for the experience and view at the pinnacle
will be worth all pain suffered.

Irate you may become,
yet soon, the peak will be a footstep away.

Finally, the breeze at the top of the hill
will soothe your anger and all struggle
will have made you stronger.

Hop on the sled and travel down
the hills on which you have suffered.

Enjoy the wondrous ride
while you still can, for possibly,
this is your last ride.

Eventually, the sled will cease and
the snow will melt.

Zack Greenberg
Kent Denver School
Englewood, CO
Grade 7

Love or Lust

Are these feelings love or lust
I know that having you is a must
I would see your face and your eyes glittering like stars
I wanted to open up and have you heal my scars
I thought and dreamed of you every day
Thought of every word I wanted to say
Every time I thought of you, I had a smile on my face
And I knew in my heart, no one could take that place
But you found a new girl to run to
And I found I could never have you
Now I wish I could be that girl
The one that revolves around your world
I know I can't and your love for her will never part
But I don't care, I'm still giving you my heart
I won't lie, I won't cheat, I'll be faithful 'til the end
I'll be your lover, your family, and always your friend
I won't hurt you or make you cry
I will brighten your stormy sky
I promise that all these feelings are true
And I promise that I will always love you

Sheena LoBach
Riverview Jr High School
Murray, UT
Grade 8

He Held My Hand

In preschool Patty stole my rag doll.
There were tears, pinches, bruises. He got my doll back.
Then he held my hand.

In kindergarten I fell off the slide. My knees were scraped and bleeding.
He handed me a Band-Aid for my wounds, and informed me that the pain would soon cease.
Then he held my hand.

In fourth grade a car hit my sixteen-year-old sister.
He came to the funeral with flowers for Annie. He wrapped his jacket around me for the burial.
Then he held my hand.

In seventh grade I broke up with my first boyfriend.
He sat by me at each recess and let me cry on his shoulder.
Then he held my hand.

In twelfth grade, the college of my choice would not accept me.
He wrote me a letter assuring me everything was going to be okay.
Then he held my hand.

In college I was expelled for smoking on the school-grounds.
He e-mailed me and told me to join him in Boston: his college would understand and respect me.
When I arrived, he held my hand.

The next letter wasn't a letter convincing me that my troubles would go away.
The letter explained that he was dying of cancer.
This time, I held *his* hand.

Lia Zneimer
Vail Mountain School
Vail, CO
Grade 7

Mother

Mother, I am afraid; could you wait by my bedside until morning?
Yes, my child I will stay with you until the end of time, if you only wish it.
Mother, what are those orbs so bright in the sky? Do you think I could have one?
I will retrieve a handful for you my child, if you only wish it.
Mother can you dream me a world as simple as the white doves over our heads?
I will dream you a world and blow it to you in the form of a kiss, if you only wish it.
Mother, as we walk down this road I see suffering and pain, can you help me right these wrongs?
I will stand by you in this war to the very last man if you only wish it.
Mother, these tears are so quick to fall; can you make them cease to flow?
Not this time, my child, even though the world's woes, only *YOU* can make these tears cease to flow,
And sadly only *YOU* can stop all this pain. I trust you, I love you, use your brain.
Mother; don't leave me here all alone, I can't face this cruel horrid, storm on my own...
The little girl waited for her mother to reply, but all she heard was silence as a tear fell from her eye.
She made it through this place,
And her childhood was over in the blink of an eye; when she needs courage now; she simply looks to the sky
Because when the wind blows or when the rain falls,
She knows her mother is proud that she kept standing tall.

Courtney Davis
Colorado Academy
Denver, CO
Grade 7

Halloween

It was Halloween night
Me and my buddies were in for a scare

Should we go trick-or-treating
I don't even care

Trick-or-treating is for young kids
Now we're older than most

Lets all get together and go to the cemetery,
Maybe we will see a ghost

Evan Orton
Kanab Middle School
Kanab, UT
Grade 7

The Light

I finally see light as they open the door,
I am glad to see it; it makes me feel free.
I want to go away and soar,
Like a little bird with a get out key.

They make us go into different groups,
And they take us in separate ways.
Yet they are just some troops,
But they take people days by days.

I don't want to be taken away,
So I work as hard as I can.
They are going to get you anyway people say,
But I still strive to become a man.

Nathan Cabrales
South Jordan Middle School
South Jordan, UT
Grade 8

The Man in the Moon

The man in the moon is the only man a girl can trust.
He listens and helps her when she is in love and lust.
He constantly cares for the girls when they need him.
He never complains or bickers or ever deceives them.

The man in the moon will never hurt or make a girl cry.
The girls will never have to sit and wonder why.
They know it is true that he's their one true friend.
He'll be there always and forever, until the end.

The man in the moon is a dream come true.
Because he understands what you are going through.
So send a wish to that man tonight.
Just close your eyes and hold on tight.
For he will lend you his ears and his heart each and every night.

Amanda Haslem
Round Mountain Jr-Sr High School
Round Mountain, NV
Grade 9

On a Summer Night

I feel so calm on those warm summer nights
when I lie in the grass and the wind's just right.

I look in the sky and find that one special place
and there I can picture your beautiful face.

You're staring right at me, into my eyes
oh how I wish you were here by my side.

I'd give anything just to be with you
I would give my soul to be up there too.

We could play and jump from star to star
or hold each other tight in a big cloud car.

We could watch the sun blossom through the mountain peaks
or swim in the milky way for weeks and weeks.

If only I knew this dream would come true
I'd give my life just for one night with you.

John Balkenbush
Bigfork Middle School
Bigfork, MT
Grade 8

President

Some people say when I tell them
That I will never make it
I know deep down inside me
This is my dream and I am going to fulfill it.

I'm not going to forget my dream
Because some people laugh at me
But when I am on the stand and I have won
I will tell them not to laugh at dreams!

When Armstrong said he was going to the moon
I bet someone laughed at him
But he made it, he walked on the moon.
And he showed every one of them.

It will be a long road
To becoming the first woman president.
"If there's a will, there's a way!"
That's what I am told and I believe it.

I cannot get there by saying, "I can't!"
I always have to be positive in my mind
I should be like The Little Engine That Could.
Then suddenly you turn around and . . .

I'M PRESIDENT

Lacey Johnson
Riverview Jr High School
Murray, UT
Grade 8

In a Perfect World

In a perfect world
we'd all be spiritually free,
and nothing would bother you or me,
the oceans would be as clean as the air,
the waters could be drunk everywhere,
there would be no famine,
nor violence or pain,
and all is received when you try and gain,
the people and animals
would all get along,
and many races of many cultures
would sing the same song,
there would be no killing nor evils away,
for everyone would be kind and peaceful each day,
money wouldn't be an issue,
nor dangers or lawsuits,
and the world would never go askew,
but we live in a world imperfect every day,
for we too are imperfect in every way.

Christina Chiang
Our Lady of Snows School
Reno, NV
Grade 8

Clear

What is clear?
Clear is the sound of flowers talking.
The sound of a breeze flying through the trees.
Clear makes me feel happy and cozy.
When I read a book I think clear.
Clear is the sound of children laughing.
When I play outside in the snow,
    clear is all around me.
When I see a flag waving I know clear is near.
Clear makes me warm thinking about it.
The sound of soft music makes me wonder about clear.
Will I ever see it?
Is it really there?
But deep down I know the answers to my questions.

Shiann Baird
Riverview Jr High School
Murray, UT
Grade 7

Man

There once was a man with no face.
A man with no name or race.
A man that could not see or hear.
A man that could not smell or speak, as well.
But this man saw all he needed and heard all he wanted.
But this man was not like all the rest for he saw and heard
and understood and lived a life no other would.

Wade Hutt
Norwood Middle School
Norwood, CO
Grade 8

A Friend

A friend is someone who cares very much.
They care what you do and what you don't do.
They give everything the right touch.
They can cheer you up too.

Everyone needs a good friend to talk to.
Whether they're a guy or a girl, who cares!
Does that give you a clue,
To who really cares?

So next time you see a good friend,
Show them that you care too!

Kelley DiVesta
Holmes Middle School
Colorado Springs, CO
Grade 8

What Is Love Worth?

What is love worth to thee?
How does it compare?
Worth riches farther than the eye can see?
You know it's not always fair.
Of all the beauties in the world,
Is it rated best?
Something so strong, you can't control.
Are you ready to be put to the test?
The thing most thought about,
Yet quite crazy.
Love is all around.
Catch it unless you're lazy!
How much is love worth to thee?
Don't tell, show me!

Jessica Jordan
Centennial Middle School
Boulder, CO
Grade 8

A Petal of Friendship

Thank you my friend, for all that you've done.
You taught me how to love someone.
How to let your joy and spirit free
How to be all that you can be.
To whenever possible try my best,
And how to fix up my life, when it is messed.
To be a good friend, when in need...
To be a strand of whatever is weaved.
To trust someone when you know you can...
And when to give out that open hand.
To never let go of that dream...
And when to smile until you beam.
I'll always be there anytime, whenever.
I'll love you always until forever.

Jackie Hwang
Centennial Middle School
Boulder, CO
Grade 8

Douglas Ivester

Douglas Ivester got his picture in Business Week.
Chubby cheeks, lips red
blend into smooth healthy skin
and glasses clean except for a finger print smudge.
His eyes opened, he thinks about
Nasdaq and the Dow Jones, his anniversary,
the hearing in the morning
while wearing his college reunion tie.
But there is a lying, cheating business man under all that,
and under his picture the question—
   "Dear Mr. Ivester:
   Why do you hurt the earth
   when it's so easy
   not to?"
   Meredith, Age 9
This fake liar just wants the image, nothing else.

Chase Lowrey
Colorado Academy
Denver, CO
Grade 9

Mountains

The mighty mountains reach across the land
Spreading in an everlasting band
These giants climb up the sky
Reaching for the clouds so high
Fragile flakes of snow fall upon the mountain peaks
The soft powder sits there, untouched for weeks
Sweet water flows down the icy streams
At the bottom they're warmed by bright sunbeams
The rivers flow right through the plains
And nourish the tall golden grains
The grain waves in the frigid breeze
That even bends the deep green trees
The sky is pure, a clear soft blue
At night it shines as if brand new
It stretches across the mountainous land
That stretches in an everlasting band

Elizabeth Gibson
Mountain Ridge Middle School
Colorado Springs, CO
Grade 8

Sometimes

Sometimes I wish I knew him,
Sometimes I just don't care.
Sometimes I used to cry,
   Because he was never there.
Sometimes I feel like falling apart,
   Because when he's gone it breaks my heart.
But then when he's around
   My happiness can be found!

Jessica Jackson
Kanab Middle School
Kanab, UT
Grade 8

Eye of the Wild

Your eyes are the color of the shining moon.
Your fur is the color of the top of the snowy mountain.
Your howl is like the sound of rolling thunder.
Your swiftness and keenest is that of the mighty lion.

Angela Wagner
Holy Trinity School
Westminster, CO
Grade 8

Grandpa*

   I will always keep you close to my heart
and I will never forget you. I just wish that
you were still here so I could tell you how
much I love you. Grandpa, I'm sorry that you
had to leave so soon. I never could express
my feelings to you. Grandpa, I know I never
showed you that I cared, but believe me, I do,
it's there. Grandpa, I'm sitting here crying
as I write this poem, I love you so deeply I
just wished you had known. Grandpa, life
is not the same without you. I really just
don't know what else to do. Grandpa, all I
want to say is I hope you're happy because
your happiness means a lot to me. Grandpa,
as I live, I just wanted to tell you again that
I love you and thanks for being a great grandpa
and a great friend.

Aniya Scott
East Middle School
Colorado Springs, CO
Grade 8
*In loving memory of Ronald Brown

Friends

Some will stay with you all of your life
Some will dwell and forget the fight
But most of them will leave you
You will also leave them
For you see you can't have everything
You've ever wanted

Some will just leave you
Others will have a message
Most just won't care
So don't fret over them
They won't believe when you've forgotten
Then they are the ones who wished they had cared.

Some will stay at trying
Others will just give up
Because you see that all of them want to be friends
With someone like you!!!

Brittany Aragon
Century Middle School
Thornton, CO
Grade 7

Life, A Great Adventure

Life on the wind
is never commanded.
Fluffy clouds,
rolling hills,
snow peaked mountains.
Who has seen it all?
Only time will tell
when we can see it up above.

Drew Broestl
Pauline Memorial School
Colorado Springs, CO
Grade 7

Love

I love you so much,
Like a calm summer's day;
As a flower too pure to touch,
At the end of May.
With the beauty of a stream,
Trickling slowly by;
You exist only in my dreams,
When I am not so shy.
You smell like the sweetest rose,
Always making me want to stay;
But I must use my nose,
To know I am not welcome today.
I will love you eternally,
I can only hope that you'll love me.

Julian Astley
Centennial Middle School
Boulder, CO
Grade 8

Insights to My Soul

When you look at me what do you think?
Who do you see?
You see a child, a little girl
Fearing herself and her peers
While grasping on to every last dream,
Awaiting to wake up
To a cold hearted world,
When truly inside I am not.
I am a growing woman
Searching for the moment to express
My true thoughts and feelings
To the rest of the world.
At that time I will leave behind
The life and dreams you see before you
To pursue a path in life I desire most.
Until that day when my soul runs free
I ask of you to think of me
More than just what you see.

Deana Davis-Burling
Limon Jr-Sr High School
Limon, CO
Grade 9

Closing Time

Time to close down the shop.
The many happy conversations
Must come to a halt.
The happy times must come to an end.
The door is locked,
The room is desolate and empty.
She is dead.
Gone forever, without return,
The happy times are over.
Conversations are gone
And I am empty.

Charlie Bathgate
Kent Denver School
Englewood, CO
Grade 7

Utah

Red, yellow, blue,
violet, and pink.
Are colors of flowers.
Singing birds,
bees buzzing,
people picnicking,
and kids playing.
The smell of barbecues,
of hot dogs and fruit.
The sweet taste of ice cream,
or cold water around you.
The perfect soft fur,
of little puppies.
This is what I love.
This is springtime in Utah.

Carolee Bennett
Mountain Ridge Jr High School
Highland, UT
Grade 9

If Only. . .

If only cows gave juice,
If only the sky were purple,
If only tight was loose,
If only it was polite to burple.

If only nothing was the same,
If only chocolate were healthy,
If only pink hair was considered plain,
If only I could sneak out more stealthily.

If only poetry were easy,
If only I could do it,
Then this would be a breezy,
And I wouldn't have blew it!!

Lauren Victor
Century Middle School
Thornton, CO
Grade 7

Flying on a Bike

As I fly through the air
Wind blowing in my hair
Only me and my bike
Seem to even be there

Flying with steady flow
I must hit the ground below
I must prepare myself
For a paralyzing jolt

A thud as I hit the ground
That is the only sound
My bike, the ground, and I
Are like glue, we are bound

Josh Young
Star Valley Jr High School
Afton, WY
Grade 8

Whispers

From the day you were born,
You can still hear.
Your mother whisper,
Kindly in your ear.

Thirty long years have past,
Your mother's getting old.
The illness makes her whispers,
Now seem harsh and cold.

It's now twenty years later,
Your mother has passed away.
But it really doesn't effect you,
Because her words seem to stay.

Brandi Holybee
Norwood Middle School
Norwood, CO
Grade 9

Fog

The harbor so quiet
Not a person in sight
As the fog drifts by
The people shall wake

So lazy and sleepy
As the fog has taken over

But as the fog drifts away
The people shall wake
And the new day
Begins

Christopher McCall
Century Middle School
Thornton, CO
Grade 7

The Flower in the Mist

It was a cold, dark, and rainy day.
Dark clouds hovered above.
And in this deserted meadow I felt alone like there was no love.
My toes were turning blue as I watched the sun go down.
I was beginning to feel afraid as wild animals gathered around.
Then upon a hill I saw a glorious sight.
A flower in the mist on this cold and frightening night.
It glowed like a streetlight up on a tower.
And it made me feel warmer even by the hour.
I watched its loving bloom until the break of dawn.
Then I fell from this world like a little dying swan.
I know I died happy and I know I died warm.
Because I felt there was a loving hand holding on to my arm.
I felt like I was kissed by a light in the darkness,
And I know that I was kissed by a flower in the mist.

Randi Combe
Rocky Mountain Jr High School
Hooper, UT
Grade 9

Goat Tying
(A Rodeo Story)

Every weekend to the rodeo we head
Up by seven, no staying in bed.

Saturday, Sunday the competition is rough.
Everyone associates with friends just enough.

As each event approaches, the nerves start to wreck.
Then next thing you know, your name is called next.

You bust through the gate, full speed ahead,
Keeping the worries and voices out of your head.

Getting off is the extreme fun of it all,
Off you go hoping you don't fall.

You land on your feet, thank goodness for that part.
Your legs carry you swiftly; off to the goat you dart.

You flip the goat, but not too high.
You wrap the string, and three legs you tie.

You throw your hands way up in the air.
The crowd is watching, but you don't care.

You back away, and wait for your time.
8.03—that will suit you just fine.

You unsaddle your horse, and give him a treat,
And anxiously wait for another rodeo weekend to beat.

Tara Romero
Sage Valley Jr High School
Gillette, WY
Grade 9

Earth

Trees, moss, rocks, and grass.
Lions, tigers, bears, and bass.

Mother Nature is our guide,
To all of her beautiful countryside.

Snow in the mountains; sand in the deserts,
Water in the oceans, the Earth is in motion.

People building sprawling condos;
The Earth will retake them, everyone knows.

Earthquakes, tsunami, volcanoes, and mudslides;
Man's progress wiped out in the blink of an eye

Earth is covered by life of all kinds,
Plants, animals, and mankind.

Earth.

Shawn Rousseau
Holmes Middle School
Colorado Springs, CO
Grade 8

Silent Stutters

Silently stuttering, the boy slinked to the alter
to speak the spoken words of the wise world,
without the quivering quietness
from the concussion of the crying crowd.

Gilmen Gasper
Redwater School
Circle, MT
Grade 8

Hope

This hollow pit I shall lay,
wandering through the mists of gray,
I dare not open my eyes for Hell I dare not find.
The crucification of my mind,
the bone biting fear traveling down my spine.
Running, running into walls,
darkest depths and long, long halls.
Dead end there I begin to turn around,
in my face fear is sitting there,
eating my image you can hear,
the swirling winds pulling me away.
For God is here to save my soul this very day.
The shining light and golden rays,
for my soul is saved,
for me the lights and golden rays,
my soul rests in peace,
for now I must lay down to sleep.

Ben Milton
Dubois Elementary-Middle School
Dubois, WY
Grade 8

Silence

Silence, a loud shriek
In the ears of many.

Silence, a word that causes
A delusion in the minds of some.

Silence, a streak of terror
Beyond sound.

Silence, an eerie sound,
The sound of something wrong.

Silence, the only sound,
For death.

Joe Kennedy
Franklin Middle School
Greeley, CO
Grade 7

Sisters

Four sassy, snotty, sisters
just waiting for revenge.
But they know they'll never
get it, cause the time
must come. But
when?

Pamela Sue Geer
Circle Jr High School
Circle, MT
Grade 8

Little Girl Speaking

Mommy I was awake,
I heard you fight,
I saw him do it,
Mommy, I know this isn't right,
Mommy, leave him
how could he hurt you so,
make him go away before
he hurts me one day,
Mommy wake up!
Where is he now,
Mommy answer me
I'm scared,
don't leave me alone,
Mommy he's coming,
get up and we'll run,
Mommy I can't fight him,
I'll be with you soon.
Mommy I love you . . .

Daddy why?

Sheena Lanegan
Rosebud Public School
Rosebud, MT
Grade 9

The Love of a Friend

We talked all day,
just about hiking and camping,
it was so interesting to me,
the way we could talk about anything,
or just nothing at all,
but it wasn't what we talked about that was important to me,
it was the time we spent together,
it was just the right friendship,
not like one of a couple madly in love,
but one of two friends,
sharing all their life secrets that they had hidden away for so long,
yet people hadn't understood this friendship,
pushing and pulling both of us farther away from each other,
till it was no longer there,
or was it?

Lindsey Sinclair
Star Valley Jr High School
Afton, WY
Grade 8

Inside

Inside my mind is a train of thoughts that never ends
Inside my mind is a corner where thoughts are born
Inside my mind cabinets are filled with memories
Inside my mind confusion comes and goes
Inside my mind are streams of burning questions that have no answers
Inside my mind my personality glows bright
Inside my mind are unexplored wonders
Inside my mind are many dreams
Inside my mind ideas blossom,
and inside my mind are unexplainable lands.

Liz Lind
North Arvada Middle School
Arvada, CO
Grade 7

Light of the World

The innocence of a child is the light of the world.
The world has no understanding of a child's worth to the future,
If only they would teach their children.

A child could be or do anything, with the help of you and I.
We would be a dim light far ahead leading them on to glory.
To help a child to do what is right; we must be the example for them.

Helping the children find themselves in this dark and fearful world,
Is the greatest glory that we can achieve.
In helping the children the entire world will TRIUMPH.

The child is blessed with the light of the world, leading the future to its glory.
Glory to the parents, who once were children.
Let the light of the world SHINE through them.

Samantha Heiner
Star Valley Jr High School
Afton, WY
Grade 8

Confused

Every night I lay awake and think
Why am I here, just answer me why

I feel like I have no purpose
To be on this place they call Earth

I think I am not a good friend
I wish I could just change everything

Then I think, wait a minute
Maybe, just maybe it isn't me

Maybe I am the good friend
It might just be everyone else

Some people won't give you a chance
It's like they see you and decide

I don't like her clothes, so I don't like her
Or, I love her new hair-do, she is my best friend

So on those restless nights
I get so confused

I wish I could just forget everything
That happens, but I can't!!

Tia Sharp
Tintic High School
Eureka, UT
Grade 8

All By Myself

Sitting in my room, all by myself
I see my best friend leaving.

She's being taken by the Nazis
I see my best friend leaving,

One, two, three, she's marching towards the cars
I see my best friend leaving,

Once she's in I know I'll never see her again
I see my best friend leaving,

One by one, they're loaded on
I see my best friend leaving,

As the train starts moving
I see my best friend leaving,

Slowly, the train is getting smaller and smaller
My best friend is gone.

Whitney Anopol
South Jordan Middle School
South Jordan, UT
Grade 8

Thunder Storm

The sky is a battlefield
with great white soldiers,
that march to and fro.
But when they meet,
these clouds put on their war paint.
and with their faces now darkened,
A great battle is fought.
The thunder is the sound of cannons,
firing great bolts of lightning.
The rain that falls is the bleeding of wounds,
mixed with tears for lost comrades.
And after this battle, the armies leave.
To grieve and prepare for the next battle,
the next pouring of rain.

Paul Winkel
Century Middle School
Thornton, CO
Grade 7

Just Breathe

Loud claps of thunder sound through the air, lightning strikes.
It rains. A rain that is gentle, soft, light.
It rolls down windows
and into the crevices of the earth.
The sun comes out.
Birds chirp, swans glide with ease
through a nearby pond,
with geese sounding in the background.
A rainbow.
It is all so mystical that you have to remind yourself to breathe.
Just watch and breathe.

Shandra Hair
Vilas High School
Vilas, CO
Grade 8

True Love

I love you so much with all my heart
I have no idea what I'd do if we ever had to part
If that day ever came
Nothing would be the same
I'll cry and cry for days and days
Because they told me you were only a phase
But I know that is not true
Because I know that I love you
You are my one and only soul mate
It's obvious why we came together by fate
We'll be together now and always
And for the rest of our days
Whenever I see you I want to give you a hug
You are my one, my only
True love

Ashley Knutson
Holmes Middle School
Colorado Springs, CO
Grade 8

Spider

Walking slowly, silently
towards me
Spinning a web around me
Slowly, silently,
Scaring me
Spinning a web to
catch me
Squiggly, squishing me
But. . .
It is only a toy

Scott Spina
Laurel Middle School
Laurel, MT
Grade 8

Clueless for You

I don't know who to look for,
I don't know who to blame.
It's just that since you left me,
Nothing's been the same.
I don't know who to distrust,
I know that sounds so lame.
Now that I don't have you,
My life is just no game.
I don't have anything now,
I don't know where to go.
And ever since you died,
I guess I just don't know.

Hana Lindsay
Powell Middle School
Littleton, CO
Grade 7

Home

Monument Valley
is the most beautiful place
in the world.
The environment is like
a beautiful pearl.

Holding this treasure in my heart
reminds me of the dark.
The rocks cast their shadow
from the moonlight
for surely this is
a beautiful sight.

In my mind I can hear
the coyotes howl.

For this makes me feel
at home right now.

Marcus Benally
Excel School
Durango, CO
Grade 9

The Hanging

It was dawn–the rope hanging dead from the gallows.
The town's people gathered in the square.
As the young woman was lead to her destiny,
A sense of unforgettable fear filled the air
Like a faint stench of a moor.
This couldn't be right.
By the look on the crowd's faces you could tell that they were filled with fright.
Had they gone too far?
Twenty people had already died.
This was bizarre.
It was too late to save this young lady's delicate paper white face.
But tomorrow's another day.
Maybe they'll learn a lesson from the horror they lived today.

Zachary Lucido
Vail Mountain School
Vail, CO
Grade 7

The Horse

The horse in the show runs around mincingly as ever,
Yet it cannot see the periphery. Its blinders prohibit the horse's view
Of his supporting fans.

He has been trained to be the best and is the best,
But something is unfulfilled. The horse is with us to be happy.
Is he happy? Stiff as a board prancing and dancing
For the entertainment of others.

The answer lies within the horse, and he knows the true answer.
He knows he must take off those blinders and see the world around him.
He needs to take in the surroundings and realize what the real point in life is.

Michael Winter
Kent Denver School
Englewood, CO
Grade 7

What Is Life

What is life is the question we sometimes wonder
Are the mistakes we make just part of a great big blunder
Is life just a circle of hate that we live in the day we are six feet under
We go to church and ask these simple questions and hope for a decent answer
But as we see some change for the good there is another death from cancer
Some go to school for a reason when others leave just to be a plain dancer
We use our heads in hope to understand and be able to recognize
But when we realize all the problems of our society we understand the great size
Our education standards lowered and kids living to be the age 18 seems to be a prize
We have heard stories about amazing saves and human fights
But how can we help each other now when a lot of people don't even have rights
Kids living without any food and a cold house without any lights
Most people thinking it will never happen to them so they have no need to worry
Hearing about domestic violence when a guy gets mad and takes out his anger and fury
If you are a victim of a dying society get help before we have another person to bury

Jason Stockley
Berthoud High School
Berthoud, CO
Grade 9

The Delicate Rose

So beautiful and bold
Yet your petals so cold,

The life and color you bring
And the hearts that you cling,

Each petal as delicate as the rest
Each petal the paleness reflects,

Your beauty is hidden but never forbidden
From the thought in which it brings,

Your beauty from the life and color you bring
Clings to the heart of the rose,

Our hearts and souls cling
To the beauty you bring.

Megan Vasquez
Ranch View Middle School
Highlands Ranch, CO
Grade 8

Lullaby

Oh, little child, so lovely and white
Hush now, don't cry, I'll be with you tonight.

The sun has gone down, the stars are shining,
And for my little baby, heaven is crying.

Oh, rock-a-bye-baby, my soft little babe
Be still and listen to my slow serenade.

Now now, hasten and soften your cries
Relax your small fists and close your blue eyes.

Oh, don't worry now, I'll stay with you all night
A little sleep now will make everything right.

You're too little yet, to understand love
But, I know you're a blessing from heaven above.

Oh, as long as you're here, right now at my side
I'll know you loved me, no matter how I've cried.

If you have to leave, know I'll understand
I can't keep you here if you're in the Lord's hand.

Oh, the time has now come to say final good-byes
And to sing you quiet, soft lullabies.

So good-bye, my young one, remember you'll always be
My little baby, who'll always love me.

Erin Purdie
North Cache Middle School
Richmond, UT
Grade 9

Change

The more things change,
the more they stay the same.
I find myself here all the time.
Always changing, but still the same.
You can never run from yourself.
Wherever you go, there you are.
So when you change, my friend,
I hope it's for the best,
and learn from past events,
'cause history has a thing with repeating itself.
Even though I know that everything is strange
I know a little saying
that bears my repeating:
the more things change,
the more they'll stay the same.

Heidi Bowden
Sage Valley Jr High School
Gillette, WY
Grade 9

The Garden

The garden of roses, a wonderful sight,
Is a river that flows, without a thought of fight.
It's a path to heaven, a one-way flight,
No turning back, you weary soul.
It's a highway home, no worries there,
For you are safe from all your fears.
The garden is a family grave,
Who knows what lies beneath their eyes.
A thought to you and all the youth,
Let your soul fly free,
In the garden of these identities.

Cory Dodson
Torrington Middle School
Torrington, WY
Grade 8

The Hunt

There I was,
Miles from nowhere.
Smelling the fresh rain,
From the night before.

Walking across the weeds as they crunch.
Looking at all the beautiful scenery around you.
No houses no cars,
Just you all alone.

You keep walking,
As you look around and realize,
It's not the hunt that gets you out here,
It's being in the wild outdoors.

Chance Warren
Star Valley Jr High School
Afton, WY
Grade 7

Nevada

N evada is the silver state
E verything has a history
V ery exciting place
A lways something to learn
D ullness is not an issue
A bsolutely great!

Anna Castronova
White Middle School
Henderson, NV
Grade 7

A Car Ride

In my car,
out there so far.
A thud, a thump and there I sat.
Just what I needed, a miserable flat.

I wanted to cry, to say "Oh no!"
Why was I not able to go.
Without a spare,
and no one there.

When suddenly a freezing snow,
a chilling wind began to blow.
I didn't want to even care,
I found that I was in despair.

A big white car comes to a stop,
a man gets out he is a cop.
My luck had changed for the best.
I hope that this was just a test.

Matt Hillam
Butler Middle School
Salt Lake City, UT
Grade 8

Summer

Beautiful weather through the weeks
Music coming from the birds' beaks
On the beach summer fun
Light beating down from the bright sun
Kids off school
And are playing in the pool
Picnics in the park
Until it's dark
Watermelon, hot dogs, lemonade
While the sun fades
So much summer fun
Underneath the sun
Back to school you can hear the bell call
Guess we'll have to have fun in the fall

Malia Hueftle
White Middle School
Henderson, NV
Grade 7

Fog

Slowly: creeping, drifting, flying
the light blue sky is transformed.

Now a cloud, the sky seems to float
Like dancing people of an Indian tribe.
Slowly: creeping, drifting, flying.

Leyla Serway
Century Middle School
Thornton, CO
Grade 7

Bummer Summer

The first day of summer,
Is really a bummer,
When you have snow,
And there's no place to go.

You can't see the things you want to see,
Then you get stung by a bee,
And fall and scrape your knee,
Then run into a tree.

Now it started to rain,
And you feel like you are in pain,
At least there's tomorrow morning,
Maybe tomorrow won't be so boring.

Lauren McPhee
Century Middle School
Thornton, CO
Grade 7

Writing

With pen in hand
and paper on table
I believe
I am quite able
to write a word or two
that just might interest you.

With my humor for some laughs
I might even write you
some paragraphs.

Then, punctuation, I did learn
has its place, in its turn.

However, writing style
takes a while
and for my editing
by my pencil you can see
I've been fret-it-ing!

Amber Daley
Powell Middle School
Littleton, CO
Grade 7

Fire

A burning cinder, fading.
Upon it, I am waiting,
For yet a chance to spark a flame.

So I sit and watch it dim,
As its glowing light from within,
Softly dies in shame.

It is born and then, it dies.
Very few of us know why,
And it has nothing but its light to wane.

So am I—a dying cinder,
Waiting for a breeze to render,
To me the help to become a flame.

So the wind blows,
And it is I who knows,
That I will become...

A fire.
A raging fire.
I will be free
And a fire
That will never cease to be.

Jordan Eads
Cortez Middle School
Cortez, CO
Grade 8

God

Even though,
This is why our founders came,
We can't talk about God,
Not in school any way.
They came for religion,
They came for Christ,
But now there is Satan,
And Christians pay the price.
Teachers get in trouble,
For speaking of him.
They battle and debate,
But who will win?
Is that the reason,
For the shooting at school,
That Satan is now "in",
And is considered cool?
I look at my life,
Thinking I couldn't do it without Christ.
And if something could bring him back,
I'd pay the price.

Emma O'Connor
East High School
Pueblo, CO
Grade 9

Dear Dog,

Dear Dog,
   I think you stink,
You remind me of a rabid mink!
You seem to like my pepper spray,
'Cause it never keeps you away!
You try to tear me limb by limb,
Which leaves me feeling oh so grim!
I hate my work I hope you know,
My wife has pants every night to sew!
You're always grumpy so I see,
Your yard's the worst place to be!
I really hope you throw a fit
When you hear the news . . .
Yesterday I QUIT!!!!

Hatefully yours,
The Man Formally Known as the Mailman.

Daniel Varas
West Jordan Middle School
West Jordan, UT
Grade 8

Fire

Fire is like the hot coals in a fireplace,
It sizzles and cracks like hot molten lava on a humid day,
Fire sounds like a thousand babies screaming all at once,
Fire tastes like a habañero pepper,
Fire smells like a field full of tires that is always up in flames,
Fire looks like the devil and his demons,
Fire has a texture like a scratchy rug burn,
Fire moves like a swift cat stalking a defenseless robin.
Fire.

Michael Shelofsky
Franklin Middle School
Greeley, CO
Grade 7

The Leaves

The leaves drop from their branches
As they slide down to the stage to begin their dance
Their dance is full of twists and drops
As they dance they are ever falling
They perform difficult turns at high speeds
Without breaking the flow of their dance
The leaves leap and glide without a sound
Still using immense energy
In every move I can sense emotion
Just what they are feeling
Their brightly colored costumes keep me fascinated
As they spiral downward the colors revolve around
Then, slowly, their dance comes to an end
As they lay down, to welcome the snow

Jeanine Bernadette Bowman
Butler Middle School
Salt Lake City, UT
Grade 8

Snow

White jewels are swirling, through the frozen air.
Tiny mirrors are whirling, reflecting winter's face so fair.

Floating and drifting, they dance a happy song.
The cloud's treasures are sifting, snowflakes fall all day long.

The clouds make merry, laughing wind,
Tossing white confetti, for their party might never end.

But alas! It must end,
Leaving white to cover the grass. Now fog is my only friend.

I look out over the white blanket, it is quite a different world.
Covered so softly is it, like a blanket of white unfurled.

There is a quiet peace, I can only hear my heart,
Singing, "May this time never cease!" May melting never start!

The cold chills my very being, the white makes me feel filthy,
For what I am seeing, is a white kingdom so wealthy.

My heart is crying, snow, please stay!
But the wind is sighing, remember the sun's golden ray.

When I arise the sun is out,
And the snow is just a memory.

Amy Bredehoft
Home School
Longmont, CO
Grade 8

Splash,

As I jumped into the clear pool,
I looked up at the blue sky,
There was no puffy clouds there,
I got a chill, it was a light breeze,
Everybody left the pool,
I put on my wet sandals,
We went inside,
And my lips touched that cold juicy popsicle,
Someone handed me a glass of ice yellow lemonade,
I said no thanks,
I gnawed on my yummy popsicle,
"Kaboom!"
The air conditioner broke,
That reminded me of storms,
Winter storms,
I left the house with the popsicle in my mouth,
And as I reached my room,
I saw winter clothes packed away in my closet,
And I was glad that school was out,
That I knew I was going to have some summer fun.

Nicole Hunter
Riverside Jr High School
New Castle, CO
Grade 7

Fairytale Poem-Rock Soup
A town full of greedy people
Three soldiers returning home from war
Hungry as hogs
A soup of rocks
Made into a gourmet meal of trickery
Turn the soldiers into stuffed pigs
Stuart Webster
Colorado Academy
Denver, CO
Grade 9

Lost and Alone
You wander off, someplace
No aim, nothing in life to chase
Knowing the vultures are there
Waiting to take the first tear

Something in your heart
Is tearing you apart
So afraid you won't be found
So afraid you're going to drown
Giving up is not the way
So get on your knees and pray
Gerda Korneev
Century Middle School
Thornton, CO
Grade 7

School
School is so boring
School is so dumb
Staying home is
So much fun

Playing computer
Playing games
Chatting with people
Chatting with gangs

Playing baseball
Playing sports
Having fun in
Our little forts

Going out
Planting seeds
Going to lunch at
Black Eyed Pea

Still at school With Mr. Mitch
I might as well
Just go and ditch
Daniel Suh
Ranch View Middle School
Highlands Ranch, CO
Grade 8

The Holocaust
In the horrible year of 1942,
Hitler was cruel to every Jew.
He beat them and tortured them until their sad deaths,
Then haunted their souls after their last breaths.
He burned down their houses for no apparent reason,
Then accused them of committing a terrible treason.
Hitler's Gestapo picked up Jews of all ages,
And took them to camps in damp boxcar cages.
He starved them and worked them all day and all night,
And unmercifully shot them if they put up a fight.
In the end Hitler had killed over five million Jews,
He gassed them and beat them with his militia killing crews.
If this evil man taught us anything through his big killing spree,
It was to treat people of different race, color and belief, equal and free.
Tess Phillips
Connect Charter School
Pueblo, CO
Grade 8

A Friend Is...
A friend is someone to play with or sing with
A friend is someone you can take a walk with
A friend is someone who will write you a letter or call you on the phone
A friend is someone with whom you can spill the contents of your heart
A friend is someone who you may laugh and have fun times with
A friend is someone who will tell no lies
But most of all a friend is someone who will always be right next to you
During your most troubled times
A friend to you may be a bit different, but however you look at it
A friend will always last a lifetime
Christina Vogel
Plentywood Middle School
Plentywood, MT
Grade 7

For the Love of Dogs
(Lilly and Abby)
Through thrashing storm and violent thunder
Pounding rain or sunny shine
Your undying companionship seems never to asunder,
and your everlasting love seems always to be mine
You always greet me at the door with your tails a wag
Even when I yell and have been cross
You comfort me when the tears start falling or when I am just plain sad,
and you're there to play catch with when I am at a loss
Your puppy playfulness never has an end,
and after a long belly rub and pet
A wet slobbery kiss you're always ready to lend
I knew the moment that we met
You are the best dogs around
That give the truest love that can be found
Megan Downing
Centennial Middle School
Boulder, CO
Grade 8

I'm Not Sure

Some people say there's a perfect person for everybody
I'm not so sure
Some people say there's no such thing as love
I'm not so sure
Some people say there is death
I'm not so sure
Some people say there is no pain
I'm not so sure
Some people say there is no such thing as happiness
I'm not sure
I'm not sure what's what in this world,
But I'm sure I'm here.

Betty May Elder
Norwood Middle School
Norwood, CO
Grade 9

100 Acre Wood

A golden bear filled with wonder,
A little pink pig afraid of thunder;
A bouncy tigger fiddle fadding,
A great owl who can't stop chatting.
A little blue donkey who's always gloomy,
Even when the flowers are blooming;
A little boy in the trees above
And for each other they all feel love!

Jenevie Sisneros
Laramie Jr High School
Laramie, WY
Grade 8

Fire

A fire is an angry lion,
roaring through the valley,
ruler of all creation,
no one in its way.
Living.
Breathing.
Pulsing.
Adrenaline thundering through fiery veins,
seeping into its mind,
urging it
faster, Faster, FASTER
to the ultimate.
Blood red flames playfully seducing prey,
tongues licking at the air,
ready for revenge.
Savaging through the dry foliage,
devouring any life in its path.
A fire is an angry lion.
Breathing. Pulsing.
Alive.

Shannon Kelly
Lakewood High School
Lakewood, CO
Grade 9

Best Friends

Friends are always there to help you out,
And always know what you're talking about.

They never leave you in the dust,
And never leave you without trust.

They always treat you the very best,
And never like you are a pest.

During life's roughest miles,
Friends can help you through your trials.

Even with the many trends,
We can all be the best of friends.

Shelly Jo Honey
Kanab Middle School
Kanab, UT
Grade 7

A House Versus My Home:

The difference between a house and a home is
a house is where you keep your 'stuff',
a home is where you keep your love.
A house is full of nothing much,
a home is full of such things as;
family, memories, love, and hope.
A home is where you go to cope.
So it is up to you, do you want to live in a house or a home?

Jessica Kernan
Ranch View Middle School
Highlands Ranch, CO
Grade 8

My Dog Sadie

My dog Sadie was a
Happy, joyful, playful dog
She always stayed by you
When you were alone
And always licked your hand with
Her wet slobbery tongue
She was never mean and always friendly
Until one day she got sick
I took her to the vet and
She had to be put down
I held her head in my hand
As I fought back the tears and told her
It would be okay
Now she is gone and I miss her deeply
But I know she is up in heaven
And is a happy, joyful, and playful dog again
How I miss
My Dog Sadie

Krista Guerin
Century Middle School
Thornton, CO
Grade 7

Do I Care?

There is a little girl,
who rides my school bus.
She is on before I am,
and always she says to me,
"Sit by me, please."
My heart breaks,
each time I see,
her mussed hair and bright blue eyes,
so filled with hope and her eager smile,
her heart-shaped face upturned,
waiting . . .
My stomach flip-flops,
I don't want to.
But I have seen how, when she asks
the kids her age, they just pass by.
My eyes moisten and my heart tears.
Then the big question is asked,
Do I care?
Can I just pass by and pretend,
ignorant indifference,
Or do I care?

Janna Tomsheck
Sunburst Elementary School
Sunburst, MT
Grade 8

I Know

As the sunrise
beats without you,
I know my strength
won't hold on.

I hold on to you,
but you pull away so fast,
I can't breathe.

I know, I know,
I can't hold on
so long without you.

As I see your face
looking down on me,
I think of the days
alone with each other.

Even though you're gone,
I still feel you here,
around me.

I know, I know,
I can't hold on
so long without you.

Lisa Krieger
Powell Middle School
Littleton, CO
Grade 7

Life

As he sits on the bench with his duffel bag at his side
He watches the people go by
And he knows that tucked deep inside their minds
Are all their troubles and worries
He wonders to himself, how do they do it
He wonders how they can keep going with all the complications in life
But then he thinks, that's it: *LIFE*
What is life?
Life is a gift
No single one perfect
But every one different
But as his train comes to a slow he picks up his bag
And heads out into the world with a new chance at life

Kendall Granle
Sierra Middle School
Parker, CO
Grade 7

The Poet

The milky white parchment lies in front of him,
Intimidating the sheets may be, as is the inky black quill.
Yes, but what a thrill.

The Poet thinks and looks to the window,
The window whittled of wood and set with single separate panes of glass.
Beyond that lives
The fisherman and his cat.
That unusual cat, wearing a coat of orange and black.

And the Poet dreams of many plots
But only one shall suit his thoughts.
The plot of a poet and his thoughts.

Tom Day
Powell Middle School
Littleton, CO
Grade 8

My Number 1 Dream

Waves splash against the rocks,
As if clapping at some hysterical joke.
Footprints lead to the water's edge,
As if they are leading to your destination.
Seagulls fly overhead screeching,
As if crying a mournful song.
Seashells scattered along the beach,
As if a giant hand gathered them up and tossed them into the air.
The sun glistens down on the water,
As if reaching, reaching toward a magical mirror.
People sit around the water's edge,
As if dying of thirst for beautiful scenery.
This is where my dreams are made,
As if, someday, they will come true.

Heidi Brough
Star Valley Jr High School
Afton, WY
Grade 7

Millennium

I have a dream
That was once said
That was a theme
After he was shot dead

Four score and seven years ago
That was once declared
After he stepped on a train cart
With the help of one man's hand

One large step for man
One giant leap for mankind
Echoed through our heads
When we lined the flag
And stepped on the moon

This has all happened before our millennium
But now it is gone and it shall not be forgot

Michael Massé
West Jordan Middle School
West Jordan, UT
Grade 8

Peppermint Paper

Wouldn't homework be a treat
If everything tasted sweet.
Essays would be okay I think
If I could write with frosting ink.

Licorice pencils,
Marshmallow erasers,
I'll get an A on all of these papers.

I wouldn't mind math one little bit
If paper was made of peppermint.
Reading I would never hate
If the pages were made of chocolate cake.

If you ever need a snack
Then just give your homework a whack.

Jessie Eaton
Century Middle School
Thornton, CO
Grade 7

What Bugs Me

When my Dad says to clean my room.
When I have to eat a mushroom.
When I have an extremely large Math lesson.
When I need to go to confession.
When my doggy barks all night.
When I am scared in fright.

Kimberly Kutt
Academy Charter School
Castle Rock, CO
Grade 7

The Face in the Clouds

I sit in my chair and think of the past,
Great memories come to my head very fast.
I think of the smiles, the pain, and the sorrow,
And just to think
I won't see her tomorrow.

Marc Mariani
St. Jude Thaddeus School
Havre, MT
Grade 7

Darkness

The day begins I think of pain.
As the day goes on it stays the same.
I try to think it will be okay,
but it just gets worse through out the day.
I try to think of sun and shine,
but the darkness takes over that time.
Some people say not to even speak
I can't I'm just too weak.
They tell me to think of flowers and things,
but the darkness takes over those things.
I know that someday it will be over,
but until then it seems like forever.
I have to be strong and let it go,
but I am too small and I think it shows.
They tell me to rest and to sleep,
they hope but it is too deep.
One day I hope to be free
free from pain and agony.
Praying for God to take my soul,
praying for God to take me home.

Sapphira Meir
Overland High School
Aurora, CO
Grade 9

Winter Silence

Silence fills the world.
Snow falls gently outside,
as the earth is covered in a white blanket.
The sky is filled with a white misty fog.
The ground sparkles as the sun peeks through the clouds.
Rippling water fills the silence,
as the snow starts to melt away.
Blue sky peeks through the clouds,
flowers start to bloom,
the grass turns green,
and the world is alive again.

Jamie Oliver
Holmes Middle School
Colorado Springs, CO
Grade 8

Memoirs of Home

Blaring Bajaj's,
Drivers yelling "cepat, cepat!*" as horns blare,
Foreigners with BMW's and Mercedes come through with a silent fanfare,
Laughing ladies with babies tied to their backs,
Chitter-chatter of the different dialects.
Silent, smoking men watching from the corner of their eyes, sitting kneeled—yet flat on
their feet,
Jamu women selling medicines made of...?
Smells of spicy, satay** cooking,
Naked children screaming and running through dirt roads—kicking up dust behind them,
Stray dogs bound and leap after them, hoping for a morsel of food to feed their bony bodies,
Shreds of newspapers litter the streets,
Taste of smoky air on the tip of your tongue,
Glasses filled with brownish, bug swarming water,
Rubber flip-flops float by on their way to the sewer, or to be found by a lucky person,
All while you receive your gap-toothed smiles,
For these are the sights and sounds of a busy city...my home

Nirvana Bhatia
Colorado Academy
Denver, CO
Grade 9
*Faster, faster in Indonesian
**Meat on a skewer served with peanut sauce

The Fly

Perplexed and frightened, as it soars endlessly in despair,
Depressed because of miserable inability.
Lost, contained, and trying to fly out, but in which way
Should it venture? It does not know.

Trying to find independence, to show it is brave, to show it can,
But ending up going nowhere.
Hearing stories of those who had been lost before, and their triumph before
Oblivion.
He is not like the rest at heart for he keeps striving for an exit out of unspeakable
Captivity.
However, upon failure he feels as though he is destined for the same fate as the others.

Running in circles and buzzing madly, crying invisible tears
When will his search be over?
When will he find his destined path out of sheltered-ness?
When will his heart beat a life of contentment and simplicity?
The answer he knows, is only to be found inside of himself, and it is just a matter of
Searching. Searching ...
Searching for a way out, a way to live, and a standard to live by
Not only takes place inside of a fly, but also in a boy just as trapped as he.

But in them both lies a gut-deep fire, as inspiration, a hope that brings forth so many
Emotions and tears. Their future lies in it. It is their fate. It is the way out.

Brett Perlmutter
Kent Denver School
Englewood, CO
Grade 7

My Mother

My mother is someone who is kind and caring,
Who is always caught in the deed of sharing.

She is the mother God gave to me,
When I look at her, His wisdom I see.

She always is trying to lead me the right way,
I hope that I can be like her someday.

My mother helps me when something's gone wrong,
So I am never sad for too very long.

She is my hero, my angel, my friend,
And I hope to be with her until the end.

She is a GREAT treasure, I hope she can see,
Her love has made all the difference in me.

So in the end, I will use all she's taught me,
I'll follow in her footsteps and be all I can be.

Chelsey Bunker
Briggsdale School
Briggsdale, CO
Grade 8

What Is Evil?

Evil is the representative of everything wrong;
Evil is the army against good;
Evil is what most are afraid of.

People try to hide evil;
People fight because of evil;
People discriminate out of anger.

Anger is evil in his human form;
Anger is the follower of evil;
Anger is caused by hate.

Hate fights by anger's side;
Hate is evil's apprentice;
Hate is what people do.

People aren't always evil;
People use evil;
People must fight evil.

Evil is something that must be fought;
Evil is everywhere it can be;
Evil feeds off people who have anger and hate.

And therefore, my friends, evil is a vicious animal
That hunts and hunts and hunts. . .

Adam Loner
Beacon Country Day School
Denver, CO
Grade 7

If I Die

If I die, please don't cry because this day was coming
some people dread it most people fear it
but for me I couldn't wait because finally I can rest
You feel it deep inside and this you cannot hide
because there is no stopping it
All through my life I struggled and fought
but the lessons were clearly taught
at certain times I'd sit and cry and couldn't wait
till the day that I died, but now it's
real and I can't express how I feel
So I'll leave you with this quote
For every step you take, I take
For every breath you breathe, I breathe
For every dollar you make, I make
You told me we'd make it to the sunshine
I just made it a little quicker.

Michael Galegos
Moffat High School
Moffat, CO
Grade 9

Pets

I've always wanted a fuzzy frog,
A stinky hog, a little dog,
A great big bird with a great big beak,
And a skunk that doesn't stink.

I want an elephant that is really light,
And two kangaroos that like to fight,
A little lizard that will run real fast,
Plus a piranha that will really last.

All of these would be really cool,
The piranha could even live in our pool,
But when I asked my mom for the dough,
All she gave me was a short, simple, NO!

Cole Suter
Star Valley Jr High School
Afton, WY
Grade 7

Mom

She's always there for you
Packing your lunch
Making dinner
Cleaning the dishes
You never could imagine being without her
It would be too hard
Glad she is there every morning
Every evening
Every day
To love you

Daniel Kim
Century Middle School
Thornton, CO
Grade 7

Who Are We?

Who are we?
What do we do?
Who are we under that skin?
Do we really know?
Are we what we want to be?
Are we lying? To whom?
Are we happy?
Do we dream or are we dreaming?
Do we love?
Do we hate?
Who are we?
What do we want?
Do we want money, love, happiness?
Who are we individually?
What do we want and need?
Are we proud?
Take what you have
Take it!
But still, who are we?

Adriane Bohlender
Century Middle School
Thornton, CO
Grade 7

Determination

"I'll push you," it says.
"With me, you'll feel no pain.
Farther and farther I'll take you.
I will help you.
You will survive,
Because of me
I am determination."

Ross Hammerer
Pauline Memorial School
Colorado Springs, CO
Grade 7

Snow Poem

Why won't it snow?
I do not know.
My board is getting rusty and cold.
The weatherman says,
A big storm is coming,
But that line is getting old.

Then to my surprise,
Right before my eyes,
Flakes begin to fall.
The weatherman is right,
The storm is in sight,
The slopes begin their call.

Ryan Gardner
Mountain Ridge Jr High School
Highland, UT
Grade 9

Sadness

The day is cold and filled with sadness,
For the earth knows the sun won't shine.
The wind howls like a wolf
Sitting under a bright moon,
And still the sun won't shine.
The rain beats on the roof,
Like your heart beats inside,
And still the sun won't shine.
The thunder roars like an angry lion,
Ready to eat its dinner,
And still the sun won't shine.
As all is happening, the clouds part,
And the wind stops howling,
The rain stops beating,
The thunder stops roaring,
    And finally,
    The sun shines.

Brittany Job
St. Jude Thaddeus School
Havre, MT
Grade 7

Master Poetaster

I'm the Master Poetaster
All I write is a big disaster
In my head the space is vaster
For I'm the Master Poetaster

People say my poems are bad
Surprisingly I don't get mad
But there is the occasional lad
Who says my poems aren't that bad

Read this poem and you will see
How bad a poem can really be
Even this poem is a disaster
For I am the Master Poetaster

Kit Beikmann
Century Middle School
Thornton, CO
Grade 7

Sand Dollar

The sandstone of the ocean
The shape of a windmill
The leaves of autumn
The roots of spring
The white doves within
    A pointed star
    A ridged flower
The currency of the sea

Shonda Letchworth
Colorado Academy
Denver, CO
Grade 9

Memory Loss

Alzheimer's
splitting personalities
ripping out cores of memory
feeding vultures of
"I can't remembers"
of a tribe that
remembers events
in your life
crumbling like
rain forest life
in a "slash and burn"
method of
I can't remember
what you love in me

Sarah Schlicting
Sheridan Jr High School
Sheridan, WY
Grade 8

My Love for Poems

I really hate writing stuff,
'cause poems like this are really tough.

I truly hate to write each verse,
'cause it seems to get worse and worse.

The rhyming seems to gradually decline,
it gets impossible to write a line.

I try and try with all my might,
but I just can't get the verses right.

Then I'm done with my big mess.
here you go teacher, call the press.

Grant Miller
Pawnee Jr-Sr High School
Grover, CO
Grade 8

Autumn Day

The leaves on the old oak tree
tottering to the ground.
The sun setting briskly
on the water
which causes a reflection.
Children's laughter
mingling in the hollow trees,
A fleet of leaves tumbling
across the lawn.
A perpetual blitz of wind
discovering the Autumn Day.

Mary Ann McNitt
Evergreen Jr High School
Salt Lake City, UT
Grade 9

On a Sad Little Road

On a sad little road in the middle of Poland
We drive through the devastation
That has fallen upon our peaceful country.
The tears in my mother's eyes tell me this is no small deal
And that we are not coming home.
My father tells me this happened because of a man,
A very cruel and possessed man.
I hear everyone around me talk of this man,
Our friends say he is evil,
Our enemies say he is great,
I don't know much myself but I feel hate for him.
How could such a great and wonderful thing as a human,
Do such ugly things to his fellow man?
A terrible stench fills my nostrils
As we pull up to the walls surrounding our new home.
What our new home will be like I know not,
But from the smell I know it won't be as good as Poland.
On a sad little road in the middle of Poland
We travel to meet this great evil named Hitler.

Devin Barrett
South Jordan Middle School
South Jordan, UT
Grade 8

One Soul Lives

The silent mind unknowing danger
Strolled slowly through the dewy grass.
Quiet heart beating slowly
Thinking death is maybe sleeping.

Slowly it emerges from the shadows,
Slowly silently without a whisper.
It spies its prey out of the corner of its eye
And slowly sinks to the standoffish wet ground.

Front legs outstretched for more altitude
Waiting for the perfect time to strike.
And still its prey is unaware
Not a sound has been heard except itself.

Suddenly without a moments delay
A flash, a crash, a sobbing cry.
Ripping claws, tearing jaws
One soul lives, one soul is ebbing.

The last gasp of air is the stabbing pain of passing
A moment is taken to truly thank a higher power.
The predator summons to a subnormal youth
And a moment with a loved one is praised.

Alicia Ziegler
Laurel Middle School
Laurel, MT
Grade 8

The Race

Boom! The gun goes off,
the race has finally begun.
The anticipation and nervousness
was nothing like you thought it was,
all the stamping of feet on the hard ground,
people pushing, shoving everywhere.
Through the middle, so ashamed,
too tired to go on, too sick to move.
But the thought of honor came piercing through.
You hear someone yell out, "You're doing great!"
Pushing harder you make it to the end.
You may come in first or last but at least you finished.

Cassie Revelli
Mountain Ridge Jr High School
Highland, UT
Grade 8

Music

Without music life would be dull,
We would have no way of expressing ourselves at all.
Music is what we listen to each day,
Music is an instrument we play.
Music is singing and talking too,
Music is even playing the kazoo.
Music is a rhythm of all different kinds,
Music comes with practice and time.
People think music is only playing an instrument
Or singing, that's not true,
There are many other types I'll tell you.
Talking is music with rhythm and rhyme,
Even walking is music with a certain time.
That annoying bird chirping, yes it's true,
That is music too.
As you can see music is found in many different ways
So go out and find some music in your life today.

Alexandria Pretzer
Manitou Springs Middle School
Manitou Springs, CO
Grade 7

21 years +

They never care what we know,
or what good we do.
All they care about is the blood in the snow,
and who shot who.
Always quick to judge,
slow to see our point of view.
Say our generation is sludge.
They have no clue!
We are decent people,
and shouldn't be judged because of others
mistakes.

Devin Keller
Mont Harmon Jr High School
Price, UT
Grade 8

Springing into Spring

Winter now is waning,
The snow is melting speedily.
The bright sunshine is hard at work,
Warming the muddy scenery.
Rain pours from the sky above,
It refreshes everything,
From the newborn animals,
To the blooming flowers,
Those are the effects of spring!

Becca Price
Star Valley Jr High School
Afton, WY
Grade 7

Jaysi Lee

My sister's name is Jaysi Lee.
She will soon be turning three.
She can't climb a tree
or fly like a bee.
She yells yippee
whenever she sees me!
She likes to see
Tarzan in his movie.
Jaysi loves her baby.
Its name is Maddie.
She is very special you see.
I love her and she loves me!

Cole Shakespear
Kanab Middle School
Kanab, UT
Grade 7

I'm So Sorry

Why don't you believe me?
Just because I don't know why,
And you get very mad,
And you make me want to cry.

Why do you hate me?
What did I do to you?
I try to tell you something,
And you think it is not true.

Why are you so rude?
I try to be nice,
But I guess it doesn't work,
So I won't do it twice.

This is not fair,
I try to do what's right,
You act like you don't care,
You say you want to start a fight.

Samantha Smith
First Presbyterian Church Academy
Las Vegas, NV
Grade 7

The Poem

As the fluorescent lights and the booming thunder of the sky begins
A dark figure stands at the door
He knocks and the door opens and he disappears in the smoke filled doorway.

As the figure walks into the dark murky smoke filled room
The men give a ghastly stare
The man takes off his cloak the other men suddenly stop
They stand up and say
Come and sit down and play a game of poker

Jonathan Hill
Century Middle School
Thornton, CO
Grade 7

Guilt

The judge's gavel came thundering down on the round cedar block.
But I felt no sorrow.
The catty preacher's wife was to hang.
But I felt no grief.
The minister betrayed his wife, as did the town.
But I felt no regret.
Her cold eyes hung in the air with her fringed body.
But I felt no fear.
Her cold feet would never touch the empty earth again for eternity.
But I felt no pain.
Finally the trials were over.
But I felt sorrow.

Michael Schindel
Vail Mountain School
Vail, CO
Grade 7

A Bit of Hope for the Summer

As I came to an end in the deserted,
Misty-like forest,
The quietness in the waves wrestling against the sand,
And dew dripping off leaves
Was all I could hear.
My brain was stretched in many different directions,
As I tried to think of something to do that summer.
Lingering home with a look of sadness in my eyes,
And every now and then taking a glimpse out at the shimmering sea,
Yearning for a bit of hope
My eye caught a shiny piece of metal in the distance.
As I ambled closer
I could see it,
A bottle,
Which at that time I didn't know it would change my life forever.
Inside the crisp bottle was a letter,
It smelled of lilac on an early spring morning.
It's edges were golden brown from being burnt,
And it was signed at the bottom, "Love, Chris"

Courtney Somes
Vail Mountain School
Vail, CO
Grade 7

Did You Remember

Did you remember . . .
When it was my birthday,
when I needed you there,
when I was hurt horribly?
When was the last time you remembered,
to wish me a happy birthday?
When was the last time,
you were there for me?
That is when it hurts the worst.
Do you remember,
when I was sitting in the corner?
Do you remember seeing me crying,
there in that corner?
Do you remember when I was in the corner,
you didn't even come and ask what was wrong.
I wish you could remember that happened.
You could have seen that I do have feelings.
I had tears in my eyes,
but you weren't there to see that . . .

Jennica Grimstead
Tintic High School
Eureka, UT
Grade 8

Life

Life is but a river,
Smooth, rough, fast or slow.
Some know where to go,
Others make a wrong turn.

A stream is but a baby,
River is middle age.
When it reaches the ocean that is where the journey ends.
And other lives begin.

Some rivers are evil,
Because they have taken lives.
Others are beautiful in a way.
With flowers by their sides.

They can lead a happy life,
Filled with excitement and joy.
Sadness is another story,
It sounds like crying.

But through the ups and downs.
And the hardships and laughter.
In the end it was worth it.
For another life to begin.

Mindy Ord
Century Middle School
Thornton, CO
Grade 7

Millennium

How awesome it will be to be alive in the new
Millennium.

But I wonder what will happen during this new
Millennium.

Will we have flying cars,
Or robots that can clean our rooms
And our whole houses too.

Or maybe we will have to start with
No computers because of the crash.

No one knows
Until the first day of the new
Millennium.

Emily Willis
Mountain Ridge Jr High School
Highland, UT
Grade 9

The Future Is in Our Hands

The world is small, but we are smaller.
We are but a tiny speck in the universe.
Earth is the only planet that can support us,
but even though it is small,
it is strong when we are united.
So people, people, join together
to make our planet strong.
For it is the only place we have to live.
We are free, free, free.
So people, people, join together
to make our planet strong.

Matt Liese
Circle Jr High School
Circle, MT
Grade 8

Grandma

I loved you like you were my second mom,
but in a heartbeat you were gone.
It's hard to face tomorrow
because my heart is filled with sorrow.
I can't stop crying
because you never told me you were dying.
Now without you, my heart is so blue.
I feel like I can't do anything more
because without you I feel like I can't open a door.
Now you're gone,
I know the pain will go on and on.
You're my grandma and I love you to death,
I feel like I can never rest.

Nathan Camacho
Granada School
Granada, CO
Grade 9

Presidents

Lincoln, Washington, and Jefferson to name just a few
they led our country under red, white, and blue.
Lincoln was worried for what he would do
with all the fighting of the gray and blue.
Washington the great General led the states to victory
to help set us free and give us liberty.
Jefferson gave us independence with a stroke of a pen
on a piece of paper that will never end.

Lyle Bracken
Riverview Jr High School
Murray, UT
Grade 8

Spellling

I wish I would spell, I really do
But the *postion* of the letters don't stick like glue
If I could spell my teachers would rave
And maybe I'd get some *attentiion* I crave.

But *spellling* is something that doesn't quite work,
So often I end up looking like a jerk
They really should make more worlds with just three letters
For me that would be much more better.

So give me a break when my papers you grade
Please don't let my *enthueasm* fade
My spelling is poor, I'm the first to say
But *spellling* correctly isn't my way.

Casey Swan
Century Middle School
Thornton, CO
Grade 7

Keys of Life

As I slowly pass through life with much fear,
in my heart there is always someone here.
Though I have decisions to make every day,
I know my family will evermore stay.
With parents, brothers, and sister too,
they make me feel I have nothing to lose.
Courageous and faithful is what they'll forever be,
I love them more than anyone can see.
My family is what I will never forsake,
devotions and peace is what they make.
Our families are the keys of life and dreams,
no matter how difficult families seem.
So treat them right and with respect,
for then your life is what they'll protect.
My family is who I'd do anything for,
because without them my heart will be torn.
With someone to love I have no sorrow,
because they are the only true love I know.

Espie Bada
Johnson Middle School
Las Vegas, NV
Grade 8

The Sky

The sky is everywhere,
When you take a hike, or comb your hair,
The sky is all around you,
You can't escape its grasp,
Beauty and wonder,
It's not something you have to ponder,
Just take a moment to look at it one summer day,
You'll be surprised how it mystifies you in its own unique way,
Even though it may not put you in the best of moods some days,
Be happy that it's there,
When you feel blue one day,
Or even if you don't have a say,
Remember that the sky will always be there for you,
Especially when you need the most cheering up.

Ryan Hafer
Holmes Middle School
Colorado Springs, CO
Grade 8

Wrestling

The smell of the mat,
The feel of my old tarnished shoes,
The heat of the workout room,
As the sweat pours off my head.
I reflect the images of the off season.
The weight room, the passing rocket ships
as I run down the old highway.
Dreaming. . .Dreaming big as I lay in bed,
Now I train like an animal wishing I were dead.
All of it to reach one goal.
To be the best of the best.
To be a State Champion!

Fred Spor
Norwood Middle School
Norwood, CO
Grade 9

The Road

The cowboy spends his life on the go
Never knowing what his life will behold
For every trip he makes alone
Traveling down that dusty road

The cowboy travels down this road
For it is the only thing he knows how to do
He grew up this way always on the go
Always working to keep his home

So if you see a cowboy on the side of the road
And his thumb is out waving at you
Be a pal and give him a ride
For you never know but he might win his next ride

Chad E. Wiltfang
Rosebud Public School
Rosebud, MT
Grade 9

Dreams and Hopes

All of the dreams—gone
All of the hopes—gone.
All of the beautiful children—gone.
All of the families—gone

The hate for a culture.
They were different; they were killed.
All of the Jews—gone
for what they believed
who they were.

They were killed, treated like animals
shot in the head
babies thrown into the air for target practice
thrown into gas chambers to die.

All due to one man, Hitler.
Because of one man's hate of a culture
Almost the entire culture was killed.
The Holocaust.

Jordan Deroo
South Valley Middle School
Platteville, CO
Grade 8

The Lake

My life is a lake on a warm summer's day;
Each person, every encounter, are the fish beneath the waves.

My heart shines down upon the quiet bay,
watching people come and go; in my life they play.

In my life they play, rattling my thoughts
interfering with my calm, taking away my peace.

They fish in my lake, taking what they can
taking people, taking thoughts, throwing some back.

But what they throw back doesn't return unchanged;
When a person is taken, only memories remain.

One by one, they take them all, destroying my life,
taking pleasure in my pain, leaving me in strife.

My heart is setting over the horizon,
leaving life in darkness; the memories dying.

The sun has set, the memories slowly fade
into the darkness of my life; nothing swims beneath the waves.

Brianna Freed
Vilas High School
Vilas, CO
Grade 9

The Rose

The rose sits in a vase,
Lonely,
Without solace.
Looking out on the world
Petals full of sorrow,
Petals that used to be as crimson
As red wine and as deep as the sea
Now are brown edges and shallow.
Its stem grows tall
With pride and glory.
However, the rose feels as though its heart has been rendered.
The feeling is of loss . . .
Perhaps a loss of love . . .
Its thorns do not puncture a soul that drips blood
They puncture the life of a fading flourish.
For the love does not return to the blossom.

Samantha Mogul
Vail Mountain School
Vail, CO
Grade 7

Time and What It Brings

As every second goes by
Another soul is anxiously waiting
For what seems like nothing

When each minute comes
Another mind is steadily preparing
For what seems like nothing

At the beginning of each hour
Another heart is vibrantly beating
Starting to get excited and nervous
For what seems like nothing

At the end of the day
Another soul, another mind, another heart
Is fully satisfied with what it got
Which now seems like everything

Autumn Rae Sanders
Kent Denver School
Englewood, CO
Grade 7

Help

Help,
Help me Lord,
Help me get through all this pain being caused.
Help me be courageous.
Help me return to the one I know, the one I trust,
    and the one deep in thought.
Help me repeat a chant of I will, and I can.

Kayla Squires
Custer County School
Westcliffe, CO
Grade 7

Cloud Shapes

A racing horse runs over the sky,
a cheat telling a lie,
a hamster about to jump high,
a kite that goes up and up,
and a cat about to jump.
An alligator about to chomp,
a tear from a sad sob,
a spill of milk,
a long buckled belt,
a large hunting hound,
or maybe just a cloud.

Charlotte Siska
Century Middle School
Thornton, CO
Grade 7

The Trip to the Vet

We took my dog to the vet,
for a check.
She said my pup is a nice pet.
They took her far in the back
and sat her down on a mat.
She looked in her ears
without fears.
It's time.
The table was cold and depressing.
The needles were long and gleaming.
They came with a mask,
before I could ask,
she jabbed her hard in the rump!
Then my poor dog fell with a thump.
The vet began her fast task
with a snip here and there.
She soon walked out with her mask
and said, "It's over,
so take great care."

Cody Knight
Jarbidge School
Jarbidge, NV
Grade 7

Teddy

He is soft and fluffy
squishy and furry
light and not heavy.
Two little arms
two little feet
and on the left foot
you can squeeze
and then there comes
a little squeak.

Tiffany Valdez
Century Middle School
Thornton, CO
Grade 7

To Touch the Sky

To reach a dream that's way up high
You must be sure to touch the sky
Although it's hard you'll never fail
If all you do is follow the trail

You grope, you cry
You soar, you fly
You whine, you fall
You win, you crawl

That is part of reaching your goal
But if you stop it'll pay it's toll
From bad to worse soon it'll get
Though if you wait it'll change your fate
You'll be strong and mighty
Powerful and free
All from waiting and continuing

So go for dreams
Be fearless of falls
Pursue those mighty, potent walls
And if you win, all will be well
You'll feel good 'bout yourself
And everyone can tell!

Kim Ross
Centennial Middle School
Boulder, CO
Grade 8

The Race

The gun goes off; he starts the race,
To stay ahead he must keep pace.
He has started the race.

Zooming down the last long stretch,
His family cheers him from the bench.
He is now close to the end.

Through hard work and perspiration
He finally reaches his destination.
He has won the race!

Michael Bradley
Challenger School
Sandy, UT
Grade 7

School House

English, kids
Talking, eating, learning
Scratching, pencils—worksheets filled
High School

Katie Borden
Boulder City High School
Boulder City, NV
Grade 9

A Golden Statue

A golden statue stays inside,
Leaving a force of patience,
a single tear it catches . . .
is washed away.

A golden statue keeps me safe.
It holds a spirit
Locked within an image of perfection
Handing out chills,
but I stay warm.

My heart offers weakness,
But a heart of gold
erases an image of emptiness . . .
being locked inside
A golden statue.

Chelsea Martinez
Sage Valley Jr High School
Gillette, WY
Grade 9

Questions of Love

Does he love me?
Does he care?
Will I ever know?
Do I have a prayer?
Will he ever tell me?
How will I know?
Does he want to be free?
Does he feel chained?
Chained to the ground?
Do I make him feel unfree?
Do I make him feel bound?
Some say, "What do you know,
You are only a youth."
But I know I need answers!
I know I need the truth!
Do I know what I want?
Do I have a clue?
There is only one thing for certain.
It is that I will always love you.

Robin Rene Richter
Round Mountain Jr-Sr High School
Round Mountain, NV
Grade 8

Windmill

My life is like a windmill.
It keeps going around in circles.
Until the day the wind stops blowing
And my life stops going.

Kody Nunley
Round Mountain Jr-Sr High School
Round Mountain, NV
Grade 9

Bare Feet

Here I am looking down at them.
My damp, withered feet,
Hovering over the dark, icy, stone surface.
Torn, shattered, and bruised,
They lay there limp.
But they weren't always this way.
I used to run and jump with my family
And not have a care in the world.
Then a dark cloud drifted over us
And I never felt the sun again.
It tore my family out of
My hands, my heart, my life.
My only memories are screams,
Echoing through my mind.
... No! Please, NO! ...
... He's only a BOY! ...
... JEW! ...
Now I stand alone,
Looking at my bare feet,
And asking
Why?

Jeffrey Farnsworth
South Jordan Middle School
South Jordan, UT
Grade 8

The Prairie Storm

The dark mysterious clouds rolled in.
The sky is as black as night.
The prairie is silent
As the first drop falls.
Then all hell breaks loose.
The thunder rolls across the sky,
Nothing there to stop it.
The lightning strikes without warning
And the rain starts pouring down.
The grass whips and twists,
And the wind howls
The rain shoots to the ground.
It shatters like broken glass.
The thunder rumbles and crackles.
The ground shakes.
The lightning flashes across the sky
As though being hurled into the distance.
And without warning the storm ends
And the clouds roll away into the distance.
And again the prairie is silent and at peace
As though nothing ever happened.

Sheena Rasmussen
Sage Valley Jr High School
Gillette, WY
Grade 9

The Shores of Your Soul

the ocean whispers to my soul
as I walk along its shores
not knowing quite what it's saying
but listening anyway
for some reason I'm able to see
the end but I keep going
not wanting anything to end
wanting it to last forever
but nothing ever does
happiness never lasts
neither does sadness
so what do you do in between?
walk along the shores of your soul to find
yourself and continue on.

Angelina Randall
Pleasant Grove Jr High School
Pleasant Grove, UT
Grade 9

Hoping

If only you knew how I felt,
Every time I see you my heart melts.
You don't know what it's like to cry yourself to sleep,
I only wish you were mine to keep.
Wherever I go, you're on my mind,
I'm like a puppet that only you can wind.
I love you more and more every day,
Those are the words I wish you could say.
You are my fantasy, as well as my friend,
I hope in time my heart will mend.
You've put me in a black hole and I can't get out,
But when I look into your eyes, I wonder what you're all about.
I dream day and night about only you,
And I pray, you dream about me too.
You get me so confused I don't know what to do,
Should I stand around and dream, or tell you I love you.

Mandy Klimeck
East Middle School
Colorado Springs, CO
Grade 8

The Face*

I wish that I could see your face just once more.
The face with a bright and loving smile.
The face I didn't say good-bye to.
This is the face that I'd love to see once more.
You are mine, all mine.
Please come back to me.
This is the face that rises from the mist.
I know you.

Felicia Taylor
East Middle School
Colorado Springs, CO
Grade 8
*In loving memory of my Grandma Phyllis Avery.
Forever your only granddaughter, Felicia.

Getting Ready for the Hunt

Boom! went the gun
as it shot the bullet through
the air, straight as an arrow
it was going straight for the target
"Wham!" it hit the tin can full of water
and sent it sailing through the air
I am ready for the hunt!

Duston Turner
Star Valley Jr High School
Afton, WY
Grade 7

The World Is . . .

The world is big,
The world is small.

Pretty soon,
There'll be nothing at all.

The world is calm,
The world is loud.

If you count all the people,
It's quite a crowd.

The world is dirty,
The world is clean.

If we all work together,
We'll create quite a scene.

Sterling Glover
Kanab Middle School
Kanab, UT
Grade 7

Fiery Red

Today I'm red, so you see
I have a fiery red personality,
tell me what to do
and watch me rebel,
but in an adventurous situation
I adapt very well.

I like to be the boss
and I'm a good decision maker too,
I am very self motivated
so keep your distance and let me do.

I'll protect you from harm
and am very caring for you,
compassion's my middle name
and I'm intelligent, too.

Krysta Pecharich
Riverview Jr High School
Murray, UT
Grade 8

Scuba Diving

The water overpowers me as I submerge into the vast tropical sea,
My ears begin to ring as I descend,
The reef, with a hundred colors, is a beautiful wall,
The fish in the school scurry as I draw near,
The sound of my regulator releasing bubbles of air becomes a steady pattern,
When I look above, I see the sparkling sun,
Octopuses and eels poke out of the reef, and a white-tipped, shark circles above,
When I look past the reef, the gray ocean flows forever,
As I slowly rise, up to the surface.

Grant Goerzen
Holmes Middle School
Colorado Springs, CO
Grade 8

Volcano

Spewing, thundering,
angrily trembling and grumbling, releasing out
emotions of utter disgust,
anger, bottled-up stress,
causing tremendous

havoc and terror,
as it watches the unlucky
inhabitants flee for their lives,
far away from this old, maddening
senile demonic existence as it laughs at all
of the helpless and needy ones, it rumbles with
a sickening, sadistic delight, as it erupts numerous
glistening, red-hot, embers, sparks fly all over, surrounded
by a hazy and misty screen of evilness as a thick, flaming liquid
blanket oozes down along the grooved, cracking sides, covering the
deserted homes in a heated boil, enveloping all that was, will, and possibly ever be.

Danchi Nguyen
Riverview Jr High School
Murray, UT
Grade 8

My Luck Star

When then sun starts to set
And everyone leaves I sit alone and start to think.

Long ago and far away,
We fished and swam throughout the day.

He held my hand and helped me learn about the stuff that now is old.
And then one day I walked alone, without his hand never again to hold.

I miss him tons and will never forget about the fun we had,
And the time that we spent together I now cherish.

The stars still twinkle and are bright at night,
But mine is gold and will always shine bright.

Kate Griffin
Star Valley Jr High School
Afton, WY
Grade 7

Changes

"Change is not bad, it is only different."
Does anyone really believe this?
This change couldn't have been for the best,
Could it?
You once were always there,
Now you don't seem to care.
I remember the day we met
Our plan of always together seemed to be set.
You changed so much
Since those days of swing-sets
And shy words.
Or perhaps it was me who changed?

Maureen Maguire
Century Middle School
Thornton, CO
Grade 7

The Simple Things in Life

Living in the world today
you can take it as you may
there is hunger, depression, and poverty
these are the things that are not meant to be
the world should be a happy place
not one run by disgrace
we can help it you and me
so help yourself by helping others in need

Matthew Estell
Bigfork Middle School
Bigfork, MT
Grade 8

Stories

When you open a book,
There is a birth of a story.

You read on,
Through the beginning of the story.
Through the beginning of life.

You keep reading through
Happiness and conflicts,
Triumphs and defeats,
Each story different.

Some are boring, some are interesting,
Some end in tragedy, some end with happiness,
Each story different.

When you close the book the story stops.
Life doesn't go on until
Someone opens the book and the story starts again,
Each story different.

Courtney Olsen
Kent Denver School
Englewood, CO
Grade 7

Rich

A man,
Trapped in his own personal hell,
Self-created,
Terrified of what's below him in the streets.
Family, friends, money,
All without substance.
He ignores his conscience,
He owns much,
Knows that he doesn't deserve it,
Deep down, screaming at himself.
His soul reaches out but he swallows it,
Good manners, the American dream, exploitation,
All parts of high society,
His mind squelching his heart.
Staring at an empty glass of himself,
A pill to end it,
No more fighting himself,
No ignorance, yet bliss.

Peter Host
Custer County School
Westcliffe, CO
Grade 7

Stop and Smell the Coffee

Ever go outside after a small rainstorm?
You know the smell, the look, the feeling you get
You need to.

Have you seen the sun rise
Over a beautiful range of mountains in the summer?
The sun is the earth and the colors of the solar system.

Ever go cloud gazing?
I tell you what, that is a blast.
You can see all sorts of shapes
If you have an imagination.

These are gifts from God
To make our day brighter.

Do you let a friend know what you like to see in them.
Do they know the real you?

Do you know the real them?
Have you ever spent more than a few hours with them?
You might want to.

Stop and smell the coffee.
Really, you never know what's out there.
The different people, places, things, you are missing.
The fun you could be having, it's all up to you.

Tonya Nuzum
Sage Valley Jr High School
Gillette, WY
Grade 9

The Reflection of a Summers Day

Upon the waters front
The ripples o' so clear
A stone breaks the silence
No movement is near
A thrash of panic is delayed

As the waters still
The sun shines through
The day is almost a new
The water seems to show
The reflection of summers day

Shanda Miller
Ranch View Middle School
Highlands Ranch, CO
Grade 8

Angel's Little Rain

They fall to the earth like shooting stars
Coming from above
They're angel's little kisses,
Falling to the earth
If one falls upon you,
You'll be blessed in many ways
Angel's little kisses
Carry your life away

So next time you see the rain,
Don't be down, just go outside
And dance in the rain
And the raindrops fall upon you
Kisses from an angel

Christina Jacobson
Minturn Middle School
Minturn, CO
Grade 8

The Last Ride in the Wagon

Here I am,
in the wagon,
my last ride,
The solid chilling cold chains,
on my tepid delicate body,
that tries to warm them,
For this is the day of my death
My last ride,
on the flat firm floor of the wagon
nailed down with nowhere to go
I will certainly miss,
all the gentle grinning faces,
my little boy's helping fragile fingers
I will miss them all,
My last ride

Sasha Windisch
Vail Mountain School
Vail, CO
Grade 7

Rocking Away

It seems like only yesterday,
We were planting sweet peas in a garden with tulips high and blooming.
And his sweet smile always made me happy even while we worked.
He was an old man, my Grandpa, bent over leaning on his cane.
Soft hands were worn and strong from all the hard days,
Thin snowy white hair was long yet barely there,
The blue faded overalls were worn and soft against my cheek.
He seemed sad those last days, like he knew
The days had caught up with him, and he was weary
Too many days spent alone.
One day he rocked silently in his chair and let the angels take him home.
I miss the conversations even though we had few,
And how he smelled of aftershave,
But most of all I'll miss his touch, strong and comforting as we hugged goodbye.

Janie Rayback
Star Valley Jr High School
Afton, WY
Grade 7

Deaf in the Darkness

I often feel alone in the darkness.
I will never be able to hear the violin play its soft medley,
    or a firework burst in midair.
For I am deaf.
I can see a colorful picture hang on a dull white wall,
    but I will never be able to hear the painter tell why he painted it.
My hands complete me.
Without them I am an angel without his wings.
I sometimes feel as though I am the only one existing.
I can see and feel people talk but I never will understand their world.
I know I am one and only one, but I do not feel like it.
Words are nothing to me.
My mouth is nothing to me.
The only things I have are my hands and imagination,
    because with my imagination I can hope for a better tomorrow.

Tom Berryman
Pueblo West Middle School
Pueblo West, CO
Grade 8

Colors of the Rainbow

The colors of the rainbow are beautiful.
Each one filled with another and different mystery.
Red is outgoing, original and very beautiful.
Blue is shy but extremely intelligent, also very beautiful.
Purple is unique, very self-sufficient and very beautiful.
Yellow is funny, the class clown, and very beautiful.
Orange is soothing, shy but also outgoing, and very beautiful.
As you may have figured out by now this has nothing to do with a rainbow,
It has to do with diversity and acceptance.
Everyone is different but somehow the same.
You must always accept people for who they are.

Barbara Vucasovich
Powell Middle School
Littleton, CO
Grade 7

Thunder

The thunder roles across the dark sky.
With shouts of complaint following close by.
Each force beckons a child's fright.
This mysterious action creates all light.
The leaping lights leave many people shocked.
But when all has ended the sky is then locked.

Wendy Kwan
Butler Middle School
Salt Lake City, UT
Grade 8

The Tortoise and the Hare

There once was a hare that wanted to race
But no one could keep up with his pace
Then a tortoise decided that he had nothing to lose
And so he polished up his running shoes

The day of the race rolled around
And it started with an awfully loud sound
The hare flew as if he were to bust
Leaving the poor tortoise in a cloud of dust

Soon the hare neared the finish line
That's when he noticed a comfy pine
So he decided he had time to take a nap
Because he knew that beating the tortoise would be a snap

That tortoise marched on without a care
And soon approached the sleeping hare
He was the winner without debate
Because that cocky hare woke up too late

Anna Davis
Mountain Ridge Middle School
Colorado Springs, CO
Grade 8

Do You Ever Wonder...

Do you wonder if a doll ever sleeps at night?
If its eyes are wide open, or closed very tight?
Do you ever wonder if it sleeps or if it walks?
If it smiles, if it laughs, but mostly if it talks?
Do you ever wonder if it moves, if it sees?
If it could, do you suppose it might sneeze?
Do you ever wonder if it sees us walking by?
If it has a voice, very lightly, could it sigh?
Do you ever wonder how it acts at night?
If it moves when you're not looking at it just right?
Do you ever wonder if we're just tiny dolls?
If at night, there's giants up making soundless calls?
Do you ever wonder why we can't know for sure?
If we could, we can't help it, for there is no cure.

Colette Miles
Kanab Middle School
Kanab, UT
Grade 7

Graham Cracker

Pull it from the box, smell the sugar and cinnamon
   Step out to the cold crisp air
The graham cracker if you will
Put it to your lips
   Lips tingle as the air swirls and twists from inside
Snap! Take a bite in
   Breathe again...yes that feeling again
The crumbs drop and scatter
   Snow falls all around
Relish taste in the mouth
   Relish sights of pure untouchable white
Savor sugar on the tongue
   Savor snow on the nose
More bites
   More snow, sled, ski, build men of the cold
Dust hands of sugar and crumbs
   The trees are dusted with sugar
      Skeletons of winter
Lick fingers
   Enjoy to last flake
      Until melted and gone

Ari Leventhal
Colorado Academy
Denver, CO
Grade 9

Patrick's Dream

There once was a person, named Patrick Cortera,
Who vacationed somewhere, by the French Riviera.
He was trying out, for the French Baseball Team,
   But he couldn't fulfill, his big lifelong dream.

When he hit the ball, he ran fast to first base.
But about half way there, he fell flat on his face!
He's accident prone, and he doesn't know why,
And sometimes he wished, he'd just fall down and die!

But one day this fellow, he smacked the baseball,
And then he thought he hit, the very best hit of all.
The ball hit the fence, Patrick ran past first base,
   But then yet again, he fell flat on his face!

His slid and he slid, and the pain made him shout,
   The umpire said, "So close but you're out!"
Patrick Cortera, had just one more try,
   But the way he saw it, he was gonna fry.

It was finally his turn, so he stepped up to bat,
And that time he swung, and strike one just like that.
The baseball was thrown, Patrick hit that ball well,
That ball went quite high, past the fence the ball fell.

Chris Arena
St Vincent De Paul School
Salt Lake City, UT
Grade 7

What If?

What if the sky was green
And the grass was blue?
What if the truth was a lie,
And lies were true?
What if Santa was skinny,
And Michael Jordan was fat?
What if boxes were round,
And the earth was flat?
What if pillows were heavy,
And concrete light?
What if night was day,
And day was night?
What if all these things did come true?
If they did, what would YOU do?

Alivia Olson
Century Middle School
Thornton, CO
Grade 7

Fog

Fog weeps
Weeps itself to sleep
It sits wondering
Watching and staring
Eyes wet and puffy
Vision unclear
Slowly moving in silence
Twiddling thumbs
What to do next
Weeping softly
Hear nothing
Think nothing
Do nothing
Fog weeps

Lauren DeQuiroz
Century Middle School
Thornton, CO
Grade 7

A Fly

Buzz buzz in my ear
Buzz buzz it has no fear
Smack
Buzz buzz that fly is fast
Buzz buzz it's the last chance
Smack
Buzz buzz that ugly fly
Buzz buzz why doesn't it die
Smack
Oh dear I think I killed it
Oh dear what a mess

Tish Lopez
Riverview Jr High School
Murray, UT
Grade 8

The First Step

Every step you have taken,
every crawl you have crawled,
your first step is always mistaken,
your second follows applause.

Your first step is always amazing,
your parents shall rave with joy,
then they will go browsing,
to buy you a brand new toy.

They will make a special dinner,
just for the occasion,
they make you feel like a winner,
at the amazing celebration.

When dinner's done,
and the food is all gone,
dad says "Good night Hon,"
and they sleep until dawn.
For every step you have taken,
will live on and on.

Benjamin Wilcher
Spring Creek Middle School
Elko, NV
Grade 8

Tapestry

Tapestry of wonder and delight
of color and shapes so bright.
Every thread full of life,
colorful playing of a fife.

Beautiful, tranquil, green forest mews
in which the sparkling stream soothes.
A pool at the fountain's face
where garish eyes stare upon grace.

A maiden combs her long silver hair,
hands of slender ease and fair.
Warrior of legends untold
his vivid sword held glimmering bold.

Futile thief hides in the tree tops nigh
to the blue amulet sky upward high.
The dove soars with little rhyme
unconcerned with passing time.

As colors dim and fade
carefully woven, and made.
Places and actors of forgotten lore,
insipid tapestry behind the closed door.

Dixie Lewton-Bitner
Sage Valley Jr High School
Gillette, WY
Grade 9

Holocaust

H ideous scenes of torture
O n sight executions
L iving in the horror of genocide
O ne slim chance of survival
C oncentration camps slow death
A wful sights of insidious neglect
U nsurpassed acts of cruelty
S alvation brought by the Allies
T he sinister turmoil that once was
has now been concluded.

Garion Lee Ford
Green River High School
Green River, UT
Grade 8

Love

There is a love,
A love so true,
The love that grows deep inside of you,
A love for someone,
For only that one.

It changes daily,
You love them more,
More with every heartbeat,
Also, every time you touch.

Love is a beautiful flower,
It blooms with such passion and beauty,
It will never sour.

Love is a red, hot fire,
That burns for an eternity!

Melissa Copley
Weldon Valley Jr High School
Weldona, CO
Grade 8

Basketball

The net sang
as basketballs rained.
Sweat dripped from
my face like a leaking faucet.
I practiced for hours
escaping from the world.
Nothing entering my mind
except the hoop and ball.
The ball pounded the floor,
as I flew threw the air.
Basketball's just a game
But it's my love.

Christopher Glockson
Norwood High School
Norwood, CO
Grade 9

A Dim Light

You barely see through the fog.
Your once bright lantern
Now is a weak match for miles of fog.
In the woods it is dangerous
But dead frightening when you are blinded
Blinded by thick fog only sounds around you.
Terrifying sounds that trick you
There is no hope
There is no light
There are only those sounds that trick you.

Jonathan Greenemeier
Century Middle School
Thornton, CO
Grade 7

Midnight Breeze

As the clock strikes 12:00
The wind begins to blow
With the force of a hurricane
It comes up so suddenly
And leaves as quick as an eagle
This happens night after night
And starts to get old

The city inhabitants don't really mind
Although it shakes the houses every night
The tourists that visit never come back
And always yell at the hotel clerk
They aren't always in such a good mood
Since they were woke up in the night
By the rumbling midnight breeze

As the clock strikes 12:00
The ghostly midnight breeze awakens

Casey O. Hendrickson
Hulett Jr High School
Hulett, WY
Grade 7

Bolder Boulder

As I run all six miles
I see the crowd and all their smiles
I wonder if I will get done so I can get out of the hot, hot sun
Two miles left in the race
I wonder if I can keep the same pace
My feet hurt, my knees ache
One mile left for goodness sake
Now up the hill
And on the field
Cross the line
Just in time

Michael Warren
Ranch View Middle School
Highlands Ranch, CO
Grade 8

Hank Aaron

He was born on February 5, 1934
He grew up in a family, poor.

At age four,
He was already starting to score.

After college he knew what he wanted to be
A ball player that wanted to be seen on TV.

In 1954 he began to play for the Braves
He played and won many, many games.

People compared him with Babe Ruth
Are you serious? Is that true?

He wanted to beat Babe's record, he had his goal set
He wanted to be the first yet.

In 1974 he hit his 715th homer
Since then, he wasn't anymore a loner.

In 1976 he retired from the big leagues
With much accomplished and very fatigued.

Hank was inducted into the Hall of Fame in 1982
He has always been a legend and his fans always knew.

Amanda Payne
Fremont Middle School
Las Vegas, NV
Grade 7

Perfect Stereo Type

Label me, I'm no one without one.
I need it to know what I can be.
Label me.
I don't know who I am, tell me so I can keep on living.
I want to be a stereo type.
I know what you want me to be.
The perfect stereo type:
You know you want to be like me.
Perfect Stereo Type.
Got nothing to lose so I'm not going anywhere.
I'm the perfect stereo type.
Label me.
I don't understand who I am.
Just tell me so I don't have to figure it out myself.
I want to be a stereo type.
Vicious Cheer Leader.
A.V. Nerd. Stupid Jock.
Punk Loser. Preppy Fox.
I'm so perfect, just label me.

Erin Gardner
Johnson Middle School
Las Vegas, NV
Grade 8

A Poem

A poem is special.
You can tell a whole story inside just a few sentences.
But the story you tell will not be lame,
but will have such expressive words that the reader will catch every detail.
A poem can tell the story that you never thought was true, and make you believe it.
Poetry can make you feel grand or sorrow.
Did I forget to mention that in a poem the author
always leaves the reader with something to think about?

Dwight Lutz
Powell Middle School
Littleton, CO
Grade 7

Canyons at Night

Unilluminated, towering cliffs all around me cast shadows on the ground
From the bright, glowing moon and stars
Cottonwood trees encircle our small camp lit from our campfire
The breeze rustles through the leaves of the trees and the crevices of the canyon wall
The smell of the damp, musty ground from the early morning
Blankets our small habitat
The taste of dew as it lounges on my still body settles in my mouth
As it falls down my brow like sweat
Coyotes, like little children screaming, howl away, deep in the twisting canyon
Previously chopped logs lightly get flung into the devouring fire to keep it blazing
The sandy earth below, filters through my fingers
My worries glide away and peace settles in my soul

Kody Dodge
Vilas High School
Vilas, CO
Grade 9

Schizophrenic Dreams

Black sunshine rains down on me, melting my soul.
Voices echo from wall to wall, saying nothing, just an utter of pointless mumbling.
The mind numbing silence, is loud with screams of terror, a noise, shattering pained glass.
Drowning in your tears of sorrow, repeated death and agony.
Run towards the light, cry out for help, fall to your knees and cry.
Why is this happening to me? Walk by a stream, thick with blood, from the earth.

Touching my lips with your fingertips, wiping my tears with your innocence.
Wash your dirty thoughts in the stream, cleanse your mind of this poor planet's filth.
Help me escape to the other side of paranoia, breathe in what comes from nothing.
Us sinful children of the earth, exiled from our freedom,
Dreams of our imaginations give us peace in what we cannot see.

Cry for me, open up to suggestions of the insane,
Take a chance to find yourself, breathe in your nothing.
Take in your everything.

James Hunter
Superior Academy
Superior, WY
Grade 9

Why...

Why was he so rude to me?
Why did he make me cry?
If I could ask just one question,
Why do I wonder why?

Why did I have to tell him
The way I truly felt?
Why couldn't I do just one thing?
Keep my feelings to myself.

Why did my feelings hurt so much?
Why did I feel so sad?
Why couldn't we have just been friends?
Be happy with what we had?

Why did I have to push it?
Why did it make him mad?
When I think of what I supposedly did,
I guess it was pretty bad.

I don't know exactly what I did,
Maybe someday I'll see.
Right now I have just two more questions.
Why? Why me?

Darcy Claiborne
First Presbyterian Church Academy
Las Vegas, NV
Grade 7

Secret Friend

I have a secret friend,
That I look to around the bend.
I can count on him through thick and thin,
The two of our strengths can break through and win.
He is my friend.
I talk to him for hours on end,
Our friendships will never need to mend.
Because we are best friends so far, far away,
I know in my heart we will never stray.
He is my friend.
He is always there for me, to comfort me...
Saying encouraging things,
Telling me to shine and spread my wings.
We are so similar, when he is sad and blue,
I will comfort him, and help him through.
He is my friend.
He will never hurt me, and this I know;
Through the years, he will watch me gain and grow.
I look to him for truthfulness, wisdom, and advice,
I know I will love him for the rest of my life.
He is my one true, cherished friend.

Allison Barker
Excel School
Durango, CO
Grade 9

Tears

Tears from above cry down on the earth
To give life to creatures below
On the skin one drop of water
Makes you cheerful and clean
Tears are so innocent and pure
That you could never act mean
Catch one tear and forever remember
The fabulous times when you went outside
To catch tears on your tongue
And remember those joyous days
Until you grow old and die
The smell of the air after it's done
Left you a feeling like you were alive
The way it falls and cleans itself up
Is incredibly neat
The way it is, is the way it will always be
So calm, loving, and sweet

Randi Myers
Powell Middle School
Littleton, CO
Grade 7

Police Man

Quietly he sits,
Waiting for those who dare oppose the law.
His radar detection working against
The speeding travelers.
And when the moment is right,
He strikes!
Lights and siren flashing and wailing.
The prey willingly succumbs,
They try to make excuses,
But they are punished nonetheless.

Adam Armstrong
Colorado Academy
Denver, CO
Grade 9

Stop Pollution!

Pollution today is out of control
We're slowly being sucked into an endless black hole
If we don't act fast
We will get our butts kicked by trash
It doesn't make any sense to mess up our air supply
Without it we may even die
People say killing the ozone layer leaves no care
Tell me when they remove your hair
Cleaning up the earth is a must
Above all it will take a lot of trust
Let's take action and do a good job
Or pollution will rule us forever in its own mob.

Tyler Stubbs
Mountain Ridge Middle School
Colorado Springs, CO
Grade 8

The Desert

A man hot and hungry
in the huge desert.
Hauling heavy jewels
halfway through the
hell like land.
Seeing hallucinations
of helicopters coming to
rescue him from this
horrid dream.
Hallucinations of
hand-maidens
serving him in a
huge mansion.
HEAVEN he will see soon.

Megan McLeod
Laurel Middle School
Laurel, MT
Grade 8

The Monster Under My Bed

There once was a monster under my bed
Maybe his name was Ted or Fred
Is he green or is he white?
Does he eat red dynamite?
Maybe he has one eye
Maybe he has two
He could possibly be red, white or blue
Now this monster under my bed
Does he even have a head?
Is it big or is it small?
Is it square or does it look like a ball?
Oh well good night
I'm going to bed
Good night Fred or Ted
The monster under my bed

Jessica Powell
Century Middle School
Thornton, CO
Grade 7

Stars

As I look up at the stars
Twinkling in the night,
I listen to the birds singing
Their lullabies to the stars,
Telling them to go away.

Soon, dawn comes and
The stars take a nap.
But, then again at dusk
The stars wake up
And shine again all night long.

Doylenn Enstrom
Norwood Middle School
Norwood, CO
Grade 7

Last Breath

With hollow, blank eyes she stared at me,
I quickly turned away.
I could not bear to see her chained to misery –
or listen to her pray.
She walked by, and brushed my hand,
our eyes met for a fleeting moment.
A push came from behind and she was slowly urged away.
Bellowing voices told me to open the doors for shower time.
I grasped the handle and yanked and pulled.
Voices crowded my head – confusing me.
The door fell open – mass hysteria broke out.
People were shoving, running – thousands of people, all the same.
Suddenly, the door slammed shut.
Wait! Didn't they know I was in here? It wasn't time for my shower yet.
I backed into a corner and sank to the floor –
not crying yet. I would be brave.
Gaseous fumes filled the air,
I took my last breath and prepared to die.
Then a small child, with blank and hollow eyes took my hand.
And together, we moved on.

Bobbi Kordsiemon
South Jordan Middle School
South Jordan, UT
Grade 8

We Do Not Understand

I tell you the tale of a friendship lost,
Because of something called the Holocaust.
Mary was a Christian and Leah was a Jew.
They both were six years old in the year of 1942,
And they did not understand.

"Why did they take my bike away so I can't ride it to my new school?"
"Why does that man in uniform stare at me with a face so hard and cruel?"
"Why didn't Daddy bake a cake or buy presents for my birthday?"
"How long will I have to wait until Mary can come again to play?"
"I do not understand."

"Why does Leah and her family have to ride on that big train?"
"Why don't I get to wear a yellow star too, aren't we all the same?"
"Doesn't Leah love me? She didn't even remember to say goodbye."
"Why is Mommy trying to smile at me while tears are pouring from her eyes?"
"I do not understand."

To these children, war was incomprehensible, why did people have to fight?
But this blindness to the world gave their hearts a perfect sight.
People are people, divisions among them are created by weak minds,
Mankind poisoned itself in its own bitter hatred, a solution they would find.

The same words echo in many now-silent voices: "We do not understand."
And we will spread the message so it doesn't happen again.

Brooke Downs
South Jordan Middle School
South Jordan, UT
Grade 8

An Excerpt From My Dynamic Love Life

I know that love is mandatory,
or life might be a fraud.
But the bigot that made a move on me,
must have thought he was a god.

His sarcastic comments,
about my rustic ways,
was a colossal mistake on his part.
I've had more tranquil days.

He thought he was innovative,
but was just an outspoken boy.
Like he had an incentive,
to treat me like a toy.

Now I submit
I'm not perfect
I may have a flaw.
This guy will never know me,
He ruined it with his jaw.

Hillary Folkvord
Three Forks Middle School
Three Forks, MT
Grade 7

Prisoner

A prisoner
Each day guarded; hidden from view
Behind the fences of lies
And the stone of untruth

I lie, alone
No one knowing what I am like
I stay in my own private world
I live in the cell of humiliation and embarrassment

Behind the walls
And protective covering, I am me.
I am unlike the "person" you see, hear, and talk to every day—

And when I am taken into the town square,
People ridicule me, tease me, and throw rocks at me,
Just to beat down my own self.
They force me to become one of them.
And I play along,
Pretending every day.

And as the moon comes out
And darkness settles in,
I reveal myself, my *real* self,
To the people who aren't watching.

Lauren Meehan
Minturn Middle School
Minturn, CO
Grade 8

Mrs. Jones

Mrs. Jones is quite a sight.
She doesn't know wrong from right.
She cries when she's happy, and laughs when she's sad.
She frowns when she's calm, and smiles when she's mad.
She eats breakfast for dinner, and dinner for lunch.
She doesn't eat breakfast, and always skips brunch.

Elizabeth Rosa
Academy Charter School
Castle Rock, CO
Grade 7

The Funeral

When I thought about it,
it wasn't bad.
The day of the funeral,
I was very sad.

I had never been to one before,
but this one made my heart sore.
I cried a lot,
and I haven't forgot.

I wish I could see you again,
but I know it won't happen.
I pray for you every night,
because that's what I feel is right.

I miss you very much,
and I wish I could feel your touch.
The doctors said you wouldn't make it through,
but I didn't think it was true.

I never got to say good-bye to you.

Heidi Hibbs
Sage Valley Jr High School
Gillette, WY
Grade 9

Wind

Wind whirling through the forest,
Trees swaying with the breeze,
Stronger, stronger,
Howling through the night,
Stars shining in the sky above,
The moon, vivid, smiling on the earth below.
Wind, the only thing disturbing
The peace of the town below.
The wind slowing, slowing,
The wind is dying.
Everything is still.
Peaceful and calm at last.

Jenna Galvin
Franklin Middle School
Greeley, CO
Grade 7

My Crush

I see you from afar
You do not know I stare
You captured me with your looks
But you kept me with your sweetness
And enticed me with your humor

I could be your genie
And grant you wishes three
I could make you very happy
But you never noticed me.

Melissa Williams
Norwood Middle School
Norwood, CO
Grade 7

Springtime

Butterflies fly
way up in the sky
maybe over a man
who's out getting a tan
as he lets out a sigh

over a rose or a girl's nose
by a house
and over a mouse
onto someone's clothes

it could land on a daisy
butterflies aren't crazy
get caught by a boy
and fall on a toy
because butterflies aren't lazy

Celia Gardner
Franklin Middle School
Greeley, CO
Grade 7

Together Forever

I'm here.
You're there.
We are not together.
This isn't fair.
I want your arms around me.
I need to feel your touch.
I would give you my world,
To show you all my love.
We should be together.
Why are we apart?
Together we'll be forever.
Maybe not in distance,
But always in the heart.

Alisha Stewart
Big Piney High School
Big Piney, WY
Grade 9

Spring

Spring is like a breeze,
It blows right through,
Bringing a wonderful treasure
Beyond any other pleasure.
Buds begin to blossom,
Leaves begin to cover trees.
Grass is at its fullest color.
Spring is a gift from up above.
Many birds like a dove.
Spring can brighten up our lives.

Whitney Trujillo
Kanab Middle School
Kanab, UT
Grade 7

The Reason for My Headaches

My bratty, baby brother
likes to scream and squall all day.
He sits and hits you if
he doesn't get his way.
He also enjoys
pounding the pretty pans
against the hard wood floor.

The pans go crash... *bang... BOOM!*

Ashley Irion
Circle Jr High School
Circle, MT
Grade 8

Long Ago

I remember a time when love
was endless and innocent.
When music roared throughout my soul
shattering the silence of
moonless nights
till streams of golden liquid
poured forth from the shadows
and summoned me from
my sweet dreams to dance
and sing again.
How I hunger for that passion
I so deeply felt all
those splendid nights!
How I long to love so freely
without these piercing eyes
without this unwilling spirit!
For I can only remember
and shall never again savor
that tremendous fire once felt
in a time when love was endless.

Mario Chard
Morgan High School
Morgan, UT
Grade 9

Mother Nature

Everyone has a mother,
And that's a fact.
You shouldn't keep to taking
Without giving something back.

There are special days,
Like birthdays and Christmas, too.
Presents on these days are a "give-me"
Just something you should do.

But our mother gives every day.
She sure is a special friend.
We soon take her for granted;
Thinking her gifts will never end.

I'm not talking about your father's wife.
It's Mother Nature to whom we refer.
Oil and trees and all the world's wonders
Are the presents people prefer.

So let us be cautious.
Mother Nature's gifts are only on lend
Let's return to our giver
Recycle, restore, and mend.

Andy Spruell
Cortez Middle School
Cortez, CO
Grade 8

My Dog Bailey

A golden retriever
Who sleeps in my bed,
Barks at the cat,
And loves to be fed.
She loves it a Grandma's
For there she is spoiled,
She loves her friend Whiskers,
And together they toiled.
She loves the lake
For there she is free,
All the family loves her,
So they come to see.
She has a nick-name,
I call her "Goose,"
She plays with the hamster,
And is always on the loose.
She is a silly, sweet dog,
And I love her very much,
Every day I pet her,
And she feels my loving touch.

Kristi Brazell
South Valley Middle School
Platteville, CO
Grade 8

Quiet

It was the most important night
I was going to make a name for myself,
I was meeting new people,
I listened deeply,
Taking every word in,
Everything they had said was so uncommon,
I could not relate,
What do I say?
How do I react?
Instead of showing my true self;
I closed all emotions,
I said nothing!
Now they do not know me,
Will they like me?
Why is quietness a crime?

Aharon Robertson
Pawnee Jr-Sr High School
Grover, CO
Grade 9

Life Is . . .

Life is a wheel,
When it stops, no one knows;
It is barbed wire,
Always finding some way to rip you apart;
It is a flower,
Beautiful and fragrant, but when you get close to it,
A bee stings you;
It is a stairway,
It has its ups and downs;
But most of all,
It is a lighted match,
Its flame sometimes burns out too quickly for you
To light the candle.

Lindsay Beardall
Riverview Jr High School
Murray, UT
Grade 8

The Storm

A storm of hounds unleashed fury,
The very sky turns black with their passing,
The taste of over salted pretzels,
Entwined with the curtain of black,
Bellowing throats can be heard,
With the unleashing of fiery fury,
Claws griping fiercely at one's hair,
Blowing,
the stride of numerous beasts can be seen in the waves,
As the menacing monsters recede,
A bright curtain in close pursuit

Alec Norton
Colorado Academy
Denver, CO
Grade 9

Wildlife and Wild Lands

The wildlife and wild lands
Are dear to every rancher.
he struggles to take care of his home
The forests, meadows and pasture.

He loves to look at all this land
By truck, foot, or horse.
It makes him bitter when people litter
And leave the land looking coarse.

He loves to take care of the meadows
He improves them by irrigation.
He also maintains the pastures
By using cattle rotation.

A rancher's job is more than pastures,
More than meadows and cattle.
It is also the wildlife, streams and trees
It is long days in the saddle.

So don't gripe about the old rancher
He has watched the land when nobody cared.
He watched over the animals
As he made his last stand there.

Nik Kennedy
Cozy Hollow School
Rock River, WY
Grade 7

Big Cat Creation

In the snows of Siberia
In the night winter glow
A male tiger sits feeding on its victim,
A water buffalo.
On the savanna,
On a hot summer day,
A few female lions lie waiting
For vulnerable prey.
Close on a hill
Lies a cheetah family,
Playing in a termite colony.
Up in the mountains,
Hiding in the trees
A mountain lion starts feeding its cubs,
A deer's offspring.
Off in the jungle,
Up in the trees,
A black panther and his mate
Are sleeping.
And up above somewhere in the universe,
Mother Nature is watching her creations on our planet Earth.

Robbie Clark
North Arvada Middle School
Arvada, CO
Grade 7

The Storm

The bolt of yellow has hit the ground
the rain has started hitting my roof
oh, how much I hate that sound.

I ran to the covers on my bed,
and threw them over myself
then there it was again in my head.

I threw the covers on the floor,
and jumped off the bed;
I soon was out the door.

I ran into my mom's room to her side;
soon I felt just fine
and had no reason to hide.

Jonathan Wickes
Challenger School
Sandy, UT
Grade 7

Child

The speeding object
Punches me in the face
I was born out of wed-lock
Nothing but a mistake
I close my eyes
Trying to picture a life less painful
One more strike to the face
A stream of tears
Flow down my bloodied face
My body is throbbing
Like the fast beat of a heart
I don't talk
It will only cause more
Bullet speed hits
Just lying there lifeless
Until she feels she has torn me enough

Trista Emerson
Shelby High School
Shelby, MT
Grade 9

Autumn Leaves

Autumn leaves fall from the
lonely trees,
Brilliant colors of orange,
yellow, green.

Floating like smiling, beautiful
young dancers,
Then drift away like Comet
and Prancer.

Kiersten Ritland
Fort Benton Jr/Sr High School
Fort Benton, MT
Grade 9

Misery of the Holocaust

Hitler took the lives of six million Jews;
This sickening crime of hatred made international news.
Hitler believed in a pure race, blonde hair and blue eyes;
Any other religion should be looked upon with despise.

They rounded up the Jews, like cattle on a farm;
And placed them in old ghettos, without hope or any warmth.
When the time came to be put down, the German official came;
And gathered up the Jews like it was some kind of game.

The Jews were shipped to death camps, a dreadful scary place;
Where they were tortured and killed, with despair on their sad face.
A towel and soap were given to them, and they were taken to the shower;
But the poison gas would soon them overpower.

Few survivors were of this heinous crime;
For the few short years it lasted, for many a sad time.
Out of hatred Hitler took six million from this Earth;
And destroyed the mystery and the miracle of birth.

Now that the Holocaust has ended, one can only hope;
That such a disgusting crime shall never again develop.
Keep with you forever, a feeling of respect;
For those who died in the Holocaust – it had a profound effect.

Ted Nicholls
South Jordan Middle School
South Jordan, UT
Grade 8

?!?!?!Crazy?!?!?!

Some people think I'm a little bit crazy
I tell them no, I'm just a little lazy
Other people think I'm a little weird
I tell them yes, my life-long goal is to grow a beard
When I talk about my favorite subject – cucumber skins
They run away, while I just grin
Someone sent me to this mental institute
All they let me do there is play my imaginary flute
They gave me this pretty jacket that was leather and white
They told me to be nice and never to fight
I stay in a big white room with squishy walls
My imaginary friend and I always play with a ball
I don't have anything to do, so I think of things
Stuff like carrots, and lime green wedding rings
I think about aliens who teepee Jupiter's moons
Can you believe it, they eat cheese with staplers instead of spoons
I see little men in coffee cups, my supervisor drinks
Then he goes away, and I start to wonder how he blinks
Now that everyone knows I'm a little crazy
I can tell you, I like striped daisies

Bess James
Century Middle School
Thornton, CO
Grade 7

Seasonal Change

At the start of the year, it's winter
Most people say, "It is coldest in the winter."
There is snow and it is so much windier
And feeding it really does hinder

Then it changes to spring
When some people fling
Vast parties and get-togethers
And little kids find lost bird feathers

Spring goes to the hot summer
Some people ride in a Hummer
And while some sunbathe
Others like to grow maize

Summer goes to fall
To go Thanksgiving shopping we go to the mall
We harvest our barley and wheat
And butcher unwanted cattle for meat

Fall fades to winter
And we start over again
With the seasons changing
They go from cold to warm and back again

Eli Berry
Reedpoint Jr/Sr High School
Reedpoint, MT
Grade 7

Michelangelo

When we were little, Michelangelo,
not more than five,
we would lie on the floor,
of the matted rust carpet.
We'd look to the left, then to the right,
seeing how to save the world; again.
There, in the dark,
he reached for his numb-chucks,
I for mine.
As we approached we watched for booby traps,
that would drop us into pits with no bottom.
Through the dark he flew at us,
with a flying kick.
We ducked and grabbed,
in one swift move we saved the world.
As I was cleaning out the closet,
I saw you, but I didn't seem to care.
I felt like saving the world,
but with another,
the Power Rangers.

Michael Hoepfner
Butler Middle School
Salt Lake City, UT
Grade 8

Cerebration

I scream a thousand deaths beneath the repulsive sky,
And manipulate the delicate moments gone by.
I recall a rose essential to one,
A purple mist above the sun.
I always envision a languid day,
Delirious dreams of frantic play.
A sordid moon soars through time,
A tiny whisper says we will shine.

Teardra Pedersen
Wasatch Jr High School
Salt Lake City, UT
Grade 9

A Precious Child

As you are trying to sleep,
you think of how ugly and stupid you are.
Why can't you be like them?
Those beautiful women or handsome men?
A promise you made, but cannot keep,
to not hurt your emotions, but you scar it too deep.
You hate yourself and make the wrong choices,
as you turn bad and evil in a way.
You hear rumors and familiar voices saying: you are not cool
and why do you stay?
Why do you stay in our school anyway?
And as your tears shed to what they have said,
about who you are and how you look.
And now that you're alone with pills in your hand,
you sweat, you tremble, you cannot withstand.
You drink, you swallow the numerous drugs,
and fall to the ground.
Another child has died, but it is simply homicide—
the criminal: school mates.
It is their fault for all the words they have said.
A precious child has died, a precious child is dead.

William Soule
North Davis Jr High School
Clearfield, UT
Grade 9

Junk Food

Chips, chocolate, cake, galore
I think I want a s'more
Ice cream, cookies, and candy too
These foods are so good for you
Coke, Surge, milkshakes and more
You'll never be able to fit through the door
Shall we go to the store?
Snickers, Reeses, and Twix,
Also some brownie mix
I think I finally got my fix

Melissa Pickett
Century Middle School
Thornton, CO
Grade 7

Penguin

There goes a penguin
quickly sliding down the hill
he hits the water.

Mark Shepard
Riverview Jr High School
Murray, UT
Grade 8

Have You Forgotten

In the sky after a rainstorm
Hangs a rainbow every time
The rainbow is a vision
A million colors combined

When you see that spectrum
Shining against the backdrop of blue
Do you think pots of gold
Fantasizing the one who finds it is you

Or are you practical and don't dream
Illusions, that's all they are
Have you forgotten the magic
Of the colors you see from afar

Are you too old to remember
The land in which you once called home
Have you grown, only to forget
That land that you once roamed

Melissa Mills
South Sevier High School
Monroe, UT
Grade 9

Bubbles

Big, round,
Floating upwards,
Reflecting the
Beauty of every color,
Showing the dreams
Of every person,
Revealing
The beauty of yourself.
Telling you secrets.
Magical, mystical things,
Fragile things,
Whisked away
By the breeze.
Floating downwards
To the death
Of a ten second life,
Hitting the ground,
Bursting.

Suzanne Smith
Pine View Middle School
St George, UT
Grade 7

Always Have Faith

Always have faith. Dreams are voices of comfort throughout
     the night. Dreams are the light which guides our thoughts.
Always have faith. Dreams are paths you strive to go down.
     Dreams are the sun that is waiting to shine through darkness.
Always have faith. Dreams are the rose, waiting to bloom.
     Dreams are clouds that change with the wind.
          Always have faith.
               Dreams conquer,
                 burning fire
                 sprinkling rain
Set your goals high, be free to dream.

Dixie Poyner
South Valley Middle School
Platteville, CO
Grade 8

Day Forgotten

I remember the days when I used to dream
     of things not heard by anything.
I have not forgotten those good old days
     of when I was a little boy.
I remember the days in my youth
     when the days were cold and short,
     when my pop and I would sit by the fire.
O that day I remember, and it filled me with glee.
I am glad I have forgotten that day, twenty years ago.
In my thirties I remember the time when my little boy left forever.
     I see him each year and I wish he would stay,
     so he could help me remember those days forgotten.
In my old age I forgot all the days of my youth.
Now I just sit and I try to remember those good old days,
     the days forgotten forever.

Ben Leddick
Powell Middle School
Littleton, CO
Grade 7

The Letter

You probably do not know this but it rained today.
And as if it fell I thought of you so very far away.
I thought of words I would try to write to tell you how I feel,
     but they just come out all jumbled and often sound unreal.
I know it would be easier if I could have you here,
     if I could look into your eyes and hold you near.
I would tell you what is in my heart,
     all of our secrets we could share.
I would give you the smile I have saved just for you,
     the one that says "I care."
But since I have not yet met you and don't even know your name,
I'll put my dreams back in their box until the next time it rains.

Nate Brush
Laurel Middle School
Laurel, MT
Grade 8

Inspired

Every night she sat by the ocean waves
And watched the water come upon the caves.
Then she saw a bottle with a message inside.
It quickly floated up on the coming tide.

The content was a beautiful note
That had no name, for someone anonymously wrote
The short little message, she really admired.
Though it was small, to her, it was inspired.

She went home and tried all that night.
She couldn't come up with anything so beautiful or so bright.
And every once in a while, in late afternoon
She'd see a new bottle in the sea, under a rising moon.

In all the letters there was no trace of depression.
No sorrow, no hatred, no sign of aggression.
Just a strange little note that held something true
A depth of creation, not something just anyone could do.

It was an unsolvable mystery.
Who could the magnificent writer be.
Wherever he is, there lies a great man.
Someone who strongly holds poetry in his hand.

Brittany Meyer
Carbondale Community School
Carbondale, CO
Grade 7

Environment Poem

The environment,
Oh how it used to be,
Like a little boat at sea.
Running jumping and playing,
Isn't how it used to be.
Even our lakes for swimming,
Or our trees for climbing,
Are sitting there being polluted
By the advertising.
Pop cans, toys, and food
Aren't used how they should be used.
Wrappers, papers, and trash
Are burning this planet up into ash.
Won't you help us be,
A little boat at sea.
Oh please, oh please, oh please
Put our minds to ease.
Oh please, oh please, oh please
Send the earth to ease.
The environment,
Oh how it used to be like a little boat at sea.

Kelly Geha
Century Middle School
Thornton, CO
Grade 7

The Unknown Grandpa*

Grandpa was fun
Grandpa was kind
Grandpa was stubborn
Grandpa was loving
Grandpa was smart
Grandpa was loud but had a big heart
Grandpa was helpful
Grandpa was happy
Grandpa was grandpa and that's what makes me happy

I never got to meet my grandpa before he passed away,
But I know these things about him in my own way.

Thanks Mom

Teara Berchtold
White Middle School
Henderson, NV
Grade 7
*Dedicated to Grandpa Crane

Vacation

On the road we go on vacation.
In the car, the beautiful scenery passing by.
The trees with their orange and red leaves.
The grass just barely turning green, with summer coming.
Most beautiful of all, the bluish-green ocean.
The ocean with boats and people, so beautiful.
On the road.
Music in my ears, the bumps in the road.
They blend together in harmony.

Chris Astle
Star Valley Jr High School
Afton, WY
Grade 7

Sailing

Sailing on a moonless night
Across white water
When the time is right

Sailing across the seven seas
With men on deck
Always helping me

Sailing through the Bermuda Triangle
Taking a risk, hoping and praying
I'll make it through the dangerous triangle

Sailing under bridges
And over seas
For the golden keys

Curtis Roundy
Kanab Middle School
Kanab, UT
Grade 7

The Nile

I never saw the tombs of Cairo,
I never tasted the old rusty dust of the sand,
yet I know the Nile river still runs cold,
with ancient stories of old.
I never heard the faint cries of the past,
nor be blinded by the reflections of their treasures.
Yet in a distance a long while,
I will be the one walking next to the Nile.

Mike Martin
Boulder City High School
Boulder City, NV
Grade 9

Abortion

I was swept away like a piece of glass in the path
Mother didn't want me just like she didn't want the weeds
in her garden
I'm like trash that's been thrown away
I'm like static on the radio, just skipped over
Don't you want to see your own eyes
Don't I deserve a chance
I guess not
I'm up here in heaven
With your mother who wasn't pro-choice
Apparently it skipped your generation
That's why my life has been a forgotten voice

Jeb McCandless
Laurel Middle School
Laurel, MT
Grade 8

The Page Turned to Spring

Spring comes with gentle breezes,
it's time to overcome coughing and sneezes.
The flowers are proudly full with bloom,
miracles are born from their mothers' womb.

The sky turns from gray to blue,
the clouds billow soft and new.
The birds sound with song in the trees so high,
spreading their wings for an early morning fly.

The fish whirl around endlessly in the pond,
as speckled frogs leap from frond to frond.
The turtles awake from their built-in homes,
and enter the cool water, clear in tone.

The butterflies flutter, greeting the new flowers,
the bees buzz and hum hour after hour.
It's time for the new goals and dreams;
when everything's full of life, you'll know it's spring.

Kim Kummer
Sage Valley Jr High School
Gillette, WY
Grade 9

I Lied to You

I lied to you,
and I don't blame you if you hate me now.
I gave you pain, for the lie that I lied.
Even though I lied to you, I know that I love you.
If I could bring the moon down for you to show
how much I love you, I would.
If I could burn the fire in the angry sun, I would.
If I could make every day happy and nice for you,
I would.
If I could give you all the money that you want, I would.
If I could have you see me at night with the tears in my eyes,
because of what I have done to you, I would.
If I could give you all you want, I would.
But all that, I can't do.
But all I can say is I love you,
and hope that I'll be forgiven by you.

Nada Shabana
Milford High School
Milford, UT
Grade 7

Grandma

A cage is strong like you,
with a bird locked inside.

You are nestled in an overstuffed, blue couch,
too inflated for your taste.

I stare intently into
your brown glassy eyes.

They burn with painful memories
of the past.

As you speak of a lost daughter,
beautiful as hard work,

the bird inside
struggles.

A thin layer of clear, salty liquid
coats your eyes.

You try to prevent the liquid from escaping,
because you have been strong so long.

The cage breaks
and the bird flies free.

That was the first time
I saw you cry.

Hana Russo
Falcon Creek Middle School
Aurora, CO
Grade 8

Holding Me Back

I'm deciding whether to go or stay.
I want to go, to leave.
But you are holding me back.
One swift push with my foot,
And soon I would be gone forever.
But you are holding me back.
I don't understand the power you have over me.
I want to jump and fly, to leave.
But you are holding me back.
I think about how loud I could scream.
It would haunt you forever. I want to jump,
But you are holding me back.
You are not present, you are near, though.
I want to push with my foot, I have no fear.
But you are holding me back.
I don't want to hurt you.
I'm not going to jump.
Thank you for holding me back.

Jessica Edwards
Platte Canyon High School
Bailey, CO
Grade 9

The Meaning of Life*

As I walk the rolling fields of summer,
Or perhaps among the falling leaves of fall.
I wonder if I know the meaning of life,
Or then again, maybe not at all!

I wonder if it is happiness,
Or being all you can be.
Then again I really don't know,
But does it really matter that much to me!

Fools wander around wondering,
About the meaning of their life,
And while we all stare perplexed,
We kill our brother in strife!

Perhaps its meaning is much more simple,
Right in front of our face.
Maybe it is love of one another,
Of everyone in all the human race!

Loving is for the people,
Of the highest sense of being.
To love one another is what they've found.
Taking his troubles upon your shoulders,
While the rest of us fools just sit around!

Gage Hart Zobell
Dillon Middle School
Jackson, MT
Grade 8
*Dedicated to Norman Hart and Dale Royer

To the Harmless Spider

As the drowning water took you under
As you were flushed away from this world
Around you went
But unexpected you did not know
How was it?
You finally got treated the same way
What shame was brought upon your soul
But you deserved what you got.

Leslie Richards
Moffat High School
Moffat, CO
Grade 9

Red, White and Blue

Red is for the wars in the past,
For the soldiers who lived and died to win it all,
Who gave the freedom for people who were too infirm,
For the blood that was shed in the former year.

White is for the freedom we got,
For independence we fought,
For love of the country,
And smartness and such.

Blue and its stars,
Is for the states who were in it all,
In the civil war and wars away very far,
Who gave people to strengthen it all,
For the *Red, White* and *Blue*
The place that we love.

J. Krische
Kanab Middle School
Kanab, UT
Grade 7

Wishful Thinking*

When I am big and bad and buff,
I shall be very mean and tuff.
Then I will tell anyone I like,
To get their bottoms off my trike.

When I get very big and tall,
I will have long legs and all.
Then I can just stand there and see
All the stuff they hide from me.

When I am on the football team,
I shall be very big and mean.
Then when I dump milk on the floor,
They cannot ship me out the door.

Ray Miner
Kanab Middle School
Kanab, UT
Grade 7
*Dedicated to my little brother, "Drewsie."

The Corsage

Put together with such care.
One rose surrounded
With babies breath.
The aroma it emits.
The sweet smell
It leaves you with.
Trapped in your nose
For the night.
The florist with memories
Of her own.
Each put together
Like the corsage.

Remy Onstad
Colorado Academy
Denver, CO
Grade 9

Will I Find

As I gaze out my window
With posters all around me
I wonder if and when
I will find that special someone.
My posters are mostly guys
From TV and movies.
Though many girls
Say they will marry him, it is unlikely.

I gaze from poster to poster
Looking at the men.
Will my guy be tall, brunette
Or blonde, muscular or skinny?
What kind of stuff will he like?
Will I like it too?
When will I find him?
I'm sure that I will find him soon.

Kelsey Jordan
Sage Valley Jr High School
Gillette, WY
Grade 9

Saying Goodbye*

Saying "goodbye" is always hard.
It brings change and much pain.
Sometimes it feels like someone has
Stirred your whole world up with a stick.
In the end God's will, will prevail.
Change will come,
But with much prayer and God's help,
There's always hope for the future.

Andrew Oliver
Gillette Christian School
Gillette, WY
Grade 9
*Dedicated to my Grandmother.

Biking

I think of what's ahead
If I miss I know I'm dead
I pedal
Keep my feet on the metal

As I lean back
I hear a crack
I fall
And call
To no one

I sit and scream
Lose all esteem
I try to get up
But my leg is messed up

I sit there
And swear
Alone I sit
With no one to help, not a bit

Ben Curley
Mountain Ridge Middle School
Colorado Springs, CO
Grade 8

The Awesome

The awesome Rocky Mountains.
The western slope is where I live
With underground fountains,
And animals galore to give.

The awesome rocky hillside.
I watch out of the car,
Loving every moment as I glide.
I hope I go far.

The awesome mountain range.
I love watching out the car window,
And painting page after page,
That will never change.

The awesome mountain springs.
Gurgling out of the earth.
The plentiful food the mountain brings.
The new life it gives birth.

The awesome Rocky Mountains.
Beautiful in every way.
This is where I live, the mountains.
Sweet as the golden sun's rays.

Megan Snode
Riverside Jr High School
New Castle, CO
Grade 7

My Room

My room is my room,
It's a private place for me,
It's a place where I can go,
Just to be.

Doing what I like,
Doing what I please,
My room is my room,
Where I feel at ease.

When I'm in my room,
I have space to go,
Wherever I want to be.
Far away from life's concerns,
A life that's just for me.

Wes Johnson
Century Middle School
Thornton, CO
Grade 7

His Love

His love was a wonderful feeling,
His love was a wonderful smell,
His love was a growing feeling,
His love knew me very well.

His love was like a light summer breeze
Full of careless mistakes.
His love was the most wonderful
Thing that ached.

His love had a way of touching people,
His love had a way of understanding.
His love was as long as a big steeple,
Never ending, always going on, forever.

Abby Chambless
Sage Valley Jr High School
Gillette, WY
Grade 9

Dream-Carrier

Sleeping quietly
Above me, skipping
From cloud to cloud
Comes the little dream-carrier.
I hear her bell-like laughter
From far away.
Her bag comes open
And a dream
Falls out, and enters my sleep.

Miranda Hannasch
New Horizons Academy
Las Vegas, NV
Grade 7

Saying Goodbye

I knew this day would come
when we say goodbye.
Please be strong.
And please don't cry.

I don't know why this day came so soon,
but we can be friends I will assume.
I tried too hard to make you stay,
but I will still love you more each day.

I wish you could stay and not turn away
from the love that we had.
My heart is so broken,
but I guess that's okay,
because in my heart you will always stay.

Love can be painful and shameful at times,
but sooner or later those times will pass by.
I'm thinking of you and the fun that we had.
We would argue at times, but it wasn't so bad.

Love can be frustrating and confusing at times,
but love can also be fun, just like making rhymes.
I am going to miss you, I just thought I'd let you know,
that I really don't want you to go.

Matt Pangborn
Spring Creek Middle School
Elko, NV
Grade 8

Entrapment of Reality

Across the walls that enclose me in this desolate chamber,
darkness twists, stretches, and bends with the night.
Enchanting dreams are my only escape,
from the crystalline graveyards of reality.

My heart longs for the truth,
my mind longs to be set free,
from the locks and chains of entrapment,
that confine my imagination.

Shadows kill the light,
that guides me to safety.
I am trapped in their world,
and their ideals barricade me from mine.

I can only hope for the day,
that the power of my mind and imagination,
will bring their ideals crashing to the ground,
and I can finally escape,
the true burden of life's reality.

Kristina Miller
Campus Middle School
Englewood, CO
Grade 8

Happiness

Inside this body there is happiness,
a happiness far greater than life.
This happiness can turn rocks into animals.
But, sadness is happiness' rival
and makes the happiness weak and alone.
The sadness makes enemies, not friends.
Makes fights, not peace.
Makes sorrow, not joy. Makes hate, not love.
So the happiness is forgotten.

Jacob Veyploegen
St. Jude Thaddeus School
Havre, MT
Grade 7

Courage Mom

From the war zone I write to you
Before such a darkness comes
Such a price to pay,
My soul to leave; your son forgotten
Yet as I go
As a flowing river
Through the oceans of memory and eternity
You come to me
As such a soft song; so long a road home
But I do not forget to gaze back
If but for a moment of contact
One last second of brilliance
For as the sun must ignite such a fury
In the tender sky
In the seconds before the world is lost to dusk
So must I go; and whisper goodbye
For as my spirit has brought me here
It carries me away
But as I leave, I know I am not alone
For I am of you; and it is here I rest
Courage Mom

Greg Marshall
Wasatch Jr High School
Salt Lake City, UT
Grade 9

A Tiny Hill

Life starts out as a tiny hill,
Not fully completed destiny's will.
But as you grow the hill will grow, too,
Making life a mountain standing before you.
As you scale the enormous wall,
You may lose your way, slip off and fall.
Do not worry, you'll get back on track again,
And hopefully stay on the right path
Until you clearly see the mountain's end.

Sarah La Rue
South Sevier High School
Monroe, UT
Grade 9

Granny

Why does she have to be sick?
I'm hurting so badly.
She's always been there,
Now she'll be gone.

Now the doctor says "CANCER".
Why does it have to be her?
I just want to be little again and say
"Granny what's wrong?"

But I'm not,
I'm a teenager.
It's so hard to be strong,
To be there for her this far along.

When I was little I never dreamed
I always thought my granny
Would be here forever,
But she's not forever.

Now life seems so wrong.
How could this be?
The woman who'd never die,
Is about to.

I love you Granny!

Megan McGee
Excel School
Durango, CO
Grade 9

Forever Memories

Its cold walls trap all
I am wanting them to fall

All that can keep me here
Are the many who are dear

The fear of something new
Sticks to me like glue

The place I gingerly love
Will fly away like a dove

Here holds all of my past
The new will come so fast

To me everything is so old
Though I treat it like gold

So little can be taken along
The memories will never be gone

Kim Ouzts
Sage Valley Jr High School
Gillette, WY
Grade 9

The Storm

A fervent storm hangs over the dry plain,
The clouds splinter spurts of light—
They rumble
A beam of fire strikes the dry meadow
The fire illuminates the meadow like a ruby red rose blooming in the summer.
The blaze sweeps throughout the plain
It is wrestled to the ground by the moist rain—
Calm, it is not.
Life still perks out of the seared brush.

Richard Dulude
Vail Mountain School
Vail, CO
Grade 7

World

We live in a fallen world,
a world where people abandon love, hope, and dreams.
We live in a world where people need each other
but they are afraid to prove it,
a world where we hurt the ones we love, but hate to be hurt by them.
We live in a world polluted by hypocrites that say one thing
and do the other, a world where children play together.
We live in a world where love and hate co-exist,
a world where people choose which to follow.
We live in a world where hate is abundant, and love is rare
a world that is beautiful and unique.
But would it be a perfect world if we understood each other,
if love was cherished and we all thought alike?
Or is the perfection we search for all our lives,
not found on Earth?

Paulina Barrios
Brockbank Jr High School
Magna, UT
Grade 8

Colors of the World

Blue oceans and sky
Green grass and valleys high
Red roses and apples that grow on trees
Orange gleams of the sun and sand so hot
Yellow tulips and sun so high
Purple violets and plums so sweet
Blue, green, brown, are some colors of the eye
Blonde, black, brown, white, and brunette are some colors of hair
Yellow, black, brown, and white are some colors of human skin
Black and white stripes of a zebra
Black and yellow stripes of a buzzing bee
White is the color of a polar bear
Our world is full of many colors
And you are made up of many colors too

Jessica Haupt
Century Middle School
Thornton, CO
Grade 7

Gazing Upon the Earth

Once there was a little star,
Who looked down to where we are.
He took a peek from his high, high, place,
At out sweet home and bright moon's face.
He saw the oceans and the waves turning about,
And he thought, "What would happen if there were a drought?"

He started to watch the animals play,
And he heard them enjoy the summer day.
He beheld the governing mountains,
Overhearing all the pulchritudinous fountains.
He saw the rivers flowing throughout the sphere,
Glowing and shining, it's crystal clear.

He described the sapphire skies,
And he watched as an eagle flies.
He saw the sky begin to turn gray,
Anything can happen and surely it may.
He sensed the anger of an oncoming storm,
And the thunder, lightning, and microburst swarm.

He has seen all the elements, in good and in bad,
"These creatures must be so glad," he thought to himself.
"These creatures are so lucky, their home is full of wealth."

Stevie Marie Nicholl
White Middle School
Henderson, NV
Grade 7

Life

During my life I've had things good, and things bad.
Things that made me happy, and things that made me sad.
I don't want my life to change.
But I know it will rearrange.
When I get older, things might start to get colder.
When I was younger, I would always wonder.
Wonder what would happen.
Wonder what would be,
I would especially wonder what would happen to me.
How my life would change.
What in my life would rearrange.
I've lived a bit more now.
Seen a bit more now.
I've learned interesting things,
I've also discovered some not so interesting things.
I have understood, not everything can always be good.
But now I have to wonder, if my life will plunder.
But I hope for the best,
I hope I'll live long enough to see the rest.

Danny Pomirchy
Overland High School
Aurora, CO
Grade 9

Dolphins

Dolphins leaping from the jade-green surface,
Dripping crystal droplets from their tails.
A splash,
A white plume of water in the salt air.
A dolphin laughs as they fly again.
The joy of the sea,
The waves against my body,
As I dream of flying with them.

Dawn Keenan
Vilas High School
Vilas, CO
Grade 9

Looking

I feel as if I'm looking for someone or something.
I am blinded by the thick forest of life around me.
I walk through the forest trying to find you,
Yet not knowing who or what you are,
The never-ending search has only led
To a stronger knowledge that you're there.
Seeking high and low, always hoping that someday I'll find you,
I try to imagine you as a wonderful fantasy.
But deep down I know it's a lie.
I think I've found you,
And it turns out to be an illusion in my dreams.
Almost losing hope, I wait for you to find me,
Always wishing,
Always hoping,
Never finding.
Maybe someday you will be found.
Until then, I'll keep waiting and searching.

Kimberly Barclay
Mountain Ridge Jr High School
Highland, UT
Grade 8

Friendship

Friendship is a special package—
to be handled with care,
to be wrapped with caution
so what you have, won't tear.
I'd like a little money,
I'd like a little ease.
But a friendship that is faithful,
can outweigh both of these.
We didn't exactly see eye to eye,
as our friendship moved unsteadily
and years rolled by.
But thanks to our friendship
that will never end
I'm lucky today that you call me your friend.

Kristen Geary
White Middle School
Henderson, NV
Grade 7

Party

One night I went to a party. When I got there they gave everyone a Smarty.
I walked through the crowd to find my friends. We decided to go look at everyone's trends.

The music started to play, and everyone yelled, "Hooray!"
We started to dance, then I saw him in a glance.

There was a guy, who was looking really fly.
He came to talk to me and my friends, when I really noticed his trends.

His eyes were red, he looked like he hadn't been to bed.
He had something white in his hand, and he said that he was in a really cool band.

He asked me if I wanted to smoke, I said, "No" and I put on my coat.
I told my friends bye, and that I was leaving because of that guy.

When I got home I felt really good inside, because I knew if I had smoked I could have died.

Jennifer Jentzsch
St Vincent De Paul School
Salt Lake City, UT
Grade 7

Every Sunday Afternoon

When she used to hug me I could feel the warmth of her heart beating against mine
Whenever I saw her my eyes gleamed with excitement
We always frolicked in the garden, picking sunflowers
The magic she shared every time we went swimming in the sea
The joy that was teeming inside of me when she visited every Sunday
But then a dreadful summer day a bitter cold chill brushed over me
As I walked outside memories of her pushing me on the swing entered my mind.

Ashley Seippel
Vail Mountain School
Vail, CO
Grade 7

I'm Just Me

Sometimes I'm like trail mix,
Good and sweet, but sometimes the nuts separated from the rest of the group because they taste bad.

Sometimes I'm like a Chevy Suburban,
Original, dependable, durable, and all around, the biggest, baddest thing on the planet.

Sometimes I'm like a crocodile,
Amphibious, quick, and ferocious.

Sometimes I'm like football,
Full of upsets and touchdowns, bad calls and blind referees.

Sometimes I'm like the night,
Busy and full of life.

Sometimes I'm like summer,
Fun, and laid back.

Dan Evans
St Therese School
Aurora, CO
Grade 8

I Am

I am a cool guy who likes to read.
I wonder which Alien books will come out next.
I hear the movement of pages in a book.
I see the new Alien book.
I want the new Alien book.
I am a cool guy who likes to read.

I pretend to be an author of a good book.
I feel the pages of my new book.
I touch my new cover on my new book.
I worry that my new book may not sell.
I cry when there is a sad part in a book.
I am a cool guy who likes to read.

I understand that I may not be able to be an author of a book.
I say that it would be a fun job.
I dream that I could be an author.
I try to read as many books as I can.
I hope that I can be an author.
I am a cool guy who likes to read.

Kerry Peterson
Riverview Jr High School
Murray, UT
Grade 8

Be Yourself

To be yourself,
Is an important virtue.
To be an outstanding toy on the shelf,
Should be a virtue to you.

Like what you want,
It's who you are.
Don't think you can't,
It's just the added weight of another hurtful bar.

It's like showing who you are,
It's like wanting what you are,
It's like a description of who you are,
Or like being your own star.

A virtue of inside truth,
A virtue of outside truth,
Or a virtue of your own life's booth.

Be to yourself true,
Be to love true,
Be to others true,
And be your own virtue.

Kate Grubb
Dubois Elementary-Middle School
Dubois, WY
Grade 8

Teacher

A teacher's job is what they do,
When they must teach me and you.
We must obey their lesson plan.
Whether they're young, old, woman, or man.
Their wise words teach us in time,
Listen to them, and be the next Einstein,
Listen even if you think it's a bore,
Think, all the points you could, but didn't score.
You should listen to what they say,
I didn't, but look where I am today.

Amber Ward
Crescent View Middle School
Sandy, UT
Grade 7

Spell Chequer

Eye halve a spelling chequer,
Eye got it from my Dad.
It marques all the miss steaks in my work,
Miss steaks eye kin knot find.

Eye strike a key and type a word
And weight four it to say
Weather eye am wrong oar write,
It shows me strait a way.

As soon as a mist ache is maid,
Eye will no it very soon.
Eye can make the air or write
With the help of this Amy zing tool

This poem has been threw the chequer,
There are know miss stakes in hear
eye no.
Eye no this poem is perfect bee cause
My chequer tolled me sew!

Sarah Tundermann
Century Middle School
Thornton, CO
Grade 7

Footprints of Snow

Winding paths of sun touched footprints,
Footprints of a small, delicate little girl,
Girl, the footprints along side those of her father's,
Father's enjoyment,
Enjoyment of a little girl leaving footprints in the snow,
Snow, the keeper of time,
Time, the meaning of life,
Life starts by leaving footprints in the snow.

Sarah Norton
Colorado Academy
Denver, CO
Grade 9

I Will Always Love You

I watch you. I listen.
Although you may not tell.
No matter what happens,
I will love you still.

From California to Maine,
From London to Rome.
From here to there,
I will love you alone.

It doesn't matter what you say,
Doesn't matter what you do.
I say this every heart beat,
I will always love you.

Whether big man on campus,
Or another someone out there.
Deep down inside, I claim,
I will always love you, here.

I hope you can understand,
And I hope just for you.
From here now and forever,
I will always love you!

Shaylin Flanary
Mountain Ridge Jr High School
Highland, UT
Grade 8

Solace

Music is every emotion you ever felt,
But couldn't tell.
It is the 10,000 colors
Of the spectrum
That no one ever named.
It is the longing, the hunger,
That so many people never satisfy.
It is the missing piece;
The key to the soul
That unlocks our hearts
To make us whole.

Silence is the chill of quiet;
The grey that fills in the blanks.
It is the deepest shiver of cold
That strikes your very bones
And grips your mind
And holds...

Until the solace of music.

Julian Kittelson-Aldred
Washington Middle School
Missoula, MT
Grade 8

Nightly Dreams

When the eyes of the sunset disappear
Every night
Behind God's aesthetic terrace,
The elegant stallion struts
Toward the dappled meadow of dew
To get its nightly drink
From the rustling creek.
When the edges of the depressing eclipse
Float back to block
The heaven's shining light,
The stallion
Prances majestically away,
With its sleek, rubbery, hooves
As its only weapon.
The stallion gallops
Into the trembling branches
Of the forbidden forest.
It feels the piercing bite of pain,
And slowly trots away,
Leaving a trail of scarlet blood
In its path.

Natalie Cooper
Three Forks Middle School
Three Forks, MT
Grade 7

Heart, Mind, Soul

My heart is for you
My mind is for you
My soul is for you

But do you take my heart?
No. My mind?
No. My soul?
No.

You ignore them,
And they disappear.

Do you need my heart, mind, soul?

No.
You have another's,
Your love.

And she has your heart, mind, soul
You are her slave, and she yours
Two lovers, one dreamer.

In a dreamscape that never ends.

Leah Marie Weinrich
Boulder City High School
Boulder City, NV
Grade 9

I Am Distance

I am distance
I am powerful
though I may seem insignificant

I am overpowering
I take time to conquer
and patience to overcome

I am overpowered
by modern technology
all in attempt to defeat me

I affect emotions
I bring joy and relief
or sadness and sorrow

I am a friend to enemies
and an enemy
to friends

I can weaken friendships
or I can
strengthen relationships

I am distance
I am powerful
though I may seem insignificant

Sydney Clark
Butler Middle School
Salt Lake City, UT
Grade 8

Butterflies

The butterflies,
fly across the land,
with the sky blue,
one lands on my hand,
he flaps his wings,
he flutters around,
I can't believe I found,
such a beautiful creature,
yet he doesn't have fur,
but wings like silk,
he's very colorful,
cute as a button,
yet I can't believe I found,
such a beautiful creature,
a butterfly who has,
a wonderful feature,
his wings.

Tiffany Sorkness-Gard
White Middle School
Henderson, NV
Grade 7

I Am, I Am Not

I am not popular.
What you call popular is the girl in front of me.
I am not pretty.
Pretty is the girl at the other end of the lunch room.
My face is nice,
But I am dirty.
I can be sweet
But not sweet like candy.
I do not have a guy.
My guy is in my dreams.
I love someone–
That someone is my family.
Guys talk about me–
About how ugly I am.
I smile at my friends,
At least I think they are my friends.
I am only but a person;
I cannot do much.
But please do this one thing for me–
Be my friend.

Rachael Patterson
Woodland Park Middle School
Woodland Park, CO
Grade 8

Rain

I love the rain.
Life just seems to stand still,
It's so easy to think,
When it rains.

Everything is at a whisper,
No one fights or argues,
Everything is perfect,
When it rains

The droplets subtly hide the tears,
Thunder quiets the sobs,
And lightning frightens the fears,
When it rains.

Then the clouds open up,
The sun comes out,
And life begins again,
Everything becomes louder,
People start fighting,
And I'm forced to come back to reality.
That's when I wish it would rain all the time.
I love the rain.

Candace Mackie
Big Piney High School
Big Piney, WY
Grade 9

Ordinary

What does it mean?
Non complex, normal, a place.
A place you see every day that has become
Uninteresting.
Or maybe...No
It means exactly what you want it to.
Ordinary to me could mean
Packalumer,
A completely meaningless word—
Causing ordinary to be...well...
Ordinary

Andrew Moores
Colorado Academy
Denver, CO
Grade 9

The Constant Radio

"That don't impress me much..."
The notes float calmly and evenly through the room,
Never off-key.
Jenna carries out the tune perfectly.
Only stopping for a quick commercial break,
A short story she's reminded of while singing and dancing.
She stays right on schedule, without letting down all day long—
It is suddenly quiet, as the snooze button is pressed,
And the radio is finally at rest.

Holly Weiss
Colorado Academy
Denver, CO
Grade 9

The Game of Royalty

The chessboard sits in the corner
The kings have their castles,
The queens have their knights,
waiting for battle
in their embroidered bone bodies
The marble green of the battlefield stands glimmering
For its inevitable use
The king peaks the sky
with its over-powering summit
The queen not far behind
with its elegant agility and grace
The bishop stands oddly beckoning to its masters
The knight,
a workhorse for its kingdom
The rook guards the corner
anticipating its chance to prove itself
The pons stand ready
prepared to use every ounce of their minute figurine body
to guard against the evils from afar

Bobby Henderson
Colorado Academy
Denver, CO
Grade 9

Cheerleading

Everyone thinks it's a cinch
Screaming and slapping
Yelling and clapping
Practice and play
It's the same everyday
A game on the floor
Bursting people in the crowds
But even through the bad,
Cheerleading can be fun.

Sarah Snyder
Norwood Middle School
Norwood, CO
Grade 7

Clouds

Wispy, weightless wonders,
floating in a sky.
Depicting tales of dragons
and horses that can fly.

Blotches of white
against a pale blue sky.
A young child's drawing
so perfect in your eye.

How you wish you could reach them,
enticing as they are.
You think you have them in your clutch
but then they seem so far.

Wispy, weightless wonders,
floating in a sky
and wonders they shall remain
until humans learn to fly.

Molly Sandler
Kent Denver School
Englewood, CO
Grade 7

Reflections

While I was walking along the beach
What did I see?
A faint reflection of you and me
You said it wouldn't matter
For we really care
And memory spans the distance
And in moments we are there
We see the smile
And hear the voice
And deep inside we know
That friends remain a part of us
Wherever we may go

Emily McMullin
Holmes Middle School
Colorado Springs, CO
Grade 8

Wondering

As the days pass us by I wonder if you still feel the way that you did,
Doing anything just to be with me.
I hope you still do.
But something in my heart tells me you don't.
It tells me that I am no longer in your heart,
In your mind or in your soul.
No longer am I your baby girl.
As the days pass us by, I feel lonelier and lost;
I don't know what to think—what to do.
So I stand here alone,
Crying and thinking about what I should do.
I continue to write what I feel
Because I can't tell you.
Words just don't seem to come out as I look at you.
Another day is passing—
So I decide to tell you that "I love you?"

Daniela Quintana
Johnson Middle School
Las Vegas, NV
Grade 8

A Memory*

I feel wet little drops pouring down my cheek.
I hear so many people sobbing over him.
He felt so alone and he was so quiet.
I know how he felt because I feel it now.
He was so important but he did not know it.
How sad but true.
We don't know how much we hurt someone till it's too late.
I feel so bad for the little boy and for people who are feeling alone and need help.
We need to stop hurting people physically and mentally.
It is wrong and not fair and it needs to stop now.
If you need help don't be afraid to ask.
Put your trust in God and everything will work out.

Stacey Ann Olson
Foothills Academy
Wheat Ridge, CO
Grade 7
Dedicated to a boy named Miles, who committed suicide.

Snow

Snow, how soft it looks, like soft clouds of cotton ready to be laid in.
For little kids to play in.
For boys to have a fight.

How cold it is on my hands and how my toes feel. Numb.
Then tingling, but at the same time pinching.

Building snowmen and making snow angels, having a good time.
Wondering how such little frozen flakes can make such wondrous creations.

Jillian Mace
Kanab Middle School
Kanab, UT
Grade 7

Burgundy

Dancing figures in dark velvet dresses
Swaying to the melody of the waltz
Love is hidden among
a girl's first lipstick
dress-up
Tired burgundy roses
wilt to the dark dying rays of the sun
The romance of the night is but a blonde head
on a burgundy pillow
An Affair to remember?
Deep and dark the burgundy music struggles to understand
A can of Dr. Pepper
The pain of a fallen flag in war
a color of sleep
and yes the deep and struggling rays of the rising sun
A day at the races
A hat that turns to catch the last romance of the
words she heard
Then fall comes
Then night comes
And burgundy reigns and rains

Rachel Norton
Colorado Academy
Denver, CO
Grade 9

Spring

Spring is a glorious time in the year,
Green trees and grass are everywhere.
There's nothing you really need to fear,
Except the bees in the air.

All the children are flying their kites,
Playing baseball and riding their bikes.
Then all of a sudden the lion started to roar,
Rain started falling and much, much more!

It's March of course,
It comes in like a lion and out like a horse.
Don't tell me you've never heard of this,
It's something you could never miss.

In spring the teenage girls like to get tans,
Laughing, swimming, and drinking pop from cans.
All the girls love to flirt with boys,
Instead of going home, and playing with their toys.

You'll always know when spring is here,
Just listen to the birds through your ear,
And say . . .
"Spring is here!"

Jenny Shelley
Kanab Middle School
Kanab, UT
Grade 7

Lake Powell

If they were to drain the lake,
My greatest joy is what they'd take.
The best part of summer would be no more,
It would not be as it was before.
Why would someone do such a drastic thing,
Knowing sorrow would be the only thing it'd bring.
Now it is accessible to everyone,
But just to a few when the deed is done.
So I ask you to cast the unconscionable opinions aside,
And listen to the voice that you hear inside.
It would say, "This is how it is supposed to be,"
And if the rest of the world would open up their eyes,
that is what they'd see.

Allen Jerome Burns
Green River High School
Green River, UT
Grade 8

Love Poem #9

I was scared right from the start.
If you said no it would break my heart.
The beauty I see when I look in your eyes.
Cannot compare to the heaven in the skies.
The way I feel when you're around.
It sends my heart wanting to bound.
I prayed each night before I would sleep.
That the next day your hand I could keep.
Held tight in mine with no way to break.
The touch of your hand sent through me a shake.
Of what may come between me and you,
I could still only think I love you.

Kevin Andrews
Mountain Ridge Middle School
Colorado Springs, CO
Grade 8

Love in the Present, Future, and Past

Love in the past was a beautiful princess.
A serenade to the radiant lady above thee
A luminous queen in a long, flowing dress
Close to her heart a dame keeps a key.
Love in the future is a bright red rose
With a drop of dew staining its petals
Its sweet fragrance floating up to your nose.
A love potion simmering in two rust-stained kettles.
Love in the present is like a big sweet cherry.
Sweet yet sour and all at one time.
It can leave thee feeling a little bit merry
Or it can leave thee feeling as sour as a lime.
But love will always and forever last
If it is in present, future or past.

Emily Shaw
Centennial Middle School
Boulder, CO
Grade 8

Dad

Tall, skinny
Drinking, driving, smoking
Eating licorice all day
Dead

Alyssa Butler
St Vincent De Paul School
Salt Lake City, UT
Grade 7

Grandpa

He made us laugh.
He made us cry.
Now we think he has died.
But when we look deep in our hearts.
We know we will never part.
He loved us all,
and kept us up when we would fall.
I thought of him as a grandpa.
But now I know he is a friend,
and my love for him will never end.
He lives in heaven and in my heart.
I'll never forget him.
Nor ever part.
I loved his body.
I loved his soul.
My memories of him will never go.
So Grandpa if you're listening
I love you.

Marvin S. Greene
Evergreen Jr High School
Salt Lake City, UT
Grade 7

The Vagabond

He walks through every city
Looking for his home, his destiny
He has left everything behind
For he is hoping to find
The real meaning of happiness
To him without it, life is worthless.

Hope is what makes him go on
And dreams are what make him live on
To him, every street looks alike
It is his way to a real life
His search is not for money,
But for a way of living happily

Freer than any other man
But still imprisoned in his world
The vagabond walks down the road
This road is called the road of faith.

David Barousse
Holmes Middle School
Colorado Springs, CO
Grade 8

What it Has Seen

This old house is just like all of the others we know
It has been here and it shows the tests of time upon it
The house is old and ragged, but not yet abandoned of memories
This house used to be afar in the country but now is in the city limits
This house has seen it all from the wars and wagons to the Model T era's
Since 1894, this house has stood tall and proud showing all its beauty
Now it is almost gone for the more important buildings and things
So every time I go past it I try to think of all it has seen
I stop to look and think of all that this house has seen

Spencer Pollock
Briggsdale School
Briggsdale, CO
Grade 9

Anonymous

A touchstone
     He's always been there when I need him.
An embracer
     Doesn't let things go that mean the most to him.
An esteem builder
     He helps raise your confidence.
Yet a rose petal easily broken
     Although sometimes he breaks down and needs help as well.
Witty
     Always quick on the spot in any situation (a joke, debate, etc.)
Diverting
     Always fun and entertaining even when you're sad.
Amiable
     He's polite and welcomes anyone new always.
A rainbow with raindrops gently falling on himself.

Margaux Weinberger
Colorado Academy
Denver, CO
Grade 9

Clouds

This skinny cloud with the wispy top next to the one that looks like a New Zealand river
That has just started flood at the beginning of the monsoon, looks like what...?
A pencil
A monstrous jet liner cruising through the sky
A skinny snake trying to camouflage itself and then before you realize it, has coiled
Around your leg
A telephone chord being wrapped around a finger
A "Post-it" wafting in a summer's breeze that stole its way into a house
The little ink sign flashing on and off
A small twiggy tree before it has started to bud
The cursor
Like a wispy, skinny cloud that floats next to the one that looks like a New Zealand river
That starts flooding during the monsoon.

Taylor Ross
Colorado Academy
Denver, CO
Grade 9

Too Young To Be This Age

People often tell me
I'm too young to be this age,
And at night, in bed, away from home
I yearn for mother's gentle touch
That's there to tuck me in.

When my mind is full of worries and I begin to stress,
I long to lay my head
Upon my mother's kind ol' lap
That's been there many times.

If I manage to get my feelings hurt,
I dream of father to help me home
To where my mother's staying.
And have her loving arms wrap around me
So that the pains no more.

Oh, so far away from home
To get along alone
Without my loving parents help
To get me on my way
Perhaps I maybe am too young
To be this age alone.

Rachel Mills
Star Valley Jr High School
Afton, WY
Grade 7

I Thank Him

Once I had this dream
It's where there is no sadness
There is only tremendous happiness
I saw other people
I heard them
Yet, it was like they weren't even there
I wondered why
Then the answer came
It wasn't a dream
I looked beside me
And there you stood
With the same enlightening sparkle in your eye
Your hair was angelically flowing in the breeze
Right then and there
I realized something
That God had blessed me with an angel
And I thank him for that
I thank him for that I can hold your hand in mine
Finally to know that
I am truly
Forever yours.

Tavis Renner
Circle Jr High School
Circle, MT
Grade 8

Reflection

As I move on in this world
my life looks as if it is only my reflection.
I hold back the tears,
hoping they won't see them in my reflection.
For time as it goes by,
it will soon be in my past.
The memory's only around when
I look into my reflection.

Elizabeth Myers
Rosebud Public School
Rosebud, MT
Grade 9

Please Remember

I'm sorry that I seem so different,
And so strange to you.
But please remember when you laugh,
I am a person too.

And please remember that when you laugh,
And point fingers at me,
It hurts a lot and makes me cry,
I wish that's what you'd see.

Please don't say, "She really doesn't care."
"She never really did."
Because just like you, deep inside,
I'm just another kid.

So please remember that when you're mean,
Making fun of everything,
That I'm just another normal kid,
Trying to be just me.

Teresa Locricchio
Holy Trinity School
Westminster, CO
Grade 7

A Girl's Afternoon

I wait for excitement.
A little black and red bug waits with me.

Little kids racing and giggling all around the playground,
Windows peering into empty classrooms,
A hornet buzzing around my head,

Yellow leaves fluttering in the wind,
Flocks of black birds pirouetting from field to field,
I wait.
The shadows slowly pass
And a flag dances in the wind.

Alicia Reyer
Shepherd 7-8 School
Shepherd, MT
Grade 8

The End

You just kind of left me there
to stare ahead into a wall
no signal
no sign
I lost track of time.

I left my chair
and traded my stare
in for a gloomy glare
I found you
but you were barely there.

I watched the sunset in your eyes
and lost all hope I held for you inside
we both kind of died
but neither cried
'cause we always knew the beginning
would eventually subside.

Susan Grytness
Sage Valley Jr High School
Gillette, WY
Grade 9

Alone

The wind blows,
But I am not afraid.
The raven crows,
And still I'm not afraid.

You are there,
Not hearing what I said.
You ignore me,
And I will only fade.

You can't see me,
I have already gone.
You can't find me,
But I'll be back by dawn.

I keep walking,
Nothing coming to my attention.
I won't stop,
Not even for apprehension.

I said that
I would be back by dawn,
But you won't see me—
The dawn has come and gone.

So now again, I am alone.

Naveen Hossain
Challenger School
Sandy, UT
Grade 7

In Dreams

Dreams.
A dream is somewhere magical.
A dream is somewhere,
beyond any child's imagination.

A dream is somewhere you can go
(in your dreams of course),
when you're down and lonely.

In a dream you can go anywhere,
or meet anyone.
You can go to a magical castle,
In a magical land.
You can meet the person you love
or even your favorite band.

So dreams are somewhere
everyone should love.
And if you've never been there,
maybe you should go, some night

Neesha Molet
Century Middle School
Thornton, CO
Grade 7

Why?

Why is the sky so blue?
Why does the rain fall like tears?
Why is the world so round?
Why do love and hate go together?

Why do right things turn out wrong?
Why do people love and hate?
Why is it hard for me to see?
Why do some people have all the luck?

Why do birds fly in the sky?
Why do people walk on the ground?
Why does time go by so fast?
Why do people become so slow?

Why, I try so hard to be,
Why, I try to make you see,
Why, that trying is better than dying.
Why do some people not try at all?

Why, why so many questions?
Why are they all so unanswered?
Why is it hard to understand?
Where are all these answers from?

Anita P. Waldner
Sage Creek Colony Elementary School
Chester, MT
Grade 8

The Can

There was a man,
Who kicked a can.
He did not know,
How far it would go.

It kept rolling,
And rolling
And rolling.
It's still going.

It was normal,
And very round.
What goes up
Must come down.

It bounced off a stone,
Then hit a pine cone.
It rolled down the street,
All nice and neat.

It is very sure,
That this can had an adventure.
He still will never know,
How far the can did go.

Jeris Oberle
St Vincent De Paul School
Salt Lake City, UT
Grade 7

I Love You

My love is true but only for you.
You and I will always be two.

I love the way you make me laugh.
You never make me half.
I am always whole for you.
You never make me blue.

My love for you is whole.
You will never be old.
You have always been true.
That's why I love you.

I love you like a bird.
You're always making me fly.
You are the one for me.
You never make me cry.

That's why I love you.

Brandi Pauley
Round Mountain Jr-Sr High School
Round Mountain, NV
Grade 9

Wyoming

I wake up from my bedroll
As you can plainly see
I have no tee shirt on
I hope the animals don't see me!

I wash my hands and scrub my face
I head to the mountain stream
In less then 40 seconds
I'm in a wonderful dream.

My line pulls tight, I give a tug.
I reel it into the shore.
I take it out and hold it high.
Then I hear a knocking on the door.

I try to open my sleepy eyes
They finally fly wide open
There is no one there
There is no since of mopin''

I went back to bed and shut my eyes
I fell asleep once more
I dream of fishing again
That is what wildlife and wild lands are for.

Will Kennedy
Cozy Hollow School
Rock River, WY
Grade 8

Calm Water

Look at the cool calm water
Look at how the waves overcome it
But then it gracefully goes back to normal
Look
Look at those Manta Rays
Who don't even disturb the calm water
They just keep the calm water colorful and pleasant
Look
Look at those dolphins
Look at how they have an ever so graceful jump
But never the less they get the calm water all stirred up
Look
Look at all of the sailboats
Look at how they only use the wind
Look at how they don't disturb any of the calm water
Look
Look at all of these things that give the ocean stamina
Look at how they give the ocean color and peace
Look at how all these things relax you
Isn't it peaceful?

Laura Carey
Powell Middle School
Littleton, CO
Grade 7

The Game of Life

It seems like just yesterday I played with dolls
Now all I do is make phone calls
I remember going to first grade
Slowly those images are beginning to fade
Years go by as seasons pass from warm to cold
Life flies by as you grow old
I'll make the best out of everything
This means having lots of fun and not smoking
I need to stay very healthy
So I can live a long life and become wealthy
Years go by as seasons pass from warm to cold
Life flies by as you grow old

Kyle Granowski
Century Middle School
Thornton, CO
Grade 7

Change

Things are changing every day.
Pictures change in the halls,
Different writings on the walls.

Things are changing every day.

Oh, yes, let's not forget, the weather is always changing,
It begins by snowing and ends by raining.

Things are changing every day.
But with change come tragedies and strife,
Yes, change is part of everyone's life.

Cambria Shimmon
Challenger School
Sandy, UT
Grade 7

The Race

I start off.
My heart is racing.
I'm apprehensive but excited.
My face is dripping sweat.
The heat hits straight on.
My legs are moving so swiftly I can't even feel them,
I swear my lungs are going to burst.
As I see the blue ribbon ahead of me,
And I'm forced to put one foot in front of the other,
I feel the racing wind pelting against my body,
And gravity pulling me down.
As I feel I can't go on,
The blue ribbon passes behind me,
And the cheering grows louder.
I have won.

Lisa Jones
Ranch View Middle School
Highlands Ranch, CO
Grade 8

Autumn

Autumn leaves falling
tumbling, tumbling down
covering the ground.

Aubrey Thompson
Riverview Jr High School
Murray, UT
Grade 8

True Love

Love is something thou shall cherish,
Something thou shall remember.
Love is something that shall not perish,
Something that burns of an ember;
One or two embers or an entire fire,
That of compassion and trust.
Take all of this into consideration
And your heart shall not perish or rust.
If you find true love,
Do not throw it away.
For if you do,
I have to say,
SHAME!

Elitha Diaz
East Middle School
Colorado Springs, CO
Grade 8

Rapids

The waterfall is gently falling
To its stream below
It's carrying our perfect love
And will not stop its flow

To where it's going we can't yet see
Because our love has just begun
The water is still flowing gently
But faster it will run

Soon the stream turns into rapids
And now we feel so lost
But if we work together
We can overcome the toss

Then finally we reach the pond
The rapids left behind
And all we see is smooth clear water
No rapid we can find.

This is our pond of eternity
Our pond of love and life
And although the rapids come and go
We can overcome the strife.

Michelle Watkins
Mountain Ridge Jr High School
Highland, UT
Grade 8

Reflection

She looks at her reflection in the stream,
"Is this me" she asks herself.
Her face so worn and wrinkled,
Her skin a leathery texture and color from when she rode horses to faraway places,
on bright summer days.
She's 80 now,
her long, gray hair still in braids,
her leather dress torn,
her life almost to an end.

Danita Chesbro
Clear Creek Middle School
Buffalo, WY
Grade 8

My Grandma

My grandma was so dear.
She loved everybody and gave to the poor.
I love my grandma.
She always played games and she would never give up.
I love my grandma.
She could hardly do anything but sit in her chair.
But she was more kind than I could ever be.
Now my grandma has passed away.
I'll never forget the moments I spent with that dear old lady I loved,
And always will love to the end.

Luke Isaacson
Fred Moodry Middle School
Anaconda, MT
Grade 8

Mother Nature's Struggle

The wind is howling, yet the sun is bright.
The clouds don't stop it from giving off it's light.
I am the earth, it's what I am for.
But the skies are not mine, and how they will act can never be sure.
The Father of the skies is the ruler of the sun.
We try to work together, and to the world we seem as one.
But it isn't so and it never shall be.
For when he makes the rains fall, I make a calm sea.
I try to be kind, to give him his ways,
But I want my own thing; warm, sunny days.
He likes the wind that makes my trees fall.
Flooding the towns and ruining them all.
But I can't accept that, yet how to prevent?
No matter what, he always seems to win in the end.
But I will stay strong, and I won't give in.
So the world will remain, and I, and Him.
And we will go on forever and more,
But when he makes the wind howl, I'll keep a calm shore.

Kelli Reynolds
Mountain Ridge Jr High School
Highland, UT
Grade 8

Millennium

5, 4, 3, 2, 1,
It is time to have some fun.
The streets are filled with people and lights,
I hope this year there aren't many fights.
The streets and cities are packed,
Lots of people are going to be at parties and that's a fact.
The streets are filled with cheers and full of joy,
The millennium baby was a cute baby boy.
3,2,1,0, suddenly there was a big, sudden shout,
Oh no! My lights just went out!

Sonny Saipale
White Middle School
Henderson, NV
Grade 7

Philosophy

Da Vinci with his flying machine
It's like nothing I've ever seen
Galileo saw the stars so bright
Columbus with his great sail across the sea
But what does that mean to you and me
We don't think about what these people have done
They're the ones who let us have fun
So when you're flying or looking at a star
You know you are not too far to dream

Jeremiah Johnson
Century Middle School
Thornton, CO
Grade 7

Waterfalls

Why do we pollute the water
That flows into the waterfalls?
We throw things into the water,
Like plastic cups and Styrofoam balls.
We don't think about where the trash is going,
Or where it turns up in the end,
We just keep on throwing, throwing,
Until the trash just seems to blend,
Into our beautiful landscapes and our trees so tall,
It even flows down the waterfalls.
On it flows, out to the ocean,
Where it harms the fish of the sea.
We don't even make a motion,
If we see trash around a birds beak.
Why do we harm the fish of the sea,
The birds of the air
And the bears in the trees?
Whey can't we learn to put our trash,
In the trash cans, where it's supposed to be?

Lindsay Arnold
Century Middle School
Thornton, CO
Grade 7

Doing it the Easy Way

Why can't we go through life with ease
Without troubles to make us sad
Shouldn't life just be a breeze
Always be good news
Instead of anything bad

No one said life was easy
You weren't promised from the start
Life is filled with challenges
Forcing you to use your mind and heart

Without change life would be boring
Knowing and expecting everything
You would not be able to be surprised
Always knowing what the next day would bring

So don't get discouraged when challenges come
Don't shun away the change
Because just when you start to get worrisome
Things will turn around
Thank goodness life isn't easy

Diana Gross
Campus Middle School
Englewood, CO
Grade 8

Why?

Why do we have things such as
hate and war in our world today?

Is it so we can have something interesting
to watch on TV, or read about in the newspaper?

Or is it because in this world we just see how
everyone is different and not how they are similar?

Maybe it's because everyone is so absorbed in their
selfishness and greed, that they don't care what happens
to the people and world we live in.

Or is it because in this world today we're
too high-and-mighty to admit we're wrong?

Could it possibly be that we just don't care anymore?

How could we have let our world
become so hate-filled and sinister?

Whatever the reason, is it really worth
the hurt and pain we cause?

Lindsay Pokallus
Sage Valley Jr High School
Gillette, WY
Grade 9

The Way Flowers Act

Flowers are so interesting,
They always look like they are resting.
They never move from their places,
They don't make any faces.

Flowers are so pretty,
Some may be really witty.
Others may be very shy,
Who knows if one is sly.

Who can tell how flowers act,
Whether or not they're afraid of cats.
Some may look ornery or peaceful,
Others may look weird or graceful.

Whether we will know or not,
Will we ever unlock,
The way flowers act!

Ameleah Bunting
Kanab Middle School
Kanab, UT
Grade 7

The Teddy Bear

The toy sat on the shelf
With a look of long years of wear.
Dusty, torn, and forgotten
Was the small brown teddy bear.

This bear was old and lonely.
It really was not fair.
He had never done a mean thing.
Sweet was this teddy bear.

He had sat upon the shelf,
And acted as if he did not care.
He would force away the tears,
But truly sad was the teddy bear.

He had waited for so long
That he hardly had a prayer.
But he still waited patiently.
Patient was this teddy bear.

One day Jake came back
And found his bear sitting there.
Finally he was remembered.
Happy was this teddy bear.

Michelle Casdorph
Challenger School
Sandy, UT
Grade 7

That Terrible Night

I walked home one day
My two sisters were with me.
School was over and it was a Friday
What could go wrong this afternoon?

The answer to that question
Came when I got home,
The door was left wide open
My parents were nowhere to be found.

I kept telling myself it wasn't true
Why do they hate us
Just because we are Jews?
I don't understand.

Later that terrible night
They came for us too,
We couldn't put up a fight
Or they would kill us right there.

My sisters were crying
They took them from me,
Without even caring
That they were breaking our hearts.

Marissa Beech
South Jordan Middle School
South Jordan, UT
Grade 8

A Friend

A friend is a person
That cares and shares
They forgive and forget
And show the specialness they bear

A friend is a person
That's as kind as can be
And plays hide and seek
Behind the old oak tree

Secrets, laughs
And tears galore
Giggles, whispers
Stares and more

A friend is a person
That's there till the end
Never forgetting
The love that they send

Amanda Ingman
Centerville 7-8 School
Sand Coulee, MT
Grade 8

Earth's Cry for Help

Oh Help!
Our Earth cried,
Come clean me up!
My beautiful oceans
Are now just big dumps!
Where are my forests?
Now they're not here!
And my once flowing rivers
Are now but a tear!
Alas! The animals!
Look at them there!
You put them aside
Like you just don't care!
I gave you all beauty,
And earthly peace
But look what you did!
I've begun to decrease
Hear me now,
And listen well,
If we all work together
We'll emerge from this cell!

Hannah Smith
Century Middle School
Thornton, CO
Grade 7

Old Friend

It makes light blind,
But is soft and yet kind,
Keeps quiet, not even a crack,
And gives you a twist,
It creeps up your back,
Just a light little mist.

Hovering around,
Not making a sound,
Shut out from the warm,
More flushes in, the warm becomes cold,
Blustering about all up in a swarm,
And yet it's so bold.

It has darkened the sky to a light gray,
It has dampened the hay,
The crops are all shaken,
The soil is tightly packed,
Holding itself down so not to be taken,
But that is all part of the act.
Fog is but an old friend,
No need to defend.

Allyssa Ramstetter
Century Middle School
Thornton, CO
Grade 7

No Hope

The tears were never ending.
They were those of a young woman,
growing up in a world of confusion, in a world of mazes.
Trying to find
happiness, love, and someone to share them with.

Yet, when she thought she had found them,
there was always another bend to look around,
another corner to be turned.

The first did not care,
the second did not love,
the third was not true.

Now she was at a dead end,
no hope of turning a corner and maybe
finding something better, another someone to ease the pain.

No hope of looking around a bend, and maybe
finding the exit to the ongoing maze,
and maybe
a reason for all of this confusion.
But now she was at a dead end of tears, with nowhere to go.

Courtney Robinson
Vail Mountain School
Vail, CO
Grade 7

Spring Is Here

I wake up in the spring,
Just to have my ears ring,
Spring is a time of peace,
You can finally quit wearing your fleece,
I love to watch the snow melt,
It's something some have never felt,
All the golf courses open up,
You can probably even get a new pup,
The only thing I hate is the rain,
For some it brings much pain,
I love spring because it's the start of track,
Better go put together a pack,
I love to get out and hike,
Always hope to get out and bike,
Have tournaments for basketball,
When I hike I try not to fall,
The mountains still have snow,
Get a baseball out and throw,
This is just some of the stuff I love,
Better get out and break in my glove.

Russel Aldrich
Bigfork Middle School
Bigfork, MT
Grade 8

Snow Is as White as a Dove

Snow is as white as a dove
The ocean is as blue as an evening sky
Snow makes the day brighter and more thrilling
A dove cannot enhance the marvelous wonders that snow
Can bring forth each day.

Snow brings about water and is a useful resource to God's earth
As more snow is laid unto the earth, grass and the earth
Are filtered from dirty things
Snow is bright, used for fun and cleansing
The snow that the earth receives is a gift from God.

Brian Skiles
Campus Middle School
Englewood, CO
Grade 8

Compassion

I sit on a pillow of bluebonnets.
While my pony grazes on the grass.
I look up while hearing the rolling waves.
I see an eagle soaring high.
I feel the warmth of the golden sun touching my soft tan skin.
Compassion reaches out her beautiful hands
And holds me in her embrace.
There is a herd of wild horses on the other side of the bluffs.
I can hear their whinnies and loud cries,
They sound so beautiful.
As beautiful as the compassion that holds me in her embrace.

Holly Stokes
Spring Creek Middle School
Elko, NV
Grade 8

Love

When love was created,
God must have been thinking of you,
'Cause when I think of you,
I think of love too.

Right now I think of love:
I think of you.

You're my dear one,
The only one I could ever care for.

Once you find love never let it go,
'Cause love is one thing you can't replace.

For love is a gift:
A gift from God!

Katrina Rodgers
Roundup 7-8 School
Roundup, MT
Grade 8

Did You Hear That?

I lay in my bed; my eyes are open wide
I have a fear of the dark I can't run and I can't hide

I get sweaty palms and shiver down my back
Courage in the dark is something I do lack

My heart starts to pound and I get really cold
Oh how I can't wait until I get brave when I get old

My fear takes over and I pull the covers over my head
I don't want to leave the security of my warm soft bed

Then I hear a sound coming from the hall
Like a mad man pounding on the blue and white wall

I try to think of happy things to soothe my awful fears
But I just can't help and I break out into tears

I finally start to analyze this situation on my hands
I came to one conclusion that I'm sure you understand

I gathered up my shaking body and headed out the door
And down the hall I crept quickly on the wooden floor

I now spotted the perfect location
My parent's room was a great destination.

Monica Marquez
Granada School
Granada, CO
Grade 9

Song of Thunder

They roll in like a blanket covering a child,
in the colors of black and gray.
Angry masses of air and water,
making their anger
known through big sounds
and angry flashes of light.
Splattering drops of
water upon the ground,
bringing life to all around.
These angry masses
are life giving killers,
sweetly singing it's dangerous song.
When he feels that his anger is gone,
he slowly weakens
and stops his growling.
He rolls out just as he rolled in,
slowly and quietly,
like a blanket covering a child.

Mellissa Bowman
Kanab Middle School
Kanab, UT
Grade 7

Baseball Bat

If I were a baseball bat,
I'd swing, hit the ball and go, "crack,"
And I'd swing until I break,
And then to the woodshop, I would go back.
Wouldn't you want to be a baseball bat?

Matt Figgs
Franklin Middle School
Greeley, CO
Grade 7

Pretenders

People talk and people pretend,
They act as if they're really your friend.

They get you thinking you can trust their word,
But then the next day everyone will have heard.

You end your relationship with a hurtful heart,
And you wish you had known from the start.

That they would do that to you,
Lie, pretend, and backstab too.

Every time you see them you give them a frown,
They laugh and bring your self-confidence down.

So pick your friends with great care,
Don't trust them too soon because pretenders are everywhere.

Heather Light
Pawnee Jr-Sr High School
Grover, CO
Grade 8

The River of Life

The world can be like a river,
Sometimes swift and cruel.
But like every river,
It can also be calm and cool.
With friends, although, the world may seem,
Like one of the most wonderful dreams.
To provide love, help, and care,
Your friends will always be there.
The more friends you have,
The richer you are.
For when you have friends,
You're happier by far.
You should also be a friend,
Where your love and warmth you can lend.
To be a friend means a lot,
To be there when loneliness is fought.

Chris Cerny
Lawrence Jr High School
Las Vegas, NV
Grade 7

The One

From the moment I looked into your eyes,
I knew you were the one for me.
You opened the door,
Made me see.
And I saw something I never saw before.
The real me.

How can I find the way to your heart?
To be with you and never let go.
I never saw the greatness of love,
And how much I can make it show.

Kara Sievers
Our Lady of Snows School
Reno, NV
Grade 8

Fog

The fog is mystical.
It rides the wind like a horse.
It slides like butter through trees.
The fog arches its back as it goes over mountains.
The fog helps the wind sing with music.
Sometimes it rises to the heavens above.
As if it were pretending to be a dove.
The fog blinds you through the night.
And maybe unleashes its mysteries.
Which it holds tight.
The fog is very mystical.

Nick Thompson
Century Middle School
Thornton, CO
Grade 7

Children

With short curls,
Waving their rich chocolate brown colors,
Their innocent eyes look to you for guidance.
With plump red lips,
They ask you what to do.
Little hands of every texture and color,
Fumble in each corner,
To search for new experiences.
With hearts of pureness and gold,
They offer their love to you.
Not knowing the hardships of the world,
They ask you to protect, love and nurture,
Yet they do not speak.
They are your future.
They are you.
Treat them right.

Jill Collymore
Kent Denver School
Englewood, CO
Grade 7

Take a Closer Look

If you take a closer look, farther down you'll see.
A lonely girl that's waiting, for someone to notice me.

Behind this face and deep down low, I'm waiting to escape.
To show you who I really am, and not someone that's fake.

If you take a closer look, you'll see my secrets kept.
The pain that I have gone through, the places I have stepped.

And although you may not see it, the longing sealed inside.
To have someone to love me, someone that in I can confide.

For the girl that you know now, is not the real me.
She's someone dressed up to fit in, she's not what you see.

Behind this scared and lonely girl, is the one I want to show
But I'm afraid that if I do, I'm not someone you'll want to know.

I want so badly to open up, I want you all to see.
The one's that stuck behind this girl, the one who's really me.

So take a closer look, and farther down you'll see.
A girl that's waiting to express, who she is, the real me.

Kiri Redford
South Jordan Middle School
South Jordan, UT
Grade 8

Friend*

Waz,
Cool little gal,
I've known you since you were born.
I've known you through my life.
You're a little crazy,
And really wild.
I'm sorry if we have fights,
I still love you.
You always put a smile on my face when I am down and blue.
I have no better friend but you.
You are blood not water, let's stay that way forever.
You always stick up for me, I can't ask for better,
I love you so much and I hope you love me too.
Let's stay friends forever.
I know you're gifted with a lot of talents,
Sometimes I get jealous,
But what can I do, I am lucky enough,
I have a friend like you.
I Love You!

Ranza Fernandez
Fremont Middle School
Las Vegas, NV
Grade 7
*To my cousin Krystle Tuano

Hurricane

The cool bitter breeze goes through my flesh and
I shiver and wrap myself more firm in my worn, shabby scarf.
I am deathly tired from doing nothing.
The ship is rocking more and more abrupt,
With crashes of waves under my unsteady feet.
I am increasingly losing my balance doing favors for my mother.
I tried to open the sodden door but it was swelled to the frame.
I fall backwards and catch myself only seeing the outline of the ship.
I find my cat at the top of the mast and I flee to the unsturdy ladder trying to dodge the pelting rain.
Climbing as swiftly as I can to get my cat when I am only four dragging steps way.
The mast somewhat collapses and I am directly over the waves that grasps for whatever it touches.
I yell and scream trying to get the attention of the crew,
But the wind steals and loses my voice in the crashing waves.
Finally the wind slows down and I manage to get down from the mast and into my bed.
In the daylight I sat up with every muscle in my body aching.
I limped into the early sun and say a prayer of thanks that it was finally the morning after overcoming death.

Alicia Castillo
Notre Dame School
Denver, CO
Grade 7

Rectangle

What is a rectangle but an escape?
It is an excursion through time by means of the vision of various people,
The breakout into a world abundant with imagination and thoughts,
With simple sheets of paper and a cover.
Escaping through the great opening,
It is a pathway to another place and time,
But pictures can be wrong, books confusing, and doors closed.

Eric Craft
Colorado Academy
Denver, CO
Grade 9

Faith

I stand in the darkness
Swallowed by my heart.
Uncaring, ungiving.
Quarrel, gurgle, judgment of faith.
Which way to lean?
If I lean left into the flaming pit,
Screams echo of dying tormented souls.
The trickster Pan laughs and smiles.
Temptation has run wild.

If I lean right I'll be swallowed by life.
Laughing, playing, no misery to come.
Instead of cries of pain it's cries of laughter that ring out.
But something's missing.

What's life without pain and suffering?
What's pain and suffering without happiness and joy?
So standing on Purgatory scared of what's to come
But whatever way I lean be strong and hold on.

Bobbi Jo Klingman
Swink Jr-Sr High School
Swink, CO
Grade 8

A Look at Life

Life's a dream of fantasy
Sometimes filled with ecstasy,
Moments of joy, moments of pain
Sometimes sunshine, sometimes rain.

Life's a journey full of dreams
Filled with possibilities,
Roads are paved with miseries
But they are all a part of life's scheme.

We learn more as we grow old
That joy can't be bought by silver and gold,
And sometimes dreams may fade away
While others come true in different ways.

We'll share the sunshine and the rain
And maybe even joy and pain,
But whatever this life brings
Someday will fly away on wings.

Judith Hofer
Sage Creek Colony Elementary School
Chester, MT
Grade 8

Winter

Look out the window, and gaze at the sky!
Do you see the falling snow?
As it curls and dances in soft flurries;
Drifting and shifting. I know not why.

Look out the window, and see the snowman!
How proud he stands and how majestic!
He wears a smile that seems to call out
"Come out little child, and be a free man!"

Look out the window, and look at the frost!
Gorgeous lace, the most delicate sort
Drapes over the window and beautifully so!
All that was green seems to be lost.

Look out the window, notice the peace?
All is calm, and all is well.
The world in a deep sleep, under a blanket of snow
Lies flat and still.

Look out the window, see the beauty!
Everything in sight has a new wardrobe!
So crisp and white are the suits,
The earth is quite a beauty.

Priscilla Wyler
Challenger School
Sandy, UT
Grade 8

Morning Sunrise

My heart stops at the rare occasion
That I see the morning sunrise
I see myself in its beauty
It lifts up my problems and worries
I grin from ear to ear
Then it's over and I wait for that rare occasion once more

Michael Lippert
Minturn Middle School
Minturn, CO
Grade 8

Love

I love my mom,
I love my dad,
Even though they make me mad.

They make me laugh when I'm sad,
They teach me what's good and bad.

I love my brothers just the same,
Even though they may be pains.

I love my friends, girls and boys,
To whom I share all my joys.

I love my pets, they cheer me when I'm sad,
They're the best friends I've ever had.

I love my home it's a place to grow,
With all my heart and all my soul.

Life is good,
Life is fine,
So I'll never whine.

Shurie Sandoval
Century Middle School
Thornton, CO
Grade 7

Night Mourning

The chintzy stallion struts only at night
when the dappled sunset hangs in the evening sky
In the morning
when the dew forms
on the little blades of grass
the dew looks like a shiny eclipse
that addles aesthetically in the night's hands
On a rubbery terrace
the stallion plodded alone
but only in the night's sky
when dawn breaks
it trots majestically away

Erika Wiedeman
Three Forks Middle School
Three Forks, MT
Grade 7

My Friend

My friend you are
Through thick and thin.
My friend you are
Whether we lose or win.

My friend you are
When hope goes away.
My friend you are
When life goes astray.

My friend you are
When times get tough.
My friend you are
When the going gets rough.

My friend you are
Through times of sorrow.
My friend you are
That I can always count on tomorrow.

My friend you are
In the morning, in the night, whenever.
My friend you are
Always and forever.

Rachel Leach
Centennial Middle School
Boulder, CO
Grade 8

Life

Girl or boy
Daughter or son
Life is hard for everyone

Mother or father
Husband or wife
Many of them have lots of strife

Aunt or uncle
Sister or brother
We all think of our dear Grandmother

Niece or nephew
Cousin or not
Everyone loves what they've got

You've been dealt a hand
'Cause life is hard
All you can do is play a card

Raena Wedel
Norwood Middle School
Norwood, CO
Grade 7

Pudding

I like pudding; it is good.
I would make it if I could.
Some is green; some is slimy,
Some is also very shiny.
Pudding's puddy yes I know,
Kind of, sort of, it does glow.
I like pudding very much,
It feels weird to the touch.

Trevor Coleman
Kanab Middle School
Kanab, UT
Grade 7

A Girl's Poem

His playful laughter flowing with cheer
His soothing voice whispering in my ear
The gentle touch across my face
His tender lips feel like lace
His chocolate eyes that stare in mine
Make me feel like I'm on cloud nine
All these things are about the man I love
Even more than the heavens above
Sure we've had good times and bad
Times of happy and sad
We even had a few fights
But we've had more highlights.
There's been some times with tears
But the word "I Love You" always
Make them disappear.

Michelle Jensen
Norwood Middle School
Norwood, CO
Grade 9

Flower

One by one,
life by life,

another petal drops,
another dead end.

Eventually, a petal grows back,
her soul is fearless.

another petal prospers,
another through street,

the last petal grows back,
along with her soul.

Allie Shpall
Kent Denver School
Englewood, CO
Grade 7

Give Me

Give me no treasures
I've no want for gold,
For coins that get dusty
And lose value when old.

Feed me no pastries
I've no want for cake,
For sugary delicacies
Who of my health take.

Build me no castle
I've no want for stone,
To sit in a tower
Of darkness so drone.

Tell me no stories
I've no want for tales,
To listen of heroes
Whose feats to regale.

But give me the one thing
I have such a want for.
Just give me your love
Now and forever more.

Kari Murray
Mountain Ridge Jr High School
Highland, UT
Grade 8

Dreams

I go to a place
where the moon lives
where the light of the sun
never exists.

The unicorns play there
with their animal friends
as they drink raspberry cordial
until the night ends.

The trees all whisper
as I walk through the park
and they tickle my face
while I sit in the dark.

I go to a place
where the moon lives
where the light of the sun
never exists . . . in my dreams.

Tanya Sparks
North Davis Jr High School
Clearfield, UT
Grade 9

Farmer

The farmer wakes up early before dawn
because he knows that it will be hotter later on.

The sun rises earlier each day
he can't believe that it's only May.

As the sun beats harder and harder,
the farmer knows there will be less water.

In the field the farmer mows
someone is watching; the scarecrows.

As the water trickles down the row
it should help the potatoes grow.

As the farmer goes to bed at night,
he thanks the Lord for all his might.

Marianne Healey
Mountain Ridge Jr High School
Highland, UT
Grade 8

My Cousin Companion

I need my family.
When Christopher died, I lost my best cousin companion.

Even though
Our ages were different
We had...the most in common.
We played games,
Laughed, and had fun.

Why did he have to die?
Where is he now?

I have a pain in my heart,
An empty space.
I will always grieve inside.
For the love of my family
Cannot cure the pain in my heart.

Together, my family rebuilt
The mental and emotional strength we have.

With our love, and our care,
Together somewhere
I will make it,
Without
My little cousin companion there.

Stephanie Findley
Mountain Ridge Middle School
Colorado Springs, CO
Grade 8

Untitled

In a way I think I'm fat
Not that that is bad or anything.
My parents won't let me go on a diet,
They say I'm as skinny as a toothpick.
I look in the mirror
And try to imagine how skinny a toothpick is
Then I think I'm not fat...my brother is!!
I try to tell him but he just laughs and laughs!

Hanna Perry
Star Valley Jr High School
Afton, WY
Grade 7

Peanut Butter Jar

It just seems to sit there, whether it's empty or full.
Yet there's something about this jar that brings back
Childhood memories.
Of eating Mom-made sandwiches,
Of the time you desperately put the butter in your hair,
Because you slept with gum in your mouth.
It's not romantic, nor is it beautiful.
Yet, perhaps, it deserves some kind of recognition.
But what?
Hmmm...
A peanut butter jar.

Noelle Brough
Mountain Ridge Jr High School
Highland, UT
Grade 8

Homework

Piles and Piles
Miles and Miles,
Boy, I sure do hate homework!
I got Language Arts, two hours, at least!
Too bad I don't have powers to complete,
Oh please!
I'm getting writers cramp
From figuring this algebra,
"Well, you don't have too much,"
Oh ha!
What a joke all this is to torture these kids
With a threat of work!
Here comes a smirk on the History teacher's face
As she passes by and gives us our fate!
Even worse is detention, No homework privileges
Or time to complete our doom.
Miles and Miles,
With Piles and Piles,
Of dreaded awful
HOMEWORK!!
(Groan)

Jaimee Kendall
Academy Charter School
Castle Rock, CO
Grade 7

As I Lie Here...

As I lie here on my back,
Looking at the stars,
I wonder if you're up there,
In the Heavens far above,
Looking down on me.

As I lie here on my back,
Looking at the clouds,
I wonder if you're making
All those shapes
Just for me to see.

As I lie here on my back,
Watching the sun set,
I wonder if you're waiting
Till we meet again in heaven.

Goodbye, my dear friend.

Veronica Broslawik
Holy Trinity School
Westminster, CO
Grade 8

Parents

Mother
kind, gentle
loving, sharing, caring
hugs, kisses, trouble, fun
running, scaring, surprising
funny, daring
Father

Rachel Riggs
Custer County School
Westcliffe, CO
Grade 7

Navy Seals

They are silent and sly.
Ready for anything,
But they never cry.
They make their weapons sing.

Smart and cunning as a fox
Always coming back
They signal without talk,
And won't cut you any slack.

Strong not weak,
Invisible in the night.
Fast, accurate, doing work flawlessly.
Able to do anything.
Navy Seals.

Peter Clayson
Challenger School
Sandy, UT
Grade 7

The Dam

Off into the wild ravine,
Down the steep, grassy sides
With cactus and yucca biting at our legs.
The wild stream, polluted with the toxic wastes of the streets above,
Rages through the ravine, carving a twisted path as it goes.
The childhood task of damming that stream daunts ahead.
With the perfect place plotted, we begin the task.
As the deer go scampering through the discarded tires and newspapers,
And the owls surprise us with a sudden leap from their nests,
The two of us collect the building materials for the mighty dam.
A huge plastic sack for the main water-ward side of the dam,
A ruptured tire for the structure of it.
Coughing the cattail seeds out of our lungs, we jump in,
About to unleash the master building project.
With elusive leeches nibbling on our calves,
Finally done, the dam holds back the water and the task is accomplished.
Scrambling back up the steep sides, back into suburbia,
Sneaking through unknowing neighbor's yards,
Back to the house to beat the four o'clock deadline
Which the mother had set three hours ago.

Rob Kesselman
Colorado Academy
Denver, CO
Grade 9

Heroes and Heroines

You're someone I look up to,
Who means the world to me.
I do everything like you.
You're all I want to be.

Whether you're a big bullying brother,
Or a small annoying sister.
Perhaps you're a famous superstar,
Or even loving parents.
I respect you.

I admire how you seem to know everything, big brother.
I admire your courage when I am sometimes mean to you, little sister.
For I wish I had the courage to do not what's wrong, but what's right.
I admire you, superstar, for having accomplished so much.
And I admire you, dear parents, for staying with me when things get tough.
For I want to stick with my dreams for achieving much in life.
I admire you.

If you're big or if you're small,
If you're known by few or known by all,
It doesn't matter, for you are my role model and
I honor you.

Ashley Schroeder
Sage Valley Jr High School
Gillette, WY
Grade 7

The Summer Debate

Frost drenching trees
Like recently
Glazed and powdered donuts,
A boy stands motionless with a
Frozen, stinging sensation
Swarming up his toes
Like termites feasting.
He wishes for
Summer's
Warmth and cool breezes.
Also thinking about memories
From earlier this year.
Tired of the
Scorching burns of sunlight
The sweat covering his young face
Wishing it was
Winter.

Matthew Shore
C S Porter Middle School
Missoula, MT
Grade 7

To Stride Farther

Take a step; take another.
Where have you gone;
But of course, nowhere.

For in this impurity of life,
There is always a better.
We will not be content,
'Till the best is reached.

"Life is too short!" they say.
But this is only true
For those who *drag* through mortality.

In order to enjoy life,
We must run.
Run as hard as we can,
To accomplish our goals.

Before we are in the hands of Pluto
We must stride as far as we can.
For that is the only way we will be satisfied.

This mortal coil of ours,
Is in itself a goal.
The goal simply is:
To stride farther.

Yang Wang
White Middle School
Henderson, NV
Grade 8

Nature's Voice

scorching deserts with their harsh and yet unique beauty
bone-chilling tundra, its pure whiteness dazzling
jagged, craggy peaks towering in the sky
remote and isolated valleys, hiding unknown secrets
peaceful, green meadows dotted with flowers,
as if mottled by a master painter's brush

could all this have evolved from nothing?
it seems absurd to consider such a theory.
to have created such a beautiful and yet diverse world,
there must be a Master of Design
His work far beyond our comprehension
deserving more than we could ever give Him

Rachel Dunham
Green River High School
Green River, UT
Grade 8

Never Ending Time

Time is something that never stops,
Whether you are reading a book or going to shop.
It may come and it may go, but it never stays,
It quickly turns from hours to days.
Time can creep slowly like a tear down my face,
Or quickly like a skier in a downhill race.
When you are young the days go by so slow,
But as you get old where do they go?
Time can never shut down,
It just keeps spinning round and round.

Marisa Lucero
Century Middle School
Thornton, CO
Grade 7

The Rainbow

Gray and dull patters the drizzling rain.
Not letting the sun show off its shimmering rays,
for days on end.
The moods of all living things suffer,
even the plants are drooping their water drenched leaves.

As if waiting for its cue,
faint colors of a beginning rainbow
peek over the misty clouds.
Gaining courage as it breaks through the gloom,
glowing with all its might to chase away the storm.

This rainbow is the breaker of the daze.
Birds sing their songs of joy,
and tulips open their velvet petals.
Lives were brightened,
by the vivid smile of a mysterious rainbow.

Alix Wilkes
Star Valley Jr High School
Afton, WY
Grade 8

It Doesn't Matter

If we were all dogs,
Color blind, you see,
We'd have lots of friends
Different than you and me
It doesn't matter
If you're white or black,
If you live inside
A mansion or shack.
No one should care
About the looks.
What if there are things in common?
Like reading the same books.
Everyone's different,
In not the same ways.
You both are different,
Each and every day.
Don't try to be like your neighbor,
Don't try to be like your friend
Everything will work out fine
People will still like you in the end.

Kelsey Warmack
Century Middle School
Thornton, CO
Grade 7

Lightning

Lightning crashes down
through a lion's roar

It runs wild
looking for a victim
dashes back and forth
throughout a vast plain

Maren Ripplinger
Boulder City High School
Boulder City, NV
Grade 9

Fog

The fog came this morning
as if it were
a can of paint
that had been spilt.

When the wind
was done wiping it up
a thin coat of frost
was left behind.

Yet the sun came out
and wore the frost away
over time.

Matt Schmidt
Butler Middle School
Salt Lake City, UT
Grade 8

Love for Her

The tragic outcry of a deceived heart mourns the loss of a once perfect bond.
The flow of the pain bursts through my heart realizing,
and remembering the loved one which I treasure so much.
Feel it, she is no more.
I hope for the day I will:
see her,
hear her,
cherish her.
As I did in weeks, months, years, gone by.
Everything accomplished in those years has had a reflection on her.
She is my grandmother.
Loving,
caring,
beautiful,
courageous.
My grandmother, always and forever.
Death cannot stop such a spiritual and magnificent bond.
Grandma, I love you.

Alexys Harvey
Evergreen Jr High School
Salt Lake City, UT
Grade 9

Death

Out of the shadows comes someone with a stick
Dressed in black and walking slow, for many months now I've been sick.
Why are you looking straight at me?
Why are you now hiding behind a tree?
Why will no one see you but me?
Why are you here and who would you be?

Come with me now he said I will take you back to our bed
The voice was low and very deep
Why am I suddenly feeling weak?

Into the shadows I walk with him
Lights are getting very dim.
Then out of the night a scream
Out of the dark a guiding beam.

"That was my mom," I cry.
"She will understand," he wearily sighs.
"But. . ." I begin to say.
"How do you feel?" "Fine." "It will always be that way."
"Where are we going?" I suddenly ask.
"Home," he replies, "you are now done with your task.
Your father will be there, just take his hand."
I say, "I think I'm beginning to understand."

Jennifer Hedrick
Century Middle School
Thornton, CO
Grade 7

Sky Diving

The plane ride skyward was really uplifting,
A moment later I'd feel myself drifting.
The clouds wisp by, like the sound of soft words,
As I watch the peaceful flight of birds.

With the engine sound shouting my way,
I try to hold my excitement at bay.
My pack's strapped so tight it clings to my skin,
My heart leaps about and bursts from within.

The door clatters open and my heart skips a beat,
I tumble outward and feel ground leave my feet.
The winds rip at my cheeks and pummel my coat,
If I lived through this adventure I would have to gloat.

Reaching for the rip-cord, I vaguely pray,
I'd land to live another day.
The chute erupts with an explosion of light,
Its unearthly glow would gleam through the night.

My feet graze the ground and I light up with joy,
Like a child on Christmas, just gotten a toy.
I unstrap my pack and reflect outloud,
"Boy this would sure make my old dad feel proud!"

Andrew Call
Star Valley Jr High School
Afton, WY
Grade 7

My Friend

I have met a friend,
A friend who's always true.
Do you know who my friend is?
My friend of course, is you.

You are always truthful,
You are always kind.
Whenever I am happy
I have you on my mind.

You help me lift my burdens,
You help me when I'm down.
You are always happy
I have never seen you frown.

You fill my life with laughter,
You fill my life with joy.
All I've ever wanted
Is to be your special boy.

Craig Dunn
Riverview Jr High School
Murray, UT
Grade 8

Spring

I like spring
I like the rain that falls
I like listening to the birds that call
I like the flowers that grow
And the streams that flow
I like how everything turns green
To make a pretty scene
I like going on hikes at noon
And summer vacation will be coming soon
Swimming in ponds and cool pools
During spring there are no rules!!!

Evan Orton
Kanab Middle School
Kanab, UT
Grade 7

Escape

Heat, how painful you are.
Your force and tremendous strength.
From sun's rays beating down on the earth,
Like a boulder of heavy weights.
I long to withdraw into complete darkness,
Escape the oven of death.
I'm pulled back to life.
The prospect of cool water on my lips.
What I wouldn't give to quench my longing thirst.
Liquid, cool, running down my throat.
Going mad for the want of a cool breeze.
Tremendous sorrow and pain.
I want to go back to subconscious slumber.
No memory of pain.
Its existence leaves my body.
Sweet precious slumber.

Stacey Newton
South Jordan Middle School
South Jordan, UT
Grade 8

The Web of Popularity

Everyone craves it; wanting to be known and liked
   by their pressurous peers.
Coming and going quickly, like a tumbleweed
   in a wild windstorm, it soon seizes your vulnerable soul.
Some swig it down, while others cautiously sip;
   maybe even spitting it out.
With it, I am suddenly a tall oak tree
   with fallen leaves all around.
Within the blink of an eye, though, the secretly hidden cat
   pounces on the dazed mouse.
Whoosh! The insecure once-in-a-lifetime experience
   blows away as quickly as it blasted in.

Kalli Peterson
Circle Jr High School
Circle, MT
Grade 8

Billy

With every light
In the arms of sleep
Let me give the world to you
Lily (my one and only)
Infinite sadness
Age of innocence
Medellia of grey skies

Cherub rock
One less moment
Raindrops and sunshowers
Germans in leather pants
Apathy's last kiss
Not worth asking

Laura Norton
Boulder City High School
Boulder City, NV
Grade 9

the shy telemarketer

He sits all day
on his hard plastic chair
his golden brown hair
ruffled from constant stroking
and scratching as he shyly
mumbles his sales pitch.
With his sticky sweaty hands
nervously clutching the phone
inches from his ear
as another "customer"
curses him and the day he was born
for interrupting his dinner.

Greg Jensen
Colorado Academy
Denver, CO
Grade 9

Diving Experience

Looking into a new world,
Of strange and unusual creatures,
With things that look like brains
And fish that glow in the dark,
Swimming about with nothing to do,
They try to ask, "What creature are you?"

Looking about this underwater world,
Of colors and coral all around you.
Soon you'll have to leave this world,
But think, you can come back anytime.

Lauren Walther
Century Middle School
Thornton, CO
Grade 7

Rain

Drip, drop, drip, drop, drip.
On the roofs of the houses,
    Racing down the street.

Amy Albers
North Arvada Middle School
Arvada, CO
Grade 7

Spring

Spring is like a
breath of fresh air,
it sounds like
birds chirping,
smells like wild flowers
everything is green
and full of life,
new life is coming
into the world,
almost everything
is happy!
except ...

Amie McCracken
Weldon Valley Jr High School
Weldona, CO
Grade 7

Sing

The flag is waiting
Waiting for us to sing, loud
The music starts, sing

Ashleigh Wieczorek
North Arvada Middle School
Arvada, CO
Grade 7

Cruel

What should I do?
Where should I run?
Where can I hide?
Life is cruel to many people
in many different ways.
Why does this happen?
What can I do to help?
So many things – drunks, gangsters,
rapists, killers, molesters, drugs.
There are hit and runs,
also drive-by shootings.
So many, which will land on me,
and when?

Charity Ortiz
Weldon Valley Jr High School
Weldona, CO
Grade 8

Thinking of You

Every summer every winter
Every fall into spring
All daylight unto midnight
I see

See us dancing
Almost prancing
We're always wondering
'Cause when I'm with you
I'm forever free

Come with me,
To the sea,
I know we're just friends,
But you're the sun when it's set

All the stars in the sky
Glimmer like you do
And I want to be the moon
Sitting right by you

Communication, concentration
Imagination too
Always laughing
Always with you

Jennifer Rabenberg
Laurel High School
Laurel, MT
Grade 9

Hatred

I try so hard not to think of the times,
the times it hurt so bad.
I can still hear the screams, the cries,
of the children that were sad.
The fear in their eyes,
was so sad as they rode in the carts.
Never in a lifetime I could ever imagine,
why so much hatred in the Nazi's hearts.
I never had time to think,
just work and work until we died.
They didn't care how we felt,
the pain and the embarrassment.
Oh, how I wanted revenge,
but I couldn't.
I know how it feels to be hurt so badly.
I knew that I shouldn't.
I try not to think of the times,
The times it hurt so bad.

Kellie Krahenbuhl
South Jordan Middle School
South Jordan, UT
Grade 8

The Trail

Find me a place where the trails never end
With steep rugged terrain that I can descend,
Dark, narrow paths speckled with light,
I must trust my instincts and hold on tight.

The smell of pine trees and stirred up dirt.
The wind in my face enters my shirt.
My wheels are bouncing over uneven ground.
The tingling of numbness in my hands is found.

I begin to climb and switch my gears.
The path ahead fuels my fears,
But I am feeling powerful and my desire is strong.
Each pedal turns as each muscle pulls long.

My heart is pounding, and I begin to sweat.
I ride through a puddle all muddy and wet.
The trail goes flat, and I stop for a drink.
The smile on my face says, "I'm crazy! I think?"

A love for the sport keeps my energy high.
I climb back on knowing the end is nigh.
The top reveals itself in a perfect ray of sun.
I stop for a moment and reflect on my fun.

Hayden Price
Challenger School
Sandy, UT
Grade 8

Pain

They trudge through the snow,
Fighting a seemingly eternal battle against time.
Unable to spare enough energy to lift their head,
Their eyes see the simple pattern of their feet.
One, another, one, another.
The pattern, repeated an infinite number of times,
Seen only by their eyes,
Their vision can hardly continue to exist.
Tired.
Too tired even to move their eyes from their feet.
Their psyche entertained by one simple, solitary thought,
Forward.
The pain they endure though,
Does come with great reward
Perhaps more to the soul than wallet.
For the pain may be addicting,
The physical pain is the mind's most beloved joy.
Like a drug, once sampled, one is addicted.
And shall never stop

Seth Chipman
Vail Mountain School
Vail, CO
Grade 7

Petals in Time

Soft, moist, like baby's breath.
The touch is sweet and pure.
They drop with tenderness
To the awaiting floor.

The sound too quite to be heard
Is almost deafening to the ear.
And though it is only a few seconds,
It seems like many, many years.

In time the baby's breath will grow cold and dry.
Time will have brought death upon this being of nature.
Life will go on, as time is reborn.
The petals grow back in a different form.

It's a mystery of nature
That living things must die,
But even so.....
Life will go on.

Tamarah Lynn Day
Spring Creek Middle School
Elko, NV
Grade 8

Cookies

Mashed around, beater beat us together
Milk rides by to bathe us
Bacterial eggs make us sick, "Achhooo..."
We do the wave while rolling on the counter
Friends and family being separated
Getting a nice relaxing, filled with radiation, tan
And slowly ride down the water slide to our new destination,
The stomach

Phoebe Coleman
Colorado Academy
Denver, CO
Grade 9

Life's Stairway

Heaven
Finding yourself
Winning the hard game
Another candle on the cake
Climbing the ladder to success
Making it to the almost unreachable goal
LIFE'S STAIRWAY
Hell
Empty inside and out
ANOTHER candle on the cake
Divorce after many years of marriage
Not realizing that two wrongs never make a right

Chelsey Friedmann
Boulder City High School
Boulder City, NV
Grade 9

Football

Like a b-ball
But not round
Sometimes slammed
On the ground

Hitting hard
Playing tough
Until you've lost
It's not enough

Running weaving
In and out
That's what the game
Is all about

Curtis Roundy
Kanab Middle School
Kanab, UT
Grade 7

Writing Poetry

Poetry may be difficult
If you don't have a clue!
Maybe the following words
Will be inspiring to you:

Speak from the heart
Rather than the mind.
Always write nicely
Never be unkind!

Don't make fun
Of any other
Or else they may
Insult your mother.

There are other hints
That may help you write
But poetry is something
Of importance, right?

Neal Beasley
Riverview Jr High School
Murray, UT
Grade 8

Life-Giver

The crimson flame
flying in the sky
like an immortal
bird of fire
burns, churns, and
turns as it sustains
life on Earth and Mars.

Chris Royer
Norwood Middle School
Norwood, CO
Grade 8

Spring

Spring is the time when the air is full of joy and happiness.
When the flowers bloom and love is in the air.
The cold, harsh, winter is over and now it is a time of joy and happiness
and baby animals are born.
The days are long but full with joy.
The bear awakes with hunger and joy.
His friend, the bobcat, has her young in late April,
but beware, her enemy the mountain lion is near.
The lake and stream are full with salmon.
The bald eagle soars proudly and free
and watches over land and speaks freely to all around.
As the weather gets warmer, the lizards and snakes arise from the cold.
Robin is in a hurry to make her nest as the Blue Jay has laid her eggs.
The bear is roaring. You can hear his thundering voice in the canyon walls
and watch her cubs scramble up the old pine tree.
The lake and the streams are full with trout laying eggs
as the deer walk carefully in the woods as the mountain lion is stalking her.
To snow covered mountains, to the lakes
and the streams, to city, to city, to town, spring is in the air.

Steven Luckesen
Lake Powell Elementary-High School
Lake Powell, UT
Grade 7

Tears of Emotions

A tear drop,
like a bead of sweat,
rolling down my face,
leaving a wake of stinging flesh.

What causes this tear?
Is it a tear of joy,
sadness,
or pain?

Could this all be leading to a tear,
animated by stress,
by the haste, aggravation, and abundance of requirements
all needing fulfillment,
today, now, immediately?!

All these emotions
piling up,
too much to handle,
can't achieve it all.
Now all that's left to do is sit,
while the tear is forced through the eye and down my red cheek.

Megan Redd
Colorado Academy
Denver, CO
Grade 9

Y2K

Was it just a big joke,
Or just a big scare?
Some seemed to worry,
Others didn't care.
People thought the power would go out,
So most kept their families from going out and about.
Some bought food, water and such,
And others knew not to buy all that much.
People went out to restaurants to dine,
And others stayed home and said, "Bye to 99!"

Kami Clementi
Connect Charter School
Pueblo, CO
Grade 7

What I'm Like

I am like an orange; sometimes ripe and sweet
yet other times bitter and sour.
I am like a '57 Chevy, somewhat old fashioned
but still looking good.
I am like a tiger, monstrous and dangerous
yet quiet and mysterious.
I am like a baseball game, sometimes slow and boring
and other times lively and exciting.
Sometimes I am like the night, quiet and unknowing.
I am like the winter, sometimes quiet and still
and other times loud and raging.

Steve Mikesell
St Therese School
Aurora, CO
Grade 8

If Tomorrow Never Comes

If tomorrow never comes,
Will I be remembered for what I've done?
Have I fulfilled my outcome,
Or is all I've done is run?
Ran and hid,
Hid from my problems?
Or have I made a difference in someone's life?
Have I made that strife?
If tomorrow never comes,
Will I be forgiven?
Or has my life been driven,
Driven by someone else?
Have I done what I should have,
During my time?
Have I made that climb,
If tomorrow never comes?

Stephanie Baer
Dubois Elementary-Middle School
Dubois, WY
Grade 8

My Trip

I'm off to the races,
Going far to new places.
I'll go to a far away land,
Past the vast oceans and white sand.
Nothing will stop me,
No, nothing at all,
A wild animal, a river, anything can fall!
I'm going to go there,
I'm packing my bags,
And I'm getting my food,
I'll even bring my swimsuit,
Because I'm in the mood.
I'm off and I'm going,
Nothing will get in my way,
Today I'm going to have the best day!!
As I travel I worry and weep,
Where in the world am I going to sleep?
I'm frantic and scared in the darkness of the night.
I am shaky and clammy
And have a big fright!
Where did my great day go?
It got lost in the night!!

Jessica Robinson
Ranch View Middle School
Highlands Ranch, CO
Grade 8

What it Means to be Black

What does it mean to be black?
Does it mean you have to act all that?
Does it mean you have to wear your hat to the back?
Does it mean you have to slang crack?
Does it mean you have to like rap?
No, it means none of that.

It means you have to love yourself
Share your self-wealth
Accept the cards you are dealt
Love yourself until you melt

Besides if you don't who will
Jesus will
That's how I feel
Go by God's will
Be thankful for every meal
And if worst comes to worst just be real

Because all of that
That's what it means to be black

Ray Traylor
Overland High School
Aurora, CO
Grade 9

Life

We are all blowing
in a whirlwind of life.
You may hit a hurricane,
and be tossed around,
but remember, you will
always hit the ground.

Haynes Goodsell
Mountainridge
American Fork, UT
Grade 9

Thinking

Today I was thinking
About my own death
And how it would feel
Taking one last breath.

Will it hurt?
Will I feel pain?
Will the sky let go
With a cold, cold rain?

Or will it be nothing,
That I feel?
Almost a dream
But uncannily real?

After my death
Will I live on
In every raindrop
And every dawn?

Or will I just
Cease to exist
And disappear
Into the mist?

Kellie Noller
Dubois Elementary-Middle School
Dubois, WY
Grade 8

Flight

Flying up so high
Cruising through the sky
The sound is loud
Plowing through a cloud
Birds' wings get sore
That must be a bore
As you can see
Flying over the sea
Flying isn't vain
When you do it in a plane

Wesley Chapman
Kanab Middle School
Kanab, UT
Grade 7

Unforgettable

When I'm alone, without you, I have my doubts about this
I wonder what is next for us,
If there's a dead end just ahead
And if all those whispered phrases will be meaningless once again
You meant so much to me, but now we're lost
And I'm tired of the pain we cause each other every night
No ending of this cycle in my vision do I see
Nor the cause and time of its beginning
It's all hidden from me
I don't want what we have now, and what we had was lost
'Twas stolen by a different pair, whose new love still retains,
That innocence and passion,
Which for us does not remain
So we must end this saddened tale
Of fights and lies and tears
Yet through the time that follows,
In regret I will not wallow
But now the chapter's come
Where fights plague our love untrue
And we must part and smile,
Though through memories I'll not forget you

Danielle Williams
Norwood Middle School
Norwood, CO
Grade 9

My Grandma

I pondered placidly at the gloomy dirges.
I thought about where my Grandma would be.
Maybe she would be Seraphim, the highest of all angels.
I walked to the casket filled with all I had ever known...
My Grandma.

The tears stream down my face. I am reminded
Of all the good things we did together. The cooking, the shopping...
Everything. I feel as though my knees will give way at any given moment.
I am quaffing syrup. I can't catch my breath.
Then again, I am reminded of...
My Grandma.

Now people are spreading flowers on her grave.
People sobbing, people sad... for
My Grandma.

Her countenance was peaceful and full of goodness.
I knew she was at peace with the Lord.
My Grandma.

Tandi Haynie
Circle Jr High School
Circle, MT
Grade 8

The Harvest Day

The sun had just peeked over the Colorado corn,
With each breeze as it swayed another day was born.
The harvest was just right and the day had just begun,
The land waited to be touched by the rising sun.
Farmers had been up for hours by now,
Waiting for the morning dew to dry so they could start to plow.
The wheat was ready and bushels were many,
The copper-tone crop shimmered like a penny.
The work day began and heat did arise,
It gets hotter than hot and is quite a surprise.
Finally the day met the beginning of its end,
And deep into the earth the sun began to blend.

Chelsey Carlile
Granada School
Granada, CO
Grade 9

Alhambra

Ancient palaces of the Moors
Echoing halls, empty doors
Where warrior kings once took their meats
And told of all their battle feats
Among the garden lark's sweet song
Where minstrels once played to the throng
Upon the battlements spy gypsy cave
Guarding the towers soldiers brave
Yet in the distance cannon shot
Hell breaks loose, the walls hold not
Forced to leave this sacred place
A single tear rolls down the face

Mark D. Phillips
Colorado Academy
Denver, CO
Grade 7

The Rain

The raindrops leap and turn,
like tiny dancers on a concrete stage,
moving to the beat of an unheard melody.

An enormous crash of thunder echoing through the sky,
like the roar of applause from the audience,
seems to encourage them to dance more quickly.
Faster and faster they leap,
spinning swiftly across the endless stage.

They finally begin to slow their furious pace,
the patter of their feet quieting one by one.
Following a final roll of thunderous applause,
the last dancer leaves the stage.

Katherine Fisher
Butler Middle School
Salt Lake City, UT
Grade 8

Ignored and Sad

I walk toward him to give him a hug.
He steps back.

I run toward him to give him a hug.
He disappears.

I turn around and find him there.
Open arms are waiting for me.

As I get into his embrace, my arms try to hold him there.
He pushes me and walks away.

"Daddy!" I scream, "Come back!"
I'm now crying.
He just keeps on walking, walking away from me.

He never turns around to my pleas.
I need him.
I need his loving arms to give me comfort.

I run in his direction, to get him to come back
And be my father again.
But he's nowhere in sight.

I feel ignored and sad.
He just left me all alone.
I'm now in a room with no one.
No father to love me.

Brittney Ahlstrom
Guinn Middle School
Las Vegas, NV
Grade 8

Dad I Love You!!

When I'm down and sad
For some reason I usually go to my dad
He always finds a way to cheer me up
His comforting deep voice
And his cheerful happy chuckle
He dries my tears away
And tells me it will all be okay
I'm one of the lucky kids who has a dad
To play baseball with
Or go to father daughter day at girl scouts
My father may be gone soon
So I need to treat him with all my respect
And cherish his presence
All I want him to know is
"Dad I love you!"

Amy Amos
Century Middle School
Thornton, CO
Grade 7

My Promise

I wonder what I did
To deserve a friend like you
You have helped me out and promised
To always see me through

I wonder how it happened
I bet I will never see
Two friends that are closer,
Closer than you and me

You make my life seem so special
And make it seem so dear
So every night I thank the Lord
That I have you here

I plan to stick by you
Until my life is through
But in case my life is taken away
Just know that I love you

Amy Farley
White Middle School
Henderson, NV
Grade 7

Clash!

We chitter chat, and talk a lot,
my friends and I, we do.
We walk into the locker room,
and oh my gosh: PEE-U!

A thousand smells that greet us,
but knock us off our feet.
A hundred different stinky things,
whose costs were all real cheap.

The lotions of all smells and size,
the perfumes on the floor.
The week old deodorant,
hiding behind the door.

The dirty socks in all the lockers,
another perfume spray.
All the month old lunches,
like moldy fish fillet.

Class is out and away we go,
another day this concludes.
We breathe up all the fresh air,
and try to avoid the gloom.

Shoko Cameron
Century Middle School
Thornton, CO
Grade 7

Zlata in Bosnia

The bombs
The destruction
No new people
The trees are gone
No trees to climb
No going outside
No new air
Using furniture for heat
People are dying every day
Tears are falling everywhere

"Anne in Holland"

The bombs
The destruction
No friends
Stuck, not able to move
Claustrophobic, not able to breathe
The loud guns firing
No new air
Even her tears had to be
silent

Danielle Nobles
Century Middle School
Thornton, CO
Grade 7

A Night of Blue

Here I sit on a night of blue
My thoughts turned to God and you

The clouds float across the sky
The moon is at its high

What is love, what is life?
I hope I live throughout this night

My mind is bent with living fear
Is there really danger near?

Every sound upon my ear
Brings a special extra fear

Remembering the times I knew
And friends, too—
And soon I will see the sun again

My time is passing, it will soon end—
I hope I never have to fight again

Jayme Combs
White Middle School
Henderson, NV
Grade 7

Fishing

Fishing is fun
Fishing is cool.
So pack a lunch,
And dinner too,
And maybe
I'll go fishing with you.
The water was blue.
The grass was green.
We dug for worms,
But they were mean!
We fished all day.
We fished all night.
When we caught no fish,
I began to cry.
Then my dad,
Said with cheer,
"That's okay,
We will get them next year."
So we came back,
But sorry to say,
We caught no fish that day.

Zane Gray
Riverside Jr High School
New Castle, CO
Grade 7

Hate for Her

She doesn't know I hate her
but she'll soon find out.
There are many reasons why,
I feel hate for her inside.
She thinks we're "best friends"
but we're not!
She treats us like we're her slaves,
but we're not!
We're human beings like everybody else
So she's going to treat us like one
She thinks she's so cool,
but she's not!
Why do I listen to her?
All she does is make fun of people
because of the way they look,
dress and talk!
Someone needs to tell her "what's up!"
Still today she doesn't know
  I hate her,
but she's going to find out
  TODAY!

Stephanie Riofrio
South Valley Middle School
Platteville, CO
Grade 8

The Old Lone Cowboy and the Rough Rocky Mountains
As the sun gets ready to set,
It stretches its rays over the peaks of the mountains.
The cowboy's shadow is cast upon the dry hard ground
With the sagebrush looking on through the dim light.
It is as if the sun and the sagebrush
Are playing a game of hide 'n' seek around the corner
To find another child hiding in the dark.
As night falls, a large white moon thrusts itself into the sky.
It throws a shadow of the mountains to the ground.
When the cowboy gets ready to fall asleep in his bed roll,
The fire crackles and burns down slowly.
And his old buddies that will always lend a helping hand
In those special times of need hand ZZZ's in the sky.
As another hot summer day comes to a slow departure,
The westerner's day is done.

Matthew Garton
Spring Creek Middle School
Elko, NV
Grade 8

Fall
The wind is blowing,
rustling the trees with a crackling sound,
the scene looks like a fresh finger painting.
As the wind blows,
the leaves scatter through the air.
The dead trees stand there peacefully
just like skeletons on a windy Halloween.
The raven-dark clouds play pinball with the sun . . .
The shotgun sounds like an avalanche
creeping through the mountains.
You may call it fall
but to me it's a simple dream.

Rye Miller
Minturn Middle School
Minturn, CO
Grade 8

Red
Red is the color of passion and fear;
it seems to mean so much,
more than it knows.
Or is it just naive?
Can one color make the difference,
make everything seem right?
If you looked at someone with red in your eyes,
would it make them cry?
If you send a red Valentine
would that make things right?
Red is much more than it knows
or maybe not ready to accept.

Nicole Griego
East Middle School
Butte, MT
Grade 8

Park Poem
A beautiful park day
sun shining, birds singing
the park is filled with:
children running
toddlers skipping
old men playing catch
merry kids
mothers reading
old friends laughing
although this is true everyone knows
a beautiful day can turn into a rainy day
and so, as if drawn by faith
dark clouds and windy behavior appear
Hard raindrops and loud skies
take over the enchantment that once took place.
Children run to their mothers
toddlers run to their fathers.
And soon the park is deserted.
All the happy sounds
that filled the air is now replaced
by angry skies.

Vanessa Tafoya
St Therese School
Aurora, CO
Grade 8

Great Grandma Lyda's House
In her yellow house, sitting on the pink rocker,
Brings inspiration to me,
Coloring rainbow colored designs for the fridge,
Just like her I want to be.

Love to watch at dinnertime,
For the dog, a warm pot pie and a salad,
Piping hot pizza for Great Grandma and me,
Always tastes homemade as if cooked in a bakery.

Watching the old television that looked fifty years old,
My Great Grandma is just like me,
"Saved By the Bell" or "Full House,"
She would always watch with me.

Even though we're one thousand miles away,
She's still my favorite relative.
Great Grandma I love you,
I wish I could always be with you and you with me,
I want to be just like you.

You are my favorite memory.

Sarah Chaney
Falcon Creek Middle School
Aurora, CO
Grade 8

To My Two Best Friends

Words are spoken and hearts are sometimes broken.
And when we don't talk and you're not there, it's like having wings but no air.
I am sorry for the things that make you mad, I'll try hard
to make you happy when you are sad.
I'll do my best to understand your feelings and thoughts, and when
you are in need of someone, I'll be there to talk.
You mean the world to me and that's what I want you to know,
and if it were between life and you, I'd be the first to go.
I love you more than life so never forget
you will always be on all of my lists.
So as time and seasons come to change
I hope our friendship will always stay the same.

Erin Altman
Laurel Middle School
Laurel, MT
Grade 8

Difference

The most beautiful butterfly you've ever seen was flying around one summer eve.
He was sitting beneath the shade of an oak tree when she spotted an ant so far below.
Feeling more beautiful than ever, she drove down to greet him.

Just as she suspected, he was an average working ant.
Nothing as beautiful as she.

She landed gently on a flower petal a few inches away and started to smooth her wings.
Waiting for a complement from the ant, no such thing did he say other than "hello".

No eyes of astonishment or signs of jealousy.

He must have known from her expression, that she had expected much more.
He then replied "Would you like to rest here awhile with me?"

Staring in disbelief the butterfly muttered, "Aren't you jealous of my beauty or filled with envy because of my wings?
You are nothing but an average ant, nothing as beautiful as me."

With no look of sadness or any signs of feelings that could have been hurt.
The ant simply replied, "Wings or beauty wouldn't give me happiness. Just being me is good enough for me!"

"How could that be", stated the butterfly.

With a smile the ant replied, "Not everyone can have wings. For they wouldn't be unique, everyone is different.
That is how it is and the way it will be."

"Difference is only bad when someone uses it to be supreme."

With that he left. While the butterfly sat under the stars on a petal which was now lit up with the moonlight.

Thinking, about what the ant had said, a tiny ant that is.
It was there she finally understood that she was special and so was he!

Shalane Parcenue
Cortez Middle School
Cortez, CO
Grade 8

Butterfly

Spring comes, cocoons open;
They were caterpillars but now butterflies,
They wake up, and fly away,
Beautiful butterflies in the sky,
Everybody is beautiful, do you know why?
'Cause God loves you.

Mandy Brough
Star Valley Jr High School
Afton, WY
Grade 7

Pressure

I try my hardest, I never get to rest,
Until my good is better than best.
Their expectations are not mine.
I try to reach them but somehow fall behind.
I think I'm doing exceptional,
But it just doesn't seem to make the grade.
They push me too hard,
And our happy memories begin to fade.
I don't know why they do this to me,
When I'm just trying to make them proud.
It makes me so mad,
That I just want to scream out loud.
Why must you push me so!
Someday I'm going to crack, wide in two.
Maybe part of me will fit your idea of perfect,
Which I am obviously not.
So stop trying to change me,
For it will not happen,
Because I am me!
Here to live and be free!

Neely Cardinal
Pleasant View Middle School
Pueblo, CO
Grade 8

The Next Generation

To the holders of the future,
What is in store for us?
We scream loud!
We show our colors!
We fear nothing!
Except the future.
What is in store for us?
We are the future!
We are the earth
AND
We will make it
We are more powerful than generations past.

We are generation next.

Natalie Brown
Colorado Academy
Denver, CO
Grade 9

Life

The curveless road goes on for eternity
night draws closer
all light dims away

I can't do anything
I'm having troubles seeing
now talking with slurred vocabulary

As I begin my quest
my foot catches a crack in
the severed sidewalk
the balance I once had is gone
just like my faith for anything noble

Maybe I should just quit
turn around, keep away from the struggle,
just like everyone else

Now the light is lustrous
dark has dissipated,
but I never turned back
I wish the light was enduring, but I know
the ruthless night will return

Danielle Ketchum
Weldon Valley Jr High School
Weldona, CO
Grade 8

You've Got to Let it Go

If sometime in your life something happens,
That feels like a knife jabbed straight through your heart,
And there's absolutely nothing you can do,
Don't try to blame it on everyone around,
Because then you'll end up hating you.

Life goes on no matter what.
Just dump your load and walk ahead.
It may be hard to really forget,
But if later you look back,
It will have been the best thing
That you would have been able to do.

And if you harbor anger towards those people that you love,
I am sure that you will find that you want to let it go,
But it's so much harder than it would have been.
So don't hold onto anger, you've got to let it go.
Just hold onto the most important things:
The love and companionship of friends.

Maria Lechner
Star Valley Jr High School
Afton, WY
Grade 8

A Peaceful Fantasy

Light dances across an endless sky,
The droplets slide down as evening draws nigh,
Thunderous roars float all around,
As the currents hustle along the ground,
Little wet droplets soon become sleets,
That fall upon mountains, buildings, and streets,
The lights appear as a magical laser show,
That sneak behind clouds and provoke them to glow,
As wetness pauses in the air,
And the rolling thunder and lights disappear,
Slowly it is all coming to an end,
Where reality and peaceful dreams mend.

De'ja Erickson
Star Valley Jr High School
Afton, WY
Grade 7

Spring

March is a month that storms in with a bam,
March is the month that goes out like a lamb...
April is a month that brings gloomy showers,
April is the month that goes out like a flower
May is a month that comes with pink,
May is the month that goes out in a blink...
June is a month that ends the fling,
June is the month that ends spring...
Once spring is over, summer begins...
And then we must start all over again!

Alison Kjeldgaard
Campus Middle School
Englewood, CO
Grade 7

Don't Leave Me

I was coming home from work,
And I was thinking about our little chat,
How you encouraged me to do things right.
And now since you're gone,
I've been so uptight.
How did you die?
When I only got a bruise.
And yet I could still be in danger,
And I don't have you by my side,
To protect me.
I have only daddy now,
I can't bear it without you.
That terrifying accident,
Took me away from you.
I know you will always look after me,
In that great big sky.
Please don't leave me here,
All alone in the world.

Brittany Messmer
Riverside Jr High School
New Castle, CO
Grade 7

Money

Some people call it the root of all evil
Those are the ones who play with the devil
They use it for whiskey and wine when they dine
They spend it so freely it must be a crime

Some people hoard it
Grab all that they can
They put it in stocks or a mutual plan

Some people use it to better the world
Buy toys for a stranger or their own little girl
They give it to churches, to shelters, to schools
And they'd never spend it on cars or fancy jewels

Some people spend it to be the big cheese
To buy fortune and fame and to do as they please
Me, I just use it for all of these

Josh Mack
Campus Middle School
Englewood, CO
Grade 8

God Is What We Need...*

It's all over the damage has been done,
Fifteen lives have been taken and we're all stunned.
Some give grief and some give blame,
Fifteen went away with peace and two went with flames.

Rachael had a belief in which she gave her life,
But Rachael had a creed and that's what made her die.
As days go by and people start to care,
They should see that what we need is prayer.

It only took two kids to make many lives change,
With hatred, and confusion in their hearts.
Their points of view they couldn't exchange,
It's all over and the damage has been done.

I look at our government and sometimes wonder,
If in our future plans we can include giving God a chance.
I've been in schools lately with many different opinions,
Where they hesitate to see God is what we need.

With God in my heart, helping in the right way,
I will continue to pray for the day we all live out our fate.
Many people say it's credence we lack,
But it seems to me that it's God we need to unpack.

Brooke N. Jenkins
Campo High School
Campo, CO
Grade 9
*In Memory of Columbine High School

Life

Life is a whisper,
and a dream,
sometimes it's hard to understand the scene,
sometimes we laugh,
and sometimes we cry,
but life goes on and so will I.
Sometimes you're ahead
sometimes you're behind
and that's the end to my beautiful rhyme.
But why the end when it can be the beginning?
Life is a place inside your mind,
life is creation,
life is only complications,
life is a whisper;
and a dream
It all depends on how you look at the scene,
just live your life
and live it good.

Mindy Howard
Bill Reed Middle School
Loveland, CO
Grade 7

Her Eyes

When our eyes met for the very first time,
I knew for certain that it was love.
although we could only watch each other
never speaking, never meeting, just watching,
it was love.

The day the trucks took me away
I thought I'd never see her again,
but I could feel her eyes around me
all the time.

They made me work the ovens,
shoveling hundreds day by day.
I saw so many faces, all heads shaved,
all faces full of terror, and relief
knowing they were in a better place than I.

I shoveled many bodies; with my emotions hard,
I never cried.
I saw neighbors, friends, and family, all with open eyes.
And then I saw them.
Her head was shaved, her body frail,
but her eyes were still the same.
I cried.

Melissa Woodbury
South Jordan Middle School
South Jordan, UT
Grade 8

Dream

Let your mind go. A dream is a stick of cotton candy,
sticking to your fingers. A dream is a scoop of
ice cream, cooling you down.
Let your mind go. A dream is an exquisite rainbow, shining
through the clouds. A dream is a soft snowflake
drifting to the ground.
Let your mind go. A dream is a melody playing through your
head. A dream is the sun, bright and warming.
Let your mind go.
Dream away
Child's favorite place
Till she awakens.

Natasha Meisner
South Valley Middle School
Platteville, CO
Grade 8

The Fearless Hawk

The fearless, mighty hawk,
Soaring through an open sky,
Its sturdy wings, spread amid the flowing air,
Escaping to the vast crevices of the mountain.

An eye is always watchful for prey.
Its prey is seized in a single, diving swoop.

A shadow crossing a broad basin
Alerts the dangered wildlife of its approach.

Caught with a breeze, ever turning,
Its talons catch the gleaming sunlight.
The fearless, mighty hawk, ever turning,
Will never reach its true destination.

Christina Cannon
Challenger School
Sandy, UT
Grade 7

A Robin

Soaring in the heavenly skies,
a robin glides through the air.
Its majestic appearance reveals,
a fiery red breast.
Its wing span engulfs,
the air beneath it as it travels.
Its primary agenda is to snatch large,
juicy round earthworms for its young.
Countless days involve protecting, securing,
and feeding its precious young.
Ascending over the hills until its final days,
the robin claims the wide, open blue,
sky as its own.

Stacy Taylor
Boulder City High School
Boulder City, NV
Grade 9

Endlessly

Lost in a sea of blue eyed ecstasy
Boring through an endless void
Running in circles, never wish to escape
We've traveled this road before
So full of guilt
Only to find at the end
Endless love
Undying endless love
Blossoming through your being
And shaking the walls of your creation
Finding inside a hungry soul
Waiting for Euphoria to come
Will it ever end?
Will the endless love ever die?
Can I cut it open and watch it bleed?
The blood of the innocent?
The fire that burns, that never stops
Could I drown it with my tears?
Endless questions fill my mind
I hang my head and continue on
Endlessly

Alex Webb and Chassidy Atkinson
Pleasant Grove Jr High School
Pleasant Grove, UT
Grade 9

Someone I Love

Your soft voice echoes when I hear it
When you're around me your
Love is so strong that I can't bear it
Your soul is like a dove
That is why I hope I find you up above.

Rhett Oler
Academy Charter School
Castle Rock, CO
Grade 7

War

You were blind,
with your eyes closed.
  You were nervous,
because of dying.
  You were pleading,
and I regretted it.
  You sobbed and moaned,
as you peered through your eyes.
  The foe had died,
and he was rotting.
  I washed your wound,
as you howled.
  As we lied,
we were isolated.

Tyler Andersen
Indian Hills Middle School
Sandy, UT
Grade 7

I Am

I am a young girl torn between two worlds
I wonder when all animals will be free to live
I hear humans and animals talking and fighting
I see no deaths of innocent creatures
I want to live free and choose for myself
I am a young girl torn between two worlds

I pretend to be a great actress
I feel the pain inflicted on all living things
I touch the land untouched by man
I worry I will be lost to my worlds
I cry when an animal is killed in cold blood
I am a young girl torn between two worlds

I understand my past and the path I'm expected to follow
I say people should be judged for who they are, not where they're from
I dream to write famous tales and scripts
I try to preserve the earth
I hope they won't be lost in human's greed
I am a young girl torn between two worlds
The world of man and the world of nature

Amy Bullock
North Davis Jr High School
Clearfield, UT
Grade 9

Montana

I would like to know, have you ever seen
One of Montana's great fields of green?

The pastures and night skies meeting half the way
Flashing purple and chartreuse at the very end of the day

Through autumn and summer and spring and fall
Doesn't matter which, I've seen them all

Horses and cows all grazing around
It's a perfect scene with not the smallest sound

The most beautiful sight I have ever seen
Was looking out over these fields of green

If you ever chance to see the mountains or the hills
You would see how they compliment the cool running rills

If you ever come upon Montana with nothing else to do
Come and see the mountains, the clouds, and the streams of bright, bright blue

Dulcie Bue
Reedpoint Jr/Sr High School
Reedpoint, MT
Grade 8

The Storm

The storm reaches out for me.
The lightning brightens the room.
Until the storm is over I will not go to bed.

At this time the rain seems to be comforting,
But the black blanket of clouds and thunder
Darken all of my hopes away,
It is dark like a black hole.

The trees reach out for me.
The wind is howling like a wolf
As if it were howling at the moon.

The only place I feel safe is under the sheets.
Everything gets quiet, too quiet, could the storm be over,
Or is this just a dangerous calm?
I can't go to bed with only the moonlight comforting me.

Finally the storm is over.
The stars have come out to play,
It is time to go to sleep now, fall fast asleep now;
The storm is over.

Andrea Garbrecht
Challenger School
Sandy, UT
Grade 7

Flight Attendant to Daughter

Well, beautiful girl, let me tell you,
life for me hasn't always been a smooth flight.
There has been turbulence,
and traffic jams on the runway,
obstacles in my path,
and there are always delays.

But every day,
I'm still gaining altitude,
I'm still pushing that cart down the aisles,
passing out peanuts, and fastening seat belts.
Sometimes, I have to trust the pilot,
going though the dark with little light to guide him,
but I still make it through the night.

So, my precious darling, don't you ever give up.
Don't ever sit down on those seats,
just because life is bumpy and rough.
'Cause I'm still gaining altitude,
and life for me hasn't always been a smooth flight.

Elizabeth Dunn
Boulder City High School
Boulder City, NV
Grade 9

Golden Sun

The rays of shining sun weave throughout the clouds
Like weaving gold thread through a soft white pillow
The hues of reds and pinks
Travel throughout the Heavens
And the charismatic voices of a thousand angels sing

The sun has cast her lovely hues
Upon all that can be reached
Dusk cannot rebuke her, nor can night
She stays alive through eternity
As the rays weave, and the angels sing
Throughout the heavens high
And she casts her lovely hues until she sets.

Katie Roberts
Campus Middle School
Englewood, CO
Grade 8

Pearls

Falling pearls, sheet of glass,
Silver fingers form a stream –
And twisted together by an unknown loom
Combing to surge unstoppable –
Falling down a cliff in a moment,
Then grinding an crashing it shapes the earth.
It goes on without looking back,
Creating life, destroying life without thought,
Then finally joins with others so grand
To lash up on beaches, to chase a whale,
And be the absolute essence of the whale,
So is the life of a raindrop.

Tyler Matthew Ricks
Mountain Ridge Jr High School
Highland, UT
Grade 8

Our Oceans

The ocean,
Blue on the surface, an array of colors below.
An underwater world filled with wonders.
Boats ride the swells; surfers ride the waves,
The creatures underneath ride the currents.
Dolphins, whales, fish, coral: all living.
This world of aquatic beings,
So mysterious to many.
Threatened by humans,
Litter drifting throughout,
Washing our troubles away into the surf,
Into the
Living,
Breathing
Ocean.

Andrea Tanny
Excel School
Durango, CO
Grade 9

Friendships

Helping, Caring, and Friendliness,
Is what makes friendships great!
Having fun together,
Is what friendships are all about!
Loving, Hoping, and Talking,
Is what friendships are all about!
Both in life and in the souls of
Thousands of great friends!
Friendships are as good as Gold!

Kristina Parker
Academy Charter School
Castle Rock, CO
Grade 7

Deep Sorrow

I have a deep sorrow,
    because I thought my dad loved me
But he doesn't.
    He said I was a mistake,
Well, not in those exact words,
    but he was thinking it.
He wanted me to be a boy,
    but I'm not.
He disowns me,
    but I don't mind.
It really hurts me to know that
    but I can try to fill in the empty space
He left in my heart!

Allie Stephenson
South Valley Middle School
Platteville, CO
Grade 8

Springtime

Spring is the time
When the grass becomes green,
When the flowers all bloom,
And when the bees go buzz.

The grass stretches toward the sky,
All green and lush,
And fruit trees
Begin to burst with blossoms.

Spring is the time,
When the rain tumbles down
Out of the white and swollen clouds,
It's when things are all refreshed.

Andrea Brinkerhoff
Kanab Middle School
Kanab, UT
Grade 7

Reverted to Abolition

Times have gone by
I have not listened to a word
I will not lie
I've not taken care of dues

Arranged in a row
All lined in midst of superstition
Most people know that they have all
Reverted to abolition

Returned to the past
Think of the people crossed
I will never say
Try to make me think
Although
Maybe I'll never rest

Crime enforcing
Why not stop it from the source

Zach Block
Campus Middle School
Englewood, CO
Grade 8

The Sleeping World of Jacob Long

The sleeping world of Jacob Long
Filled with beasts and heroes gone
And gardens filled with flowers blue
And sunsets red, and maidens true
Was seen by creatures small and fair
But not a single man was there
Save for Jacob Long.

For he alone held close the key
That let him in this world for free
And let him smile and laugh once more
Before he closed his golden door
And locked it fast and bid farewell
To this haven where did dwell
The dreams of Jacob Long.

And thus he woke, and swept in vain;
He'd lost his heaven once again
And naught but paper held the world
That his mind had once unfurled
For dreams are drifters; refusing to stay
And thus the flowers faded away
In this world of Jacob Long.

Kayla Cheatham
Vail Mountain School
Vail, CO
Grade 7

Garbage

Garbage garbage it's everywhere.
Filling up our land and our breathing air.
Contaminating everything it touches.
Making everything nasty.

All the car exhaust.
Filling up the sky.
Making unclean air,
And making it harder to breathe.

No one cares about the earth.
They think it's no big deal.
All this trash everywhere.
Making land look like junk.

I don't know how to help.
I just sit and stare.
i just think about it without a care,
While garbage is launched into the air.

We can help though.
We just need to try.
Just teach us how.

Corey Swan
Century Middle School
Thornton, CO
Grade 7

Graffiti

When you insult me
and when you lie.
When you kick me
and make me cry.
You add to the graffiti
that slowly builds up
upon the wall that hides my heart.
Eventually you will say
the few words that will cause a crack,
like an axe, hack, hack, hack.
The crack will grow
and as it does so
I'll crumble to the ground,
my tender heart exposed
to the cruelty, the abuse.
And as your words fly
and my tears cry
my heart will slowly die
and then—so will I.

Sarah Bauman
Century Middle School
Thornton, CO
Grade 7

The Twists of Time

There I sat pondering, wondering why,
There I lay dreaming of days gone by
Of lads and lasses lost in the twists of time.
Each thought and wonder bringing louder and louder thunder

Then I dreamed of acquaintances near and far.
Of lost love and childhood friends
Of fun and friendly times
How there is only rush and run, no time for fun

Where has all the past gone
Gone away, lost in the twists of time
Why does this poor soul suffer so
Because he is tossed, tossed in the twists of time

Huntington Davis
Mountain Ridge Middle School
Colorado Springs, CO
Grade 8

The Things I Love

My satin toe shoes tied up tight.
Gracefully dancing with all my might.
The sound of a crowd in the game of baseball.
Money in my pocket, a trip to the mall.
Tulips, roses, and daffodils bright.
Billions of stars on a Lake Powell night.
A beautiful rainbow with colors galore.
A "do not disturb" sign on my bedroom door.
Gracefully gliding on a frozen pond.
The snow starts to fall as I skate along.
Playing Chopin on the piano keys.
A tickle in your nose that makes you sneeze.
A window seat on a mile high jet.
A walk in the rain and getting wet.
The Maui surf I love to hear.
My boogie board and snorkel gear.
A Christmas tree with sparkling lights.
When my baby sister says "Good night."
All the things you see above,
Are all the things I truly love.

Ashley Hutchison
Riverview Jr High School
Murray, UT
Grade 8

Hockey

H ard to score
O vertime is suspenseful
C ontact sport
K icksave made by the goalie
E SPN televises the games on television
Y ounger people are better

Chris Cleary
White Middle School
Henderson, NV
Grade 7

Eternity's Blessing

You can't see it,
Smell it lingering in the air.
It takes no shape, size or form,
But you feel it's there
It's the meaning of life,
A reason to be.
A light in the dark for both you and me.
It's the pure sound of joy
That comes from our hearts,
And the bonds holding us together
So we will never part.
It's sad, happy, sweet and sour.
We will wait for it by the year
Decade, or hour.
It's the thing some people live for,
Yet never find.
But it will emanate around us,
For all times.
It's everything you could ever wish for and more.
It's love, pure, sweet,
Love.

Carol Hewitt
Linderman Jr High School
Kalispell, MT
Grade 7

The Truth About Snow White

Now that it is ever after,
We are not so happy.
   A slave in my own house.
      A stranger,
      In my world.
Once I had beautiful silk dresses
   Royal Blue, Pearl White,
   Dazzling Yellow, Brilliant Red.
Now only rags.
      He goes to bars,
      I work, I dust
         He comes home,
         I cook,
         And sweep.
            He yells at me,
            The food wasn't right.
            I tried,
            Can't win.
Maybe our "happily ever after"
Has turned,
Unhappy.

Margaret Zaegel
Colorado Academy
Denver, CO
Grade 9

Life on the Run

Life on the *run*
isn't always fun–
Being there for the bad days,
and all of the good ones!

See you there, or on the way,
but I know I'll get there . . . someday
If I arrive there before you do,
I'll be there waiting for you.

Life on the *run*–
When will I be done?
It's just . . . taking . . . too . . . long,
I can't wait to be done!

Life on the *run*
isn't always fun.
Will I ever see the end . . .
of life on the *run?*

Nick Schaefer
Sage Valley Jr High School
Gillette, WY
Grade 9

Inside a Piece of Chalk

Inside a piece of chalk are
Math equations,
Science notes,
And English sentences.
Just waiting for teachers and students
To let them out.
When all of these things
That are waiting
To be let out
Are let out
You hold the world in your hands.

Rebecca Hilliard
St. Jude Thaddeus School
Havre, MT
Grade 7

Everything

Fish in the fountain
Dogs at the door
Cat in a cradling arm
Horses in the hay meadow
Mom in the magazine
Dad at the dock
Liz at the library
Marty in the mud
Everything always has a place,
Always.

Amber Royer
Norwood Middle School
Norwood, CO
Grade 8

Fly Fishing

Standing there all day long with waders on,
Fishing pole in hand and an empty creel.
Leaving lots of flies lost,
Stuck in a stump on the other side.

If I could just lightly land a fly,
I was sure I could catch a trophy fish.
Just then a nibble came. I waited for another strike.

The next tug came like a steam locomotive.
I let it out for just a second,
Then pulled it hard to sink it to the shank.
Yes! Finally the biggest fish I ever will catch.

Bigger than my Uncle Charlie's,
I can see it now, hanging over my bed.
Oh, don't pull too hard and snap the line.
Take my time. Take my time.

Then the monster cleared the water, scales glinting in the sun.
'Twas then the three-pound line did snap.

Somewhere in this world there is happiness.
Someone playing ball and bluebirds twittering in the trees.
But there is no happiness here today,
For the monster got away.

Brandon Richardson
Carbondale Community School
Carbondale, CO
Grade 8

Fragile Hearts

A broken heart lay along with the lonely tears on the ground
So many things to say but out of your mouth comes no sound
You wonder what happened and why
Because you never cheated or even dared to lie
A hard lump lays in your throat then you start to cry
Speechless souls standing side by side feeling sad and hurt
But neither one will let the other one know
For that of a heartache would it show
You swore you would never love another guy
Until you saw a painful unloving look in his eye
No more Romeo or Juliet, they just walked off that picture perfect set
It's too hard to look at him anymore
For if you do down your face tears shall pour
Remembering his promise to stop loving you never
Yet that heartfelt promise could not stay true forever!

Paris A. Pender
Platte River Academy Charter
Highlands Ranch, CO
Grade 7

Tuck Me In

Tuck me in when I say I'm ready for bed.
Tuck me in when I'm tired.
Tuck me in when you get home from work.
Tuck me in when it's late at night.
Tuck me in and tuck me in tight.

Chesney Randolph
Powell Middle School
Littleton, CO
Grade 7

Stories

All these books surrounding me
They all hold many stories, you see
Some about ugly old men with dentures
Some about princesses, but all with adventures

I shall travel far and wide
I'll take a book and go hide
There I'll escape to another world
Sitting cozy with my toes curled

There I'll stay,
Tucked away
For another day

Safe with my adventurous stories.

Jessica Watterson
Century Middle School
Thornton, CO
Grade 7

Collecting Dust

There was an old woman who lived on Pikes Peak
she stayed in her house from week to week

Now this may sound weird, but tell you, I must
this strange old woman collected dust.

All day long she sat in her chair
while dust collected from her feet to her hair

This collection was big and yet, it was small
she had tiny grains of dust from wall to wall

The collection itself didn't cost a dime
all it took was a lot of time

So if you want to collect something that's cheap,
just sit in a chair and go to sleep.

Paul Rohde
Manitou Springs Middle School
Manitou Springs, CO
Grade 7

Basketball

Basketball,
That's my sport,
nervousness before the game.
Soon it turns to excitement,
running down the court,
dribbling the ball,
pass it, shoot it, score!
Play tough defense,
let's work as a team,
rebound the ball,
dribble it, pass it, shoot,
watch the ball sail through the air,
Close your eyes,
swish!
Hear the crowd roar,
"I made it!," Yeah!
Long shot or short shot,
have fun and show team spirit.
I love this game!
Basketball,
That's my sport.

Cori Pfalzgraff
Riverside Jr High School
New Castle, CO
Grade 7

Violence

Pain and suffering,
Hate and killing.
Dark emotions, swelling up
In a war of love and hate
For what is mine,
For what is yours.

I fight you now,
For my opinion.
I fight you now,
For my possession.
I fight you now,
For my religion.

But now I stop and fight no more.
For now I wonder why the fight continues.
For now I wonder why we can't have peace
To join together
To help each other.

I lay down my weapon,
And put aside my anger.
To turn to you, and ask you now
Why not stop the violence?

Jonathan Daniel
Vaughn Middle School
Reno, NV
Grade 8

Young Poets
Grades 4-5-6

Ode to the Salmon River

One week long is the challenging Salmon River,
With mountains and green all around,
And crystal clear water coming from all the creeks,
With ruby red cherries and the delicious flavor they provide,
There is no place better than this.
The Mole Lady tells us the story of Frank B. Lance,
While we eat cherries under the coolness of the shade.
On our plum purple raft we ride through the rapids,
Getting soaked from the water and barely missing the rocks and holes.
Now we are cold, but we go to the hot spring and get warm.
And when we're visiting the Buckskin Bill museum,
Horses and mules come and we give them cherries.
When camping on the sandy white beaches,
We kayak in the eddies and make sand castles.
And when you look into the sunset beyond the mountains,
And the green trees, all the fruit, the beautiful creeks,
You think about what's coming--your life ahead of you.
And what challenges and exciting things will come,
As you look into the sunset wondering these things,
You will also learn that life's a mystery,
And you need to just have fun.

Brittney Banning
Westridge Middle School
Price, UT
Grade 6

Cello Notes

My cello sounds are soft and sweet.
They softly come off the page,
but in different moods:
crabby, angry, sorrowful, joyful.

Once off the page,
the notes dance merrily around my bow,
then swirl around my room.

They weave through the spindles of the bed,
making my stuffed animals waltz.
They whistle through my K'Nex creation.

They travel across my glove,
visiting countries that I haven't discovered.

They sleep in my cello case,
making my rosin ready to dress the bow.

They puff my clothes with invisible life,
so when I wear them, I move with music.

Some of the notes escape from under my bedroom door,
fading in the silence.

Aaron Child
Colorado Academy
Denver, CO
Grade 5

Surprise

At my friend's house
Two cats
Sleeping, sleeping.

Squeak! Squeak!

Two cats up now
Speaking, speaking:
Meow! Meow!

Looking for that
Squeaking, squeaking.

From the bushes each cat
Thinking, thinking:

"Tasty morsel!"
Each cat
Eating, eating.

Squeak! Squeak!

Running to the porch
Leaping, leaping.

Granny in her rocker:
Squeaking, squeaking.

MEOW?

Pauletta Donatello
St John the Baptist School
Draper, UT
Grade 4

Everyone Is Important

What makes this earth a better place
Is a variety of talent and skill
For if everyone did the very same thing
We would surely go downhill.

When we compare ourselves to others,
We notice what they do the best
Then match it to our very weakest trait
It's a poor and unreliable test.

Instead we should value the talents we've got.
And appreciate those of our friends
Never feeling bad for what we can't do
On this our true happiness depends.

And doing what's right when temptations arise
Not being afraid to say "NO!"
Will also help us feel better inside
By not just going along with the flow.

Everyone has unique character traits,
That's the way it's supposed to be.
We can strengthen each other with courage and love
And help us feel guilt free.

April Harrison
Ashgrove Elementary School
Riverton, WY
Grade 5

The Storm

I sit and watch the angry storm
The thunder blows its booming horn
Threatening clouds show ugly gray,
I'm sure the storm is here to stay.

Lightning flashes yellow streaks
The wind will roar and scream and shriek
The rain will come in big, full pails
Until it finally turns to hail.

A rainbow comes to greet the end
Beautiful colors it shall send.
And then the sun shines on a hill
The storm moves on, the day is still.

Beth Hollowed
Meeker Elementary School
Meeker, CO
Grade 5

Old Friendships

Sometimes I sit in camp through the night,
dreaming of those far off days.
I'll gaze into the fire's light,
as if into a sunlit haze.

Then visions come,
of those comrades mine,
laughing, happy, so true to see.
Untarnished by the dust of time,
forever fresh in my memory.

The ways we talked,
the parties so grand,
I dream of them one and all.
When we made life size castles in the sand,
and when we strolled through colorful leaves in fall.

Of exciting adventures each new dawn,
as side by side we stood evermore.
The fire tells the story then dies and is gone,
of what true friends are for.

Brianne Jensen
Thompson Falls Elementary School
Thompson Falls, MT
Grade 6

Evening Meditation

As the sun set over the prairie grass,
The little bird chirped his song.
And the breeze whispered a secret
Of the days that had come and gone.

The mountains stood in a solemn line
As the sun sank behind their peaks.
And the wind blew through the aspen trees
As darkness enveloped the Earth.

And as I sat in the lengthening shadows,
The bird lay down his head.
A silence fell upon the Earth
Beneath the starlit heavens.

A day of glory has come and gone,
But beauty does not last.
It is but a little bird
Who flits upon the breeze.

Meredith MacGregor
Eisenhower Elementary School
Boulder, CO
Grade 5

The Urgent Message

"There is an urgent message that needs to be delivered,"
Said the sun to the dove.
So, the dove flew and flew,
Until she couldn't fly any further.
She dropped the message to the fish in the large vast ocean.

Then the fish swam and swam,
Until he couldn't swim any further.
He gave the note to the frog.

The frog nodded, and jumped and jumped,
Lily pad to lily pad,
Until he couldn't jump any further.
He gave it to the cloud.

The cloud, with a soft smile on its face,
Rose before his eyes and gave the message to the Good Fairy.

The Good Fairy nodded and then,
With the whip of her wand,
The cold winter turned to summer,
And the sun shone bright.

Lisa Marquez
McClelland Center School
Pueblo, CO
Grade 5

The Other Side of the World

Some of us think our world is just great.
Others like my Granny see it from a confused state.

We see it bright and colorful,
She sees it black and white.
We see it clear and beautiful,
She sees it dull and barely light.

The only way to see it from her point of view,
Is if you have the disease of Alzheimers too.
So enjoy your life while you can,
The other side of the world is not so grand.

Emily Reiter
Ashgrove Elementary School
Riverton, WY
Grade 5

The Hot-Air Balloon

As I rise into the air
The sun brightly shining on my hair
Down below the people stare
As my balloon flies

The balloon's colors – red, white, and blue
Over the meadows of wonderful hue
Little birds flying across from you
As my balloon flies

Looking down into the land
I see the beach's creamy sand
Out the basket I reach my hand
As my balloon flies

Down, down, down I go
Soaring with the breeze's flow
Coming near the farmer's hoe
As my balloon lands

Sharon Wu
Northridge Elementary School
Highlands Ranch, CO
Grade 4

My Grandpa
My grandpa is fun to be around.
His name is Clayton Gumbo Zander.
It's fun to be around a great grandpa.
His hazel eyes twinkle and dance with mischief as he pinches my leg to check how thick my jeans are.
When he has been outside chucking bales, he looks kind of like a scarecrow that's been pecked by crows.
After he has been wearing his winter hat when he has been feeding his cows, his hair sticks up like the fire in the wood stove.
Before he shaves he looks like a rough and tough mountain man, but after he has shaved he looks like a nice old townsman.
That's what my wonderful grandpa looks like.

My grandpa can sound many different ways.
His voice can be as quiet as a mouse when he whispers secrets in my ear.
He can sound as loud as a lion's roar when he booms "KaBoss" to get the cows to come.
And he can sound scary when I've done something that I know I shouldn't have done.

The best thing about my grandpa is how he feels.
When I cuddle up in his lap and his arms are around me I feel warm, cuddly and safe like a soft teddy bear in a little girl's arms.

My grandpa is great to be around.
He loves to tease me and I love it, even though I squirm and tell him to stop!
And I love him very much.

Casey Zander
Thompson Falls Elementary School
Thompson Falls, MT
Grade 6

I Am

I am a woman, I am peace and tranquility,
My heart is a lonesome cradle of sorrow
That asks for nothing more than love.

My soul is cushioned with soft warmth.
The things I search for don't even exist in your world but in mine.
Joy comes when love spreads through my body,
Reaches to my heart and stretches out to my soul.
A stroke of paint can make me disappear with no trace,
And I'm swept under nothing but dark coldness.
No longer do I have a cushion around my soul
Or cradle surrounding my heart for everything has gone dark in me.
My life is an open book read by many people.
Chains and shingles around my bounded wrists and ankles bind me from stopping them.
But then I wake up for it was just a dream,
A dream that is passed now just a handful of crumpled leaves
Crumpled leaves that keep me from my future like everything else.
A song of sorrow.
Nothing passes me by without leaving a burn on my swollen body.
There is a trail of blood leading me to a key.
A key to my spirit, the spirit that now has been crushed by an endless river of darkness.
A voice of a child screaming inside me, the pain, the sorrow, the forgiveness of another.

Gretchen Roesler
Foothills Academy
Wheat Ridge, CO
Grade 6

At the Demolition Derby

Five-four-three-two-one...let the derby begin,
VROOM...VROOM...roar the engines of the demo cars
The crowd goes wild with anticipation!
Dirt and mud pollute the air as cars show off their power
CRASH...the cars smash into one another
The metal of fenders goes CRUNCH, CRACK, CLANG...
Hip, hip, hooray hollers the crowd!

Trevor Drewry
Ashgrove Elementary School
Riverton, WY
Grade 4

Spring, Summer, Fall, Winter

I know it is spring
When birds are chirping
And flowers are sprouting.

I know it is summer
When the sun is bright
And flowers are blossoming.

I know it is fall
When the air is crisp
And the leaves are red, brown and yellow.

I know it is winter
When the air is cold
And the snow is fresh.

I know I love all four seasons
Because they are all different
In some way, shape, or temperature.

Britni Riley
St John the Baptist School
Draper, UT
Grade 4

Snow Day

While I was running I saw some snow
It was sparkling brightly in the sunlight

The snow was glittering
It was so peaceful to watch it come down from the sky

You can ski in it
You can snowboard in it
You can do almost anything in snow
The snow is so beautiful

I like to watch snowflakes fall down
They are breathtaking
Snow is so joyful

Bradley J. Peers
Hawthorne Elementary School
Missoula, MT
Grade 5

Take Me to a Place

Take me to a place, a place beyond our reach,
Where birds and beasts take pleasure in everything they see.

Many waterfalls live there with willows at their sides,
To keep them company through all the winter tides.

There are fairies who do good and dance and sing
And take care of all the plants.

There are horses that run free
And give the animals rides.

In an ocean nearby,
There are dolphins and whales.

There are peacocks who show off
And take pleasure in their tails.

Now we come to the king, the greatest of all
Even if he is small.

He is a mouse though that might seem queer,
But he has the biggest heart and cares for them all.

He is loyal and fair and doesn't complain,
But the animals listen to him and take his advice.

Now we have it in our minds, this land of good spirit, so...
Take me to a place, a place beyond our reach.

Kalou Eichholz
Moffat Elementary School
Crestone, CO
Grade 5

Pain

Pain is seeing a stray dog alone,
outside in the middle of winter.

Pain is when your best friend writes notes,
your personal secrets to someone else.

Pain is a loved one,
lost forever.

I'm full of pain when I see my pregnant mother,
struggle with exhaustion and discomfort.

I'm ashamed when I don't care
if I make my family very sad.

I'm glad that pain fades away,
with time.

Andrew R. Blatter
Morningside Elementary School
Salt Lake City, UT
Grade 6

Rain Forest

Always raining, falling down,
splashing, smashing into the ground.
Puddles, lakes, streams, an animal
or a reptile, a bug, a small snug bug,
a bat sleeping, a monkey screaming,
all things need rain.

Tyson Smith
Ecker Hill Middle School
Park City, UT
Grade 6

Drumming

Drumming is like flying,
You never know where you go,
Hearing the sound,
Of my stick pounding,
Like no care in the world
I play.

Cody Wales
Nederland Elementary School
Nederland, CO
Grade 6

Strangers!

Sun
warm, on fire
blasting, heating, frying
hot, never cool, cool, craters
wondering, spinning, mind rattling
no gravity, expedition
Moon

Andrea Leal
Ecker Hill Middle School
Park City, UT
Grade 6

My Bear

Once I had a dog
He was a good fellow
He was very yellow
But one day
He ran away
And never came back that day

Once I had a fish
He was a stupid fish
He jumped out of his bowl
He rotted like a smelly fish

I have a bear
He is very near
He is a stuffed animal

Sarah Ball
Heatherwood Elementary School
Boulder, CO
Grade 4

What is a Teacher?

A teacher is someone who sees each child as a unique person
and encourages individual talents and strengths.

A teacher looks beyond each child's face
and sees inside their soul.

A teacher is someone with a special touch and a ready smile,
who takes the time to listen to both sides and always tries to be fair.

A teacher is someone who can look past
disruption and rebellion, and recognizes hurt and pain

A teacher makes a difference in each child's life
and affects each family and the future of us all.

Ashley Ceriello
Adams Elementary School
Broomfield, CO
Grade 6

When I Was Little

When I was little I used to scratch on my parents' door for attention,
Like a cat pawing to come inside.
It sounded like fingertips running down the blackboard,
Or a dog trying to bury a bone in the backyard.
My parents used to say, "Is this my angel?"
Like God speaking to his messengers.
It was always in the morning when I had the case of the yawnings,
Like a tired child not wanting to go to bed at night.
It was the one time where they could make me roll around laughing,
Like a chimpanzee showing off at the circus.
I will never forget these great times and will always hold the memory in my heart,
Like an heirloom secretly locked up in a hope chest forever.

Kammie Daniels
First Presbyterian Church Academy
Las Vegas, NV
Grade 6

Michael Jordan Six Time Champion

Bang! Suddenly the lights in the United Center go off.
Then lights like lasers cut through the silent darkness.
Then you hear a voice say at guard 6 ft. 6 in. from North Carolina Michael Jordan.
The crowd goes wild when they see the great Michael Jordan.
The game starts and Michael is on fire.
He drives it to the hole and jumps to dunk it.
But something spectacular happened Michael
Stopped in mid air to let everybody see him
And when he is ready he will dunk the ball
And shatter the backboard because he is so powerful.
I know he is powerful because
If you look into his eyes you will see a
Furious bull ready to unleash his
Power!

Alvaro Guerrero
South Elementary School
Brighton, CO
Grade 5

The Sun

Shining brightly on the grass
Making rainbows on prism glass
The color of honey in a jar
The reflection on a newly waxed car
Some glitz and gleam in the air
The highlights of strawberry blond hair
A bright yellow candle smelling of fun
That's what I think of when I look at the sun

Grace K. Baumgartner
Sacred Heart of Jesus School
Boulder, CO
Grade 5

The Wind

Yesterday the wind was blowing hard.
Today it was the same way.
Tomorrow I think the wind will blow across my yard.
I like the wind, so I think I'll stay.

Yesterday the wind made me run.
Today the wind almost blew me over!
Tomorrow I think the wind will be fun.
Hey! The wind just blew in a dog named Rover!

Carrie Ann Reese
Crest Hill Elementary School
Casper, WY
Grade 6

Water

Flowing memories
clearing everything in its path quietly,
softly blowing in the breeze.

In the still soft pond
fish swim making ripples that spread
around and around.

Loud thundering ocean
waves being blown by the wind
bring seashells close to the shore.

Soon, kids will come by, pick them up, admire them,
the broken ones are left behind
going on a great journey to the ocean floor.

Across the world,
water freezes into snow pouring down
on the huge mountains glistening in the sun.

Little children have so much fun
can't wait to go outside and make their snowman
and have snowball fights.

Blakely Richmond
Morningside Elementary School
Salt Lake City, UT
Grade 6

Mountain

The mountain glistens with a morning dew.
Plants crushed under foot by a deer
a bush rustles as a lizard darts here and there
with high hopes a beetle is near.

But the dew won't last long because
the sun and its glorious light have come.
The deer goes in search of water.
The lizard stops hunting to bask in the sun.

The mountain is a great place to enjoy.
Soon the dew will be back,
the deer will be walking again,
the lizard hunting that beetle tomorrow.

Dan Cowan
Morningside Elementary School
Salt Lake City, UT
Grade 6

Fly Away

Hello, hello!
Good day, good day!
Come fly away with me.
I am quick, but my quickness is not known.
I fly around in small, slow circles on a rainbow string.
If the day is gloomy,
and you've flown off with the gloom,
just look at me, I'll make you smile.
My body is speckled with patterns of color.
I am different from all of the rest.
Flutter, hover, butter, cover.
Come fly away,
away with me.

Chelsea Ziemer
Pine Grove Elementary School
Parker, CO
Grade 4

Footprints

Footprints can lay anywhere.
If they're feeling lazy and dull.
They will nest in the soft light sand
And then they will leave.
They follow everywhere you step.
The only place footprints will not be is away from you.
Footprints will lay anywhere like,
Soft gray carpets too
Sticky brown mud.
Grassy plains or
Rocky mountainsides.
You are not in control of your footprints,
Your footprints are in control of you.

Leann Pulvermiller
Bergen Valley Elementary
Evergreen, CO
Grade 4

Battle of the Stars

As you gaze upon the stars,
What do you hear?
What do you see?
I hear a battle,
Not far along the way.
I see the Redcoats
Ready to fight.
Firearms in hand,
Swords by their sides.
They want to win this battle
Fair and square.
They don't want their slaves
To go free.
So get up on those feet
And get ready to fight.

Lindsay Hatfield
Challenger Middle School
Colorado Springs, CO
Grade 6

Bees

Bees
Silent but deadly
Stinging, flying, killing
Strong, small and fierce
Hunters

Kevin Winslow
Christ Lutheran School
Murray, UT
Grade 5

Fetch

In the spring, birds singing,
Afternoons delighting me,
Sitting underneath a tree,
Playing with Molly,
Smiling, sun shining,
Animals scatter about,
Green grass,
Flowers blooming,
"Fetch"

Alexis Anderson
Lincoln Elementary School
Miles City, MT
Grade 5

Sun

Sun.
So hot–
Makes you sweat–
Find some shade quick–
Cool.

John Molder
Washington Terrace Elementary School
Ogden, UT
Grade 6

Butterfly Love

Why do butterflies fly?
Why do butterflies do
A little dance above your head?
Why do butterflies come
Around you so much?
Why? Why? Why?

They like to fly to see you.
They like to do a little
Dance above your head
Because,
They like you. They like to
Be around you so much
Because they love you.
And you know what?
I'm the little butterfly
Who does that to you!

Andie Kelley
Lake Powell Elementary-High School
Lake Powell, UT
Grade 4

Happiness

Happiness looks like a smiling face.
Happiness smells like a fresh rainfall.
Happiness sounds like rustling leaves.
Happiness tastes like a piece of creamy
    chocolate cake.
Happiness feels like nice warm sun rays
    shining upon my face.
Happiness is sliding down a rainbow.

Sarah Mae Watson
Moore Elementary School
Silt, CO
Grade 4

Pigs Are Pigs!

PIGS ARE PIGS!
They slide in the mud,
    when they slide
    they seem to glide
while getting all dirty
    and being a pig!
They are pink and wiggly
    they squeal all giggly,
    their tail has a curl
please say they don't hurl!
They are very very fat
and look like a curled up cat!
And please remember that:
    PIGS ARE PIGS!
    And that is that!

Kristen Rothweiler
Heatherwood Elementary School
Boulder, CO
Grade 4

Spelling

fun correct
writing learning typing
pencil paper ball glue
working playing studying
fun great
school

Andrea Canela
Washington Terrace Elementary School
Ogden, UT
Grade 4

Inside-Outside

My inside self and my outside self
Are different as can be

My outside self wears normal clothes
And very tall is she
Little freckles sprinkled on her nose
With long brown beautiful hair.
And very pretty she is
With everyone to care.

My inside self is different
You can see

A beautiful horse
Running inside me.
Tail flying high in the air
Racing everywhere.
As powerful as can be,
His eyes fill with excitement,
His hair black as night,
His feet as hard as granite
As he races
Out of sight!

Amy Hutchins
Walt Clark Middle School
Loveland, CO
Grade 6

The Cat and the Rat

One day a cat came home
To his shiny golden dome
Then he finds a small rat
Under his favorite black hat
The rat looked cute
Because he wore only one boot
When he needs help
He gives you a hoot
When that was through
The cat went shopping
And the rat tagged along hopping.

Shawn Ford
Elkhart Elementary School
Aurora, CO
Grade 5

Apple Pie

I'm sorry I ate the apple pie
but I was really hungry.
I know that the apple pies are your favorite,
but I was really hungry.
I really hope you forgive me,
but I was really hungry.
I was really hungry, and it was the last one.

Conor McMillan
Ecker Hill Middle School
Park City, UT
Grade 6

There's Something the Same

Me, I am tall
My brother is small
My sister is smart
And my mom and my dad make things start.

Of course, we're all different
But there's something the same,
It's something that's caring,
But I warn you, not very tame.

Now please don't be frightened,
This may give you a start
It's something very special,
Called your heart!

Anna Christine McMillan
Stansberry Elementary School
Loveland, CO
Grade 5

To Adam With Love

Here you lie asleep in the ground
Here you lie not making one sound

I wish you were here with me
I need a friend for company

Our hearts are filled with love inside
and now your soul and spirit will hide

I had a lot of good memories with you
and now I'm feeling so, so blue

I wish I could hear your meow once more
then see you walk through God's open door

I do so miss you very dearly
but will always remember you very clearly

Love Amy

Amy Polete
Northridge Elementary School
Highlands Ranch, CO
Grade 4

Space

Look through a telescope and you will see
The things that I love and most interest me:
Stars and the planets, the sun and the moon,
Alpha Centauri and the planet Neptune.

As I gaze at the beautiful night sky,
I drift gently off to sleep by and by.
And above me the stars proceed with their dance
That no one has taught them, it's done only by chance.

Some day we will reach them, inhabit them too.
Human beings will spread to both old and new.
So when our good old sun is dead and gone
The human race will still continue on.

Chrisella Sagers
Challenger School
Sandy, UT
Grade 6

Sunrise, Sunset

Slowly rising high into the sky,
Shining bright and radiant,
The warmth covers the land like a warm thick blanket,
Snow, sleet, or frost.

The rays look like fingers spreading though the fields,
The golden color makes light for everyone.
The breeze cools things down a bit,
But soon the sun takes over after sunrise...

Slowly falling out of the sky,
Hiding behind the mountains.
The animals sleep,
The people talk,
Everything becomes quiet.

Soon the sun starts painting soft colors along the sky,
Colors of the rainbow.
Red, orange, yellow, green, blue, indigo, and violet.
Soon everything is dark as sunset comes from distant lands.

Erica Walker
Campus Middle School
Englewood, CO
Grade 6

The Big Game

One day we had a tournament.
There was two minutes left in the game.
The score was 38 to 32 we were losing.
12 seconds left in the game.
The score is 58 to 56, I ran down the court.
It was 59 to 58 we won! Everybody cheered!

Tyler J. Fralia
Washington Terrace Elementary School
Ogden, UT
Grade 4

Butterflies

Sometimes people say,
"I hate butterflies in my stomach."
They really mean they're nervous.

Butterflies can be in all shapes, colors,
And even sizes.

Black and blue,
Red and white,
Vibrant, orange, and yellow.

Have you ever
Had butterflies in yourself?

I did once.
I was sayin' a poem
And got mixed up.

Oh what a sight!
Let's hope you don't do it.

Brieann Dimond
St John the Baptist School
Draper, UT
Grade 4

The Dirt Bike

I'm sorry about your bike;
It doesn't look too bad.
You just need some new wheels
and a new handlebar.
The jump didn't look too big
I know you might be upset
because it cost you a lot of money.
I request forgiveness
I'm really, really sorry,
but it seemed so cool
as I jumped in the air.
Can you buy another bike?

Casey Bywater
Ecker Hill Middle School
Park City, UT
Grade 6

Rattler

I come outside and I see
a rattler eating something.
I get closer.
He strikes.
I grab him before he can reach
the skin on my face.
I put him in a cage.
Problem solved.

Caleb Pavy
Colorado Academy
Denver, CO
Grade 4

Rainbow

Silently they blow their trumpets, princesses of kings and queens.
Littlest angel sweeps the floor, brushing all the clouds away.
Her tears mop the earth, she wipes the tears away to reveal
A rainbow pure and sweet.

Carla Rust
Oak Grove Elementary School
Montrose, CO
Grade 4

Dream

In a spiky leaf,
Surrounded by a world of blues and purples,
A diamond encrusted sky sparkles above me,
Slowly red rose petals sprinkle the silvery lake,
And then dewdrops swiftly touch the surface spreading odd pink ripples,
Suddenly I hear bells and the tinkling of laughter,
My leaf drifts into an odd cave made of waterfalls,
I feel a wave of freezing cold and everything turns to ice,
I get out of my leaf and the ice smells sweet and is warm to the touch,
Then I sit up in bed to the waking calls of my sister.

Bryci Webber
Afflerbach Elementary School
Cheyenne, WY
Grade 6

Image

Is image everything to you and to me
When I look in the mirror is that all I see
Or can I look inside myself and find something stronger
My looks and my clothes will soon fade away
But my personality that's what will stay
The person I am is on the inside, not out
The way I perceive myself is what I'm all about
So is your life about image, envy, and wealth
Or can you look past all that to find something better inside yourself

Cassidy Blu Forrester
Knudson Middle School
Las Vegas, NV
Grade 6

My Father's Zoo

My father has a zoo,
It is really quite a sight
He has a few snakes and a few tortoises
He also has a very mean monitor lizard; I don't like him at all!
He also has an iguana, which is very skittish
He once wanted a baby ostrich but my mother said no
Instead she suggested he get a EMU
He also has two dogs, pigeons, a cat, and many fish
Now you know my father's zoo and I bet your wondering how my
Mom survives it all but stop wondering cause she loves it just as
much as my father!

Kaitlyn Lincoln
Academy Charter School
Castle Rock, CO
Grade 6

My Mom Is Like...

My mom is like a cactus beginning to bloom,
She's sweet like a popsicle on a hot summer day,
She's beautiful like a sunflower on a new summer day,
She looks like a princess riding her horse in the wind,
She's like a cup of hot cocoa on a cool winter day,
That's what my beautiful mom is.

Danette Smith
Hudson Elementary School
Hudson, WY
Grade 6

Friends

There they stand representing joy and happiness
Dancing forever
Spreading love and curing hate
Standing as one.

Grace Icenogle
Colorado Academy
Denver, CO
Grade 5

Clouds Are Like Beds for Angels

The clouds can see houses from down on Earth
clouds are like beds for angels
they take care of you and other people too
clouds look like people in the shape of the clouds
the clouds shape looks like a hand
clouds look like snow from the sky
the same color like snow
when the clouds get together it makes thunder.

Michelle Farrell
Dos Rios Elementary School
Evans, CO
Grade 4

I Am Hers

I am her masterpiece,
I am her work.
She sits and ponders
and then...her creativeness begins.
A graceful here,
a blooming flower there.
I am her masterpiece.
Her pastel paints, her cool creme colors,
I am bound to be the best.
My many objects fill me up,
she paints me, my miraculous expression.
Each one of me, has a meaningful meaning,
And for a meaningful meaning
each one of me.
My many objects are most interesting.
Me, the masterpiece.

Katelan Shaw
Pine Grove Elementary School
Parker, CO
Grade 4

Dragon

Dragon, dragon flying high,
Mystic creature in the sky

Swirling, looping through the air,
Giving people quite a scare

Toasting trolls to his heart's delight
Then crunching and munching them in flight

Please don't scorch me with your breath,
I don't want to die a fiery death

Seth Carmitchel
Roy Moore Elementary School
Silt, CO
Grade 4

Freedom

The wind floats through the links in the chains,
floats through, and cracks them.
The wind cracks the chains
that bind my tired wings.
My parched throat is soothed
by cool wind
that trickles down my throat
like crisp, sweet water.
I spread my wings
and the wind lifts me to the sky.
I embrace the sky as it embraces me.
I circle the rainbow sky as the sun sets
and darkness veils the universe.
Then the darkness is pierced by many stars all aglow, and
I call out, and my call glows and
guides me through the night.
At last, as the sun rises,
I fall, exhausted and weary,
into a warm nest all my own,
and sleep peacefully.

Caitlin Barbera
Oak Creek Elementary School
Colorado Springs, CO
Grade 4

Yellow

Yellow is the color of a happy bumblebee
the bright sunshine on a warm summer day
a vibrant colored sunflower
and the rich center of a daisy

Yellow is the color of a lemon
the feeling of warmth and comfort
a brightly colored daffodil
and the richest colored crayon in the box

Lesley Barton
Laredo Middle School
Aurora, CO
Grade 6

Trees

Whoosh, whoosh, whoosh
The wind blows.
The leaves move.
I walk through the forest listening.
Raindrops fall off the petals of flowers.
Trees shade me from the gentle rain
that splashes as it hits the ground.

Alicia Burdick
Heatherwood Elementary School
Boulder, CO
Grade 4

Rainbow Waterfalls

Rainbow waterfalls,
Flowing into rivers.
Blue sky overhead.
Green plants all around,
Animals on the ground.
Sunshine everywhere,
Clouds in the sky,
Some breeze here and there.
At night, some light from the moon,
Shines on rainbow waterfalls.
The water glows and flows at night.
This is rainbow waterfalls.

Lindsey Smith
St John the Baptist School
Draper, UT
Grade 4

Loneliness

As I drift off to sleep
in a lonely cabin
moonlight rushes over the dark forest
as if to tell me
that I'm not alone,
though I am.

The isolated cabin is empty.
I am empty.

Feelings rush through my head
as though stars in the sky,
but will soon melt away
to almost nothing.

I feel like a fox
on a lonely desert that goes on for miles
never coming to an end.

My past is being deleted
and is starting with a new beginning.

Ashley Birth
Morningside Elementary School
Salt Lake City, UT
Grade 6

Candle in the Window

In a little window,
A beacon in the night,
A candle flame is burning,
Showing you the way to light.

Masha Williams
Carbondale Elementary School
Carbondale, CO
Grade 5

Malibu Barbie

I'm sorry I took your
stash of money.

I knew you were going
to buy me something anyway.

I really am truly sorry.
Please forgive me.

I only did it because
I ran out of money,
and I had to get
my Malibu Barbie,
before they ran out.

Monica Mason
Ecker Hill Middle School
Park City, UT
Grade 6

Pets

Pets
colorful, furry
playing, jumping, flying
cuddling, nice, playful, wild
Animals

Denise Hackett
Ecker Hill Middle School
Park City, UT
Grade 6

Chips

I like chips
I can take on trips.

To South Dakota
Or Minnesota.

I eat and eat
Then itch my feet,

Until the chips were gone,
So we just drive on.

Shawn Kramer
Pioneer Elementary School
Billings, MT
Grade 6

Bad Hair Day

When I woke up this morning
My hair was on its end
And all my friends were laughing
All the way to gym
No it was not funny
No it was not good
They wouldn't have understood
It was a bad hair day
That I knew it was
Just sometimes it goes that way
That's just how it goes
I tried to wash it in the sink
As hard as it may seem
Then it started to stink
I wanted to go to bed
And awake with a new head.

Josephine Ward
Most Precious Blood School
Denver, CO
Grade 5

A Friend

A friend is someone who believes in you
and always stands by your side.
A friend is someone who you can trust,
deepest secrets you safely confide.

A friend is someone who likes you
no matter what you do.
Mistakes are quickly forgiven,
Quarrels are far and few.

A friend is someone you can call
when your day was bad.
They quickly cheer you up,
so that you aren't so sad.

A friend is truly priceless
something money cannot buy.
Your memories last forever,
they're endless like the sky.

Alison Garel
Campus Middle School
Englewood, CO
Grade 6

When My Head Fell Off

As I went out the other day
My head fell off and rolled away
But when I noticed it was gone
I picked it up, put it back on
And walked away

Desiree Huitt
Petersen Elementary School
Sunnyside, UT
Grade 5

The Victory of Moses

He was a slave, but lived in luxury
He watched his people suffer, not seeing their misery
He shot a man, and ran away
God spoke to him, while the sheep went out to play
He had a duty to fulfill,
Yet his wife was afraid he didn't have enough will
Still he went,
Through the suffering, through the rain,
And through the pain.
And Ramses, king of Egypt, would let his people go,
After blood,
After his people cried,
After Ramses beloved son died.
Moses had won,
He had been in God's hand
This was exactly
What God had planned

Claire Connolly
Holy Trinity School
Westminster, CO
Grade 6

Horses Are Peaceful

Horses are peaceful.
Horses are cuddly.
Horses are cute.
When you ride them, it feels so breezy.
They come in all colors. Horses are hairy.
Horses are smooth. Horses are a lot of work.
They are beautiful.
They are fast.
They make you go, "Oh!"
I love horses.
They are sometimes tame.
As I see them, I say, "Wow! A horse!"

Kaitlyn Walters
Pine Grove Elementary School
Parker, CO
Grade 4

Snowboard

I have a snowboard, short and stout.
I can do tricks and Mommy freaks out.
I fly through the air and don't fall down,
And now I don't look like a clown.
I can do 720 degrees and things like that,
I don't hit the ground and go *ker-splat,*
I did a 900 degree lein air,
And then I became a millionaire,
I figured out that it was just a dream.
I really didn't do that great big lein.
I'm not a millionaire and it's just not fair.

Harrison Watkins
Sacred Heart of Jesus School
Boulder, CO
Grade 5

The Mountains of Colorado

See the soft white mountain snow,
Hear the beautiful wind,
Smell the fresh rapids running down the sides of the mountain,
Feel the beautiful mountainsides.
Taste the evergreens whip into your mouth,
When I'm in the mountains I feel like a beautiful butterfly.

Keely Wheeler
Larkspur Elementary School
Larkspur, CO
Grade 4

The Delaware Crossing

On a dark wintry night
They crossed the Delaware to fight.
Their spirits were down
As they rowed into Trenton town.

It was a happy Christmas night;
The Hessians were not ready for a fight.
They came from the left and the right;
The Hessians found themselves in a sorry plight.

Nine-hundred-and-eighty-one prisoners and 30 dead
Put Washington ahead,
There was much more fighting to be done
To keep the Hessians and Redcoats on the run.

Cassy Miller
Mary Blair Elementary School
Loveland, CO
Grade 5

Pirates

There was once a pirate named Orange Beard.
Who sailed the seven seas.
He also sailed fifty lakes,
With incredible ease.

With his first mate Pink eye he sailed around the world
Seeing tropical places and frost bitten toes,
Fiery volcanoes and icy wonder lands.

He has visited the Easter Islands,
And seen Stonehenge.
He has climbed the Pyramids of Geza
And battled in the Coliseum.
He has sailed through the Bermuda Triangle,
And eaten escargot.

Orange Beard was a great great man,
A true pirate at heart.
Never had a speck of gold,
But always brushed his teeth.

Kyle McDonald
Parmalee Elementary School
Indian Hills, CO
Grade 4

Little River

Little river's blue–
As clear as marble.
I see little fishes.

Chelsie Victor
Washington Terrace Elementary School
Ogden, UT
Grade 6

Locket Memories

I have in my locket,
A special face,
A reminder of joy and love.

I feel your presence my friend,
As I sit here and see,
Your hand reaching out,
Out for me.

Remembering you leaving,
Never to return,
Your hand waving,
From the sea.

I turned away,
Too proud to show,
You made my cry,
Leaving me behind.

But this treasure reminds me,
Of our love and happiness,
And now,
You're always in my mind.

Irene Kim
Laredo Middle School
Aurora, CO
Grade 6

October's Sky

October sky's are filled with breezes and
leaves with a big crunch.

Different colors fill the hills with red,
green, yellow, orange, and brown plants.

Jack-O-Lanterns turn alive on a full moon,
goblins, ghosts and ghouls scare people
out of their pants.

Their spine turns into ice cubes,
their hair turns into nails

At dawn everything is back to normal.

Jeffrey Alan Hiltner
Moore Elementary School
Silt, CO
Grade 4

I Like Horses

I like horses
Beautiful, slender Shetland ponies with long black manes,
Slick thoroughbred horses that gallop over the course,
I like Arabian horses who hold their heads high and their tails for beauty,
And beautiful fox trotter horses who lounge in the stall,
Their coats sleek from grooming,
But the horses I like most are palominos,
They run, beautiful, with their white manes blowing in the wind,
Like the waves in the sea.

Ashley deRobles
Lowell Elementary School
Salt Lake City, UT
Grade 6

If...

If you can't face the world with courage and with trust...
If you can't face what happens in every day life...
If you can't live up to your own expectations...
If you can't hold on to your own dreams...
If you can't find what's really important in life.
If you don't know the real worth of water...
If you can't trust your own conscience...
If you can't face each challenge, give your best and know that you've tried...
If you can't open your heart with love that endures...
If you can't find enough love in your heart to forgive little mistakes...
If you don't have enough intelligence to stay off of drugs ...
If you don't always try to be kind...
If you can't respect what your friends decide...
If you don't have enough strength to show at school...
If you can't face your own friends...
If you don't have enough courage to face people you see every day...
If you can't do hardly anything in life...
If you can't face your own family...
If you can't live up to your family's expectations...
Then what can you do.

Shanan Kessler
Riverton Middle School
Riverton, WY
Grade 6

Dog Sled Race

The dogs yelp because they have waited so long to run in the race,
Your team is ready, the dogs are lunging against the harnesses,
You hear the pistol shot ring through the crisp air,
The dogs are off, racing across the snow,
You enter a forest, then cross a river,
The next thing you know, you're above the tree line,
Weaving your way through ice covered mountain peaks,
The dogs begin to tire, you think to yourself,
"We should be to the checkpoint by now, maybe I took a wrong turn,"
You come around a bend and, to your relief,
You see the checkpoint right ahead.

Nate Guenther
Hudson Elementary School
Hudson, WY
Grade 6

The Mummies

Falling, falling into endless sandy dunes of a pyramid.
Surrounded by mummies and the ancient smell of decay.
As you stare in fright you notice they start to move,
With the soft scraping noise, the mummies advance.

Torin Francis
Parmalee Elementary School
Indian Hills, CO
Grade 4

When You're Feeling Down

When you're feeling down,
you may want to drown.
Just think of all the good times,
the smiling times, the happy days.
All the ways you've smiled and laughed.
People love you even if you don't think so.
So Smile

Stephanie Cornell
Fort Shaw Elementary School
Fort Shaw, MT
Grade 5

Tweety

I am white, like a white cloud on a sunny day.
I am blue as the sky, with a touch of black, black as night.
My beak is a bright sunny yellow.
I am very cute and people love me.
When people touch me, I am soft as a baby bunny.
I am so smart.
I can say my own name—in the mornings, afternoons, and nights.
I get lots of exercise when I fly.
What I live in is gold and has stripes,
so you can see whatever I am doing.
I am a little small, but I am also light as a feather.
I am the key to my family's heart.

Kathryn Fontana
Pine Grove Elementary School
Parker, CO
Grade 4

The Consequence of Drinking and Driving

It started on a Monday night.
Everybody ran out of sight.
For she will not come home alive.
This is what happens when you drink and drive.

Should her mom get mad?
Yes, she should.
Girls and boys at the age of sixteen should not go to parties,
Not even for Halloween.
There should not be parties where teenagers drink.
It's like they have minds but don't know how to think.

Emilie Giadone
Shaffer Elementary School
Littleton, CO
Grade 6

Butterflies

Fragile creatures in the sky.
Its name is the butterfly
Floating softly without a sound
Floating softly to the ground.

It's so small, but so bold.
With it's magnificently small wings of gold
God made such a beautiful creation
He surely used is imagination.

Butterflies fly every day
And with that note I'd like to say
Butterflies deserve to be free
Because they're just the same as you and me.

Adrian Weikel
Bennett Middle School
Bennett, CO
Grade 6

Beauty

As I stroll through the garden,
beauty surrounds me.

The cool breeze fills the morning's air.
The leaves of the tall, healthy, willow tree rustle.
The calm river flows with a warm heart.
The scent of summer's flowers fills my heart with joy.

All possessing beautiful and warm souls,
as though a blanket full of warmth
was tightly wrapped around me.

Andrea Harmon
Morningside Elementary School
Salt Lake City, UT
Grade 6

Basketball

Basketball is so fun to play!
It has a round ball that bounces!
I love to play basketball!
How about you?
I've played it for five years now.
I used to play football but then
I decided that basketball is
so much funner than football
because all you do in football is stand there
And wait for the quarterback to pass it to you.
Or if you have the ball all you do is run.
But in basketball you get the ball and dribble
down the court!
It is so,so,so fun
to play basketball!!!

Jesyka Cook
Washington Terrace Elementary School
Ogden, UT
Grade 4

Sun

Sun
steaming hot
burning, shining, setting
the earth's source of heat
light

Joe Hampton
Christ Lutheran School
Murray, UT
Grade 5

Spring to Winter

Spring
Sunny, Shiny
Dancing, Flying, Blooming
Flowers, Birds, Snowflakes, Icicles
Snowing, Skiing, Sledding
Cold, Frosty
Winter

Nicole Roth
Ecker Hill Middle School
Park City, UT
Grade 6

Balloons

I love the balloons.
It is fun to blow them up,
I like to watch balloons fly.

Nelson Muhlestein
Lomond View Elementary School
Ogden, UT
Grade 4

Colorado

The sweet smell of
the Columbine.
The taste of
wild raspberries and strawberries.
The sight of
the white-topped mountains.
The feel of
the silk-like flowers.
The sound of
beautiful whistling birds.
The smell of
fresh rain on trees and wet grass.
The sight of
the beautiful blue sky.
Beautiful bright
dandelions of the sun.
Columbine flowers
softer than the softest silk.
All this in Colorado.

Joshua Johnson
Dos Rios Elementary School
Evans, CO
Grade 5

Butterflies, Oh Butterflies!

I look up, I look up
and I see little butterflies
flying up above my head.

They are flapping their wings
saying "hello"! And look at
their pretty colors. Oh look,
Oh look, they're saying, "good-bye."

I hope they come back another day!

Stephani Pitts
Pine Grove Elementary School
Parker, CO
Grade 4

Monkeys

Small body up high
Little feet dangling from trees
Weird faces like clowns

Branson Fivas
Christ Lutheran School
Murray, UT
Grade 5

My Violin

Listen to the sound of my violin,
As I place it
Underneath my chin,

In the living room I play,
I practice for
An hour a day,

I practice and practice for an hour,
To be positive
My notes aren't sour,

But then my fingers get so weak,
And I get a red mark
On my cheek,

And then my puppy starts to howl,
Some days she will
Even growl,

I think we'll play a minuet,
On the day
Of our first duet,

Someday we'll perform at Carnegie Hall,
I will play,
My dog will bawl.

Megan Griffin
West Middle School
Littleton, CO
Grade 6

Apples

Apples come in many sizes.
They can be small, big, and just right.
If you want an apple, pick me!

Chantel Dagenais
Pine Grove Elementary School
Parker, CO
Grade 4

Bees

Bees are around you.
They love to say
That special word
BZZZZZZZZZZZZZ.
They fly around you
Seeing the beautiful colors
On the bee.
Yellow and black.
They see the color yellow on you.
They think you're special
Because of that special color on you.
They wander around to find you.
They want to see that
Special color on you again.
They flap their wings above you
So the bee's thinking
"Where are you?"

Richelle Nephew
Lake Powell Elementary-High School
Lake Powell, UT
Grade 5

Stephen

S tands up for me.
T akes care of me.
E verywhere I go.
P icks on me.
H eavy brother.
E ven tough I'm mean.
N ever leave me.

Cody Hutchings
South Elementary School
Brighton, CO
Grade 5

Tigger

Tigger, my kitty
So soft and sweet
She's always on her feet
She's sometimes mean
And sometimes sweet
And I like it when she dive-bombs
My feet

Meghan Cira
John Neumann Middle School
Pueblo, CO
Grade 6

Colorado in the Autumn

See leaves falling from the trees,
Being whipped around by an autumn breeze.
Swirling, swirling, in the air,
I reach out, got 'em!
It is definitely Colorado in the autumn!
Hear the old, dry, leaves crunch under your feet.
I say to myself, "Gee, isn't this neat!"
Hear the cheers of the football fans,
As the referee again raises his hands!
It is definitely Colorado in the autumn!

Meredith Mazanec
Larkspur Elementary School
Larkspur, CO
Grade 4

Horses

Horses make my heart beat fast
Their sleek and slender bodies
Their muscles good and strong
And their mane and tail so long.
Getting on a horse
Being so high above the ground
When you start to go...
You feel like you are flying through the air.

Dapple gray and black and brown
Their color doesn't matter
White and Palomino
Their colors range from anywhere.
In the spring, now there's a sight
Babies being born.
Foals and fillies, colts galore
All staying by their mothers.

When they've grown
To be big and tall,
I think that I will buy one.

Samantha Bitter
St John the Baptist School
Draper, UT
Grade 4

The Street

The street is like a long black tape winding like a
dragon up and down right and left.

The noise is like a roar it comes and goes repeatedly
and wakes me up oh, the noise is really a bore.

The kids that play in the street jump, howl, and play
like little banshees, they scream and run and never stop.
Oh, The street.

Aris Georgeson
Colorado Academy
Denver, CO
Grade 5

Monsters

In the dark the monsters grow,
through the silence the cold wind blows.

Old and new the monsters are there,
in your face and in your hair.

Scaring you day and night,
while you take shelters battling your own little fight.

The monsters don't go away,
not even if all is happy and gay.

The monsters can mean anything,
but to me they are not even a being.

Go away, go away,
the day is happy and you are not here to play.

Rooooaaar,
Rooooaaar.

I won't go away,
for I'm your worries and I'm here all of these days.

Ian Strack
Campus Middle School
Englewood, CO
Grade 6

Show Me Your Love Through Your Eyes

Buy me a rose,
Call me from work,
Open the door for me,
What would it hurt,
Show me your love through your eyes.

Take me to dinner,
Buy me a ring,
Show if you still love me,
Please sing for me,
Show me your love through your eyes.

Give me true love,
Pick me up when I'm down,
Please don't be a thug,
Show if you still care for me,
Show me your love through your eyes.

Buy me a rose,
Call me from work,
Open the door,
What would it hurt,
Show me your love through your eyes.

Jillian Love-Stewart
Kepner Middle School
Denver, CO
Grade 6

Sun

It comes up in the morning
and goes down at night
in summer it's a delight.

Cole Eckhardt
Lomond View Elementary School
Pleasant View, UT
Grade 4

Black Night

Turns off the bright sun
Destroys the light with darkness
Blankets of the night

Jacob Topp
Christ Lutheran School
Murray, UT
Grade 5

The Rainbow and Colors

After the rain and dew
The sky appears blue and new
Way up high is a rainbow bright
Just like the dawn of morning light
Colors floating in your sight
Green grass and yellow sun
Red balls popsicle orange tongue
Blue mountain stream and purple flowers
All fill your mind with endless powers

Josh Dickey
Petersen Elementary School
Sunnyside, UT
Grade 5

My Neighborhood

Quiet neighborhood,
Very silent,
Morning comes,
Every day.

Afternoon, very bright.
Fiery rays glistening,
Windows sighing,
Very little things.

Evening comes,
Getting dark,
Stars show,
Sun goes away.

Nighttime is here,
Only stars,
No light,
No sound.

Joshua Griego
St John the Baptist School
Draper, UT
Grade 4

An Enchanting Life

If all the clouds were monsters stomping from above,
If all the raindrops were icebergs all as white as doves,
If all the trees were skeletons made only out of bones,
If all the flowers were tornadoes in the shape of cones,

Then we would be living in a place where no person could laugh or smile.
A place where everybody would face a life-threatening trial.

But, if all the clouds were ice cream cones melting deep down low,
If all the raindrops were bubble gum all getting ready to blow,
If all the trees were lollipops with flavors swirled around,
If all the flowers were cookies piled up in a mound,

Now we would be living in a place full of excitement.
A place where everybody lives only for the enjoyment.

Justine King
First Presbyterian Church Academy
Las Vegas, NV
Grade 6

School

I wake up in the morning and jump down to the ground,
I get dressed really fast and run upstairs,
I then eat my breakfast and pack my lunch,
I start the car for my mother and wait for her in the car,
When she comes we drive out'a there down towards school,
I come and turn all the computers on and walk down to my classroom,
We start school and do a few things and learn a few things,
We then go down to lunch but it seems like a brunch,
I ate real fast and it's only a quarter past twelve,
Then it was time to leave and I was happy brushing off my pencil,
I put it down and leave, but it sticks to my sleeve,
So I yank it off and run out of school, walk over waiting for my mom,
When I see her I jump in the car and drive away from school.

Rob Wyland
Afflerbach Elementary School
Cheyenne, WY
Grade 6

The Wind

The weather that breezes in my face is the wind that flies kites
or flies glider planes, it also might be the wind that blows in my dog's face
as he sticks his head out the window.
This air could also be the wind the Indians used
to get the dirt out of there hair, or rugs.
The air I feel could be the wind that Christopher Columbus used
to sail the ocean blue in 1492.
This wind could be from the Ancient Roman Cities,
That Julius Caesar could have put his thumb down to kill the slaves
or the prisoners in the Gladiator Arena.
So the wind we feel could have been from ancient times,
or the sea in 1492, any of these are OK for me.

Mark Windler
Academy Charter School
Castle Rock, CO
Grade 6

Toads

They are slimy, green, and full of warts.
They hop, they croak, and smell of all sorts.
My friends like them, but I don't.
They dare me to kiss them, but I won't.

They say they're princes in disguise,
but I see it different with my eyes.
So I'll let them stay under their spell,
until a witch can make them well.

Chelsea Beecher
Hurricane Elementary School
Hurricane, UT
Grade 6

Winter Beginnings

The quiet little wood, all covered in snow
Out comes smoke from the homes below.
I stroll to the wood in the cold, clear morn'
With a warm woolen sweater from the sheep I have shorn.
The sweet smell of pine fills up my head
While I dance on the crisp snow that is red.
Red from the death of fall;
Leaves that no longer call
and rustle
on the trees
that I see

Sydney Buchan
Steamboat Springs Middle School
Steamboat Springs, CO
Grade 6

Colorado in the Fall

See the pinecones fall from the trees.
Hear the lark bunting call when fall is here.
Smell the small crinkled leaves that fall from trees.
That's fall in Colorado.
See the squirrels gather nuts to eat for the winter.
Feel the wind brush against your face.
That's Colorado in the fall.

John T. Quintana
Larkspur Elementary School
Larkspur, CO
Grade 4

Winter

Winter
Heavy, peaceful
Sledding, skiing, freezing
Christmas, cold, presents, snow, vacation, suntan
Slipping, sliding, swimming, laughing
Warm, relaxing
Summer

Sean Butcher
Crest Hill Elementary School
Casper, WY
Grade 6

The Big Bang

BOOM, SPOOF, BANG, KABLAM, POUGHHHH!
The big bang

One small rock to the biggest thing
to ever be...

THE UNIVERSE,
It grows bigger, bigger, and bigger!

The flows of the space dust,
The colors of the planets,
The creator of the creation,

The creations creator the...
M
O
N
O
L
I
T
H

Andrew Harvison
Heatherwood Elementary School
Boulder, CO
Grade 4

My Life

When I was born I was so cute,
But I would not remain quiet and mute.
I made these hungry oinking sounds,
Which signaled my mother to come around.

Falling, falling all the time,
I was so clumsy I would trip over a dime.
I couldn't walk and I couldn't run,
But I could crawl and I had so much fun.

I used to say "Tookie, tookie,"
"No, no," it's a "cookie, cookie."
My mom would repeat,
But I would shake my head and kick my feet.

Before my first day at St. Vincent School,
I snipped my bangs with my new scissors tool.
I was so proud of my new hair creation,
I decided to debut my hair at recess recreation.

Now I'm a handful at eleven years old,
I'm snippy, snappy, and beautifully bold.
I'm Mary, Mary Rosenbury,
I'm wonderful, marvelous, and quite contrary!

Mary Rosenbury
St Vincent De Paul School
Salt Lake City, UT
Grade 6

The Terrible Sound

The sound my sister sings,
It is so terrible!
My ears might get blown off.
The windows crack.
I run out the door screaming,
"Make her stop!
Make her stop!"
Back 4 hours later,
Still singing,
I hit the baseball through the window
    into her mouth.
Finally, peace and quiet.

Gurjeet Singh
Heatherwood Elementary School
Boulder, CO
Grade 4

Ballerinas

They leap to compete
They run with their hair in buns
They prance as they dance.

Nichole Garcia
Kearns-St Ann School
Salt Lake City, UT
Grade 6

My Dog

Exciting and fast
Through the trees
And through the bushes
Running and jumping

Eva Firth
Christ Lutheran School
Murray, UT
Grade 5

Riddle

They're cute and cuddly
they're very
soft
and they're
cool
they play
and scratch a lot
it can be
black and white
its eyes can
be black in the middle
and blue on the outside
it is a. . .

Answer: A cat

Shantel Adkisson
Heatherwood Elementary School
Boulder, CO
Grade 4

The Still Tree

The giant willow branches.
Don't move but an inch.
The still willow tree.

Jared Christensen
Lomond View Elementary School
Ogden, UT
Grade 4

My Cat Named Sasha

My cat has long
white whiskers
just like an old grandpa.

She quietly
sneaks around
on her thickly
padded paws.

Her tail
is long and skinny
she has a little pink nose
and in the darkness
of the night
her tiny green eyes glow.

Her fur is soft as silk
with black dashes of ash
and when my kitty
cuddles up with me
all my troubles
seem to pass.

Danielle M. Hauf
Laredo Middle School
Aurora, CO
Grade 6

My Dog, Elliot

Elliot the dog
Is a dalmatian
With black spots and white skin.

Sometimes he smells like tuna fish.
He likes to chew toys,
Especially with squeak.

He barks so loud
You want to scream
He feels like a cotton ball with ink spots.

Don't try to put
Him in the tub.
Boy that dog is a pain.

Ashley Vredenburg
St John the Baptist School
Draper, UT
Grade 4

Wind

The
Wind whips
Through
The trees
Winding
Around the
Poles
And whirls
Itself
To and
Fro.

Kayla Steffek
Nederland Elementary School
Nederland, CO
Grade 6

The Endless Road

The endless road
An endless stretch
With nothing there
But silence

There is no rain
A cloudy sky
With nothing there
But silence

There is no sun
There is no day
With nothing there
But silence

An endless stretch
Not night nor day
With nothing there
But silence

Cheresse Burke
Foothills Academy
Wheat Ridge, CO
Grade 6

Blue World

The ontare colored birds
make me want to fly away
into a sky naturally teal
over the Baltic sea
to a town called Portofino
where there is a fortune teller
with hair of cosmic blue
and noise has a blue echo
the town bay is inhabited by
torino blue dolphins.

Jesse Tarlton
Foothills Academy
Wheat Ridge, CO
Grade 6

The Silver Backpack

One day when I was walking home,
I saw somebody's eyes.
That thing so much distracted me,
it took me by surprise.
I fell over and falling from the sky
came a silver backpack and I wonder what's inside.
I pulled out something purple,
and then came out a shoe,
and then I saw a candy bar.
Poof
It's gone!
Boo! Hoo!

Randi Lynn Sponsel
Bertha-Heid Elementary School
Thornton, CO
Grade 5

George Washington

A very rambunctious boy,
But a proud man;
Nowadays he is not known for his generosity
Or his personality,
But for his terms as president.

Not many know of his greatness
Or his role in the Revolution,
For he was not just a president
Or a great man; he was the birth of America.

Torie Derks
Mary Blair Elementary School
Loveland, CO
Grade 5

Isn't It Fun to Share?

What do you mean?
I don't like to share, I love to share!
For instance,
I will share your dog,
I will share your teddy bear,
I will share your bunny rabbit,
I will share your bed,
I will share your mom,
I will share your dad,
I will share your pens,
I will share your book,
I will share your friends,
I will share your enemies,
I will share your paper,
I will share your binder,
I will even share your toothbrush!
What? What's that you say? Share my stuff?
NO WAY!

Laurel Morrison
Ecker Hill Middle School
Park City, UT
Grade 6

Peacefulness

Peacefulness looks like someone laying
on crunchy leaves, gazing up at the blue
cloudy sky.

Peacefulness smells like a vanilla candle lit,
spreading that wonderful smell through the air.

Peacefulness sounds like the birds singing a
beautiful song.

Peacefulness is me sitting in front of the fire place
sipping on hot chocolate while it is snowing outside.

Cassi Boe
Roy Moore Elementary School
Silt, CO
Grade 4

Masterpiece

Hello!
I am a masterpiece.
A masterpiece am I.
I'll tell a bit about myself and this is how it goes,
I am a happy work of art that helps in many ways,
you draw, write, erase, and work mistakes out.
Finally, when everything has been worked out,
then you slip me, your little masterpiece,
into a drawer for another day.

Allison Welsh
Pine Grove Elementary School
Parker, CO
Grade 4

Baseball

Every year when spring comes 'round
And cool, white frost covers the ground,
Dad breaks out his big, brown mitt.

Out in the back he tosses balls.
Watching and waiting, I catch them all.
My hand stings from a hard practice.

Then game time comes and I hold the bat.
The coach claps his hand and taps his hat,
A signal for the base runner to steal.

A round, white ball the pitcher flings.
It flies at me and then I swing.
I watch it as it soars outta' sight.

My teammates exult and shout with glee.
My mom and dad are happy for me.
I guess that father-son time paid off.

Tony Speare
Challenger School
Sandy, UT
Grade 6

Mountains

See a skier swishing down the mountains
Hear the avalanche rumbling
Smell the fresh snow
Feel the fresh snow on your face
Taste the fresh cold snow
See the skier pounce like a mountain lion

Robert Lawrenz
Larkspur Elementary School
Larkspur, CO
Grade 4

The Rocket

Up! High in the air,
The wind rushes by,
The rocket ship drops,
My stomach stays at the top.
The ride is over.
Until the next time.

Trevor Jorgensen
Ecker Hill Middle School
Park City, UT
Grade 6

Texture

Sand
Gritty, hot
Waiting, sitting, heating
Dune, beach, river, lake
Dripping, drinking, flowing
Clear, cold
Water

Evan Nelson
Ecker Hill Middle School
Park City, UT
Grade 6

Friends

Friends, they come in
all different sizes,
big, tall, medium
even small.
Friends no matter what
the color of skin or hair.
Friends are also
caring and fair.
Friends are respectful
and friends are nice.
Friends are handicapped
too, but no matter
what the age is
you still spell it
Friends!!

Christian Tyler
Washington Terrace Elementary School
Ogden, UT
Grade 4

When I Was in Space

It was a starry night.
When I was in space.
It was something beautiful.
It was something beyond.
Beyond dreams or even the human mind.
Nobody has seen it before.
I still don't realize what it was.
I thought it was a star or a beautiful planet.
It really looked like some kind of design that somebody made up.
In fact, I really don't know how to explain it.

Kyle Langhart
Riverview Elementary School
Durango, CO
Grade 4

Mountains

See the birds land on the prickly pine of a blue spruce,
Hear the wind whistling through your ears on a cold, spring day,
Smell the fresh scent of wild flowers just starting to show their beauty,
Feel the dew on your feet filling up your shoe like a cold ice cube,
Taste the cool air filling up your mouth,
The mountains are a huge play place to me.

Jennifer Kmezich
Larkspur Elementary School
Larkspur, CO
Grade 4

The Endless Night

When light suddenly fades away and a thick black blanket covers the sun.
The dime silvery white moon lights the sky like a single bulb on a cold wintry night.
A trail of black smoke catches your eye and you follow it like a zombie.
The cold air clings to your face and you feel as if it's
pulling you down, down, down to the depths of eternity,
you fall crashing to the ground and the snow folds around you like a wet blanket.
You struggle to get up but the coldness is running through
your blood quickly and you know you don't have much time,
and then the blanket of snow pulls you down for the last time.
Your whole body shakes and shivers as you lay there in the thick blanket of snow.
You can't feel your hands or your feet,
and you look off in the distance to a house filled with hope and light.
You take your last gulp of air and eyes flicker.

Jessica Parker
Foothills Academy
Wheat Ridge, CO
Grade 6

Colorado Winter

Winter is like sparkling white diamonds falling on Christmas morning as I open my gifts.
Winter is trudging through heavy down falling white waist-high snow.
Winter is a vast white lifeless cold ski adventure through the arctic snows.
Winter is a close encounter with a brown viscous mad bear ripping through you.
Winter is a wrapped raging snowstorm spreading a blanket of white over the town.

Josh Davidson
Roy Moore Elementary School
Silt, CO
Grade 4

My Sister

My sister's ways are like a fairy's.
Her art is beautiful.
Her hair is as brown as chocolate.
Her heart holds joy as wonderful as you could imagine.
She lives in art
and she eats wonderful things.

Jonathan McCloy
Thompson Falls Elementary School
Thompson Falls, MT
Grade 4

Liquid Gold

A tarnished ball of gold
sinks over the horizon,
desperate to stay in the sky
for as long as possible,

transforming the grass into crude slabs of bronze,
converting tree bark to mosaics
composed from dull and bright copper one-cent pieces,

changing common houses into elaborate sculptures
of tarnished bronze,

the air is as if a bomb,
filled with powder from
a rusty old can, burst in the sky,

the brilliant colors on the horizon
dance and wave like blazing flames bursting
from a fresh-cut cedar tree,

the Great Salt Lake glows as if a slab of steel,
still hot from processing,

the roads wind throughout the city
like streams of liquid gold,

many changes in the world, and in my mind,
all caused by one beautiful sunset.

Brenden Hoffman
Morningside Elementary School
Salt Lake City, UT
Grade 6

Horses

As they run across the open plains of Colorado
    they shimmer in the sunlight,
And during the night when their tails are aflame
    their manes are full of constellations,
And when they run it seems they are translucent
    but can violate stone.

Jessica Williams
Cortez Middle School
Cortez, CO
Grade 6

Pain

Pain is green like the stem of a rose that prickles me.
It makes me want to scream as loud as I possibly can!

Jenny Oilar
Most Precious Blood School
Denver, CO
Grade 5

Snow

Small little snowflakes,
drifting on my nose.
I can feel the coldness touching,
and it leaves a shiver to my toes.

The white, soft blanket
covers far and wide,
and covers everything up
with a blink of an eye.

I can see the children,
playing in the snow.
Just to see their merry faces
makes me want to glow.

The snow has stopped,
and everything is calm.
All the children have gone home
soon the snow will be gone.

The snow has melted all over town.
Oh, how I miss the snow!
How I miss everything around,
but another year will come and go
and soon the snow will return back home.

Xiaoxi Cheng
Challenger School
Sandy, UT
Grade 6

I Wonder

I wonder if the birds, that fly just so high
Fly higher than the airplanes, that take you through the sky
I wonder if the bears, the population getting scarce
The ones you see in zoos, and the ones on the news
I wonder if the lakes, the ones with all the water snakes
They seem to be so far, far enough to take a car
I wonder if the geese, the ones you speak of far the least
I wonder if the crocodiles, the ones who save their rage
The ones I speak of here, on this very special page
I wonder if the land, the animals, the creatures and
Everything I speak of, that spends their time in sand
I wonder if they know,
That they'd look perfect in the snow

Davis Stone
Bergen Valley Elementary
Evergreen, CO
Grade 4

Wishing

Driving through traffic
wishing you could die
thinking what it's like to fly
to find out what it's like
from a bird's eye.

Kyle Joseph Hallaran
Cherry Valley Elementary School
Franktown, CO
Grade 4

Gum

Sticky and chewy
Lumpy and gooey

Yum, yum, yum

Minty and fruity,
Also fruity tutti

Yum, yum, yum

Under tables it sticks,
That's what my brother licks

Yum, yum, yum

This is gum and how it does taste,
Just try not to get the kind
That tastes like paste.

Ben Bradshaw
Morningside Elementary School
Salt Lake City, UT
Grade 6

Life Is Like a Painting

Life is like a painting,
Fragile and rare.
Life is like a painting,
Do anything you dare.
Life is like a painting,
Something you can touch.
Life is like a painting,
I love it so much.

Life is like a painting,
So much to see.
Live is like a painting,
I'm glad it includes me.
Life is like a painting,
Let me see some more.
Life is like a painting,
See more, and more, and more.

Jenna Stodghill
Shaffer Elementary School
Littleton, CO
Grade 5

They Come

Dakota,
He's gone,
He ran and ran.

We look for Dakota,
Over mountains,
Over hills,
For Dakota.

While in the distance we hear,
The rumbling of horses getting near.

Through the coughing river,
Over the mountains,
And across the scrunching snow,
They come.

The roaring sound
Of their hooves hitting the ground,
As if being chased,
They come.

Jessica Gillan
Shrine of St Anne School
Arvada, CO
Grade 6

Cloud Watching

As I look into the sky
I watch the clouds go by.

I watch them as they move
across the light blue sky
up so high.

I try to identify every cloud
by what they look like,
I see a bunny, a whale, I even see
a cloud that looks like Italy.

Cloud watching is so much fun!
I could do it all day long.

Leslie Robinson
Morningside Elementary School
Salt Lake City, UT
Grade 6

Yellow Jacket

Bees
Black, yellow
Buzzing, humming, gathering,
Lovely sparkles of gold
Yellow jacket.

Gennie Allumbaugh
Christ Lutheran School
Murray, UT
Grade 5

Peace

Lying in the lush green grass,
Tall trees all around me,
Reaching toward the sky.
Up above me,
A welcoming waterfall,
And a large blue lake beside me.
Beautiful, colorful flowers all around.
And happiness overwhelms me.
Suddenly I'm on a cliff,
Looking down at the lake,
And like the rushing water,
I fall down into a rush of blue,
And a sensation of peace and happiness
Comes over me.

Melanie Wilson
Afflerbach Elementary School
Cheyenne, WY
Grade 6

Little Box of Memories

Little box of memories,
Bordered with gold E's,
Bring me back a sweet memory,
To share with all my family.

Little box of memories,
You now belong to my family,
Memories here, memories there,
Collecting memories everywhere.

I'll open your lid,
To see what's inside,
Maybe something,
From before my grandpa died,
Little box of memories,
Keep our little memory,
Tucked way down inside.

Jonathan Hedger
Afflerbach Elementary School
Cheyenne, WY
Grade 6

Balloons

I am blue, I got picked for $1.00.
I was tied to a hand but,
I noticed a big swoosh of wind then,
I noticed I kept floating and floating,
then I landed on Jupiter.
I also met some other balloons.
They were Purple, Yellow, Orange
and another one of me,
a blue balloon.

Erica Treat
Pine Grove Elementary School
Parker, CO
Grade 4

A Day in Heaven

Going to Cloudy Heaven High School one day,
I look through the clouds at kids who play.
I jump off my bike,
I wave at my best friend Mike.
My first class is angel choir
taught by the teacher with big red lips and hair like fire.
In my second class,
taught by Big Head Bass,
He teaches about famous angels,
and constantly quotes the Bangles.
Other classes are harp and home ec,
history, science, and heaven tech.
After school I attend a seminar
of Michael's defeat of the centaur.
I have tea with JFK,
and that almost concludes my day.
I fall into bed,
dreams fill my head.
That was a heavenly day.

Emma Black
Lab School
Fort Collins, CO
Grade 6

Mirror

All those people trapped in the mirror
Chained within
With no hope of being unleashed.

When the glass is shattered
They crack but do not care
Only imitating through broken eyes.

Forever unknowing with hidden secrets
Looking back at you but not being able to see
A small piece of you will always be there.

Hilary Mulhern
Slavens Elementary School
Denver, CO
Grade 5

The Growth of a Sunflower

I had a little seed
that one day would be
a flower, a sunflower.
I had never seen such a thing.
Some said they are as big as the sun.
Others said they are just little yellow flowers.
But after growing mine, I discovered that's not true.
A sunflower is a little bit of love,
a pinch of beauty,
and a drop of truth.

Alicia K. Leece
Most Precious Blood School
Denver, CO
Grade 5

Fall

Fall sun sees leaves falling to the bare dry grass
with every crunching step looking up to the fall sun
running out of shining energy.

Derek Ochreiter
Foothills Academy
Wheat Ridge, CO
Grade 5

I Like Flowers

I like flowers
Tall, tangy, tulip flowers with red petals,
Soft fuzzy flowers with petals that make me feel happy,
I like red roses that look like hearts in the breeze,
And yellow daisies that sparkle like gemstones in the sun,
Their long stems invite bouquets and gifts,
But the flowers I like best are marigolds, yellow, full of petals,
Whose beauty is like the fair princess Odet's.

Cheryl Kauer
Lowell Elementary School
Salt Lake City, UT
Grade 6

Trouble

This weekend I had lots of fun
In New York City in the sun.

But now I'm home and have the blues
Because I have so much to do.

I never thought it would be this bad,
Right now my mom and dad are mad.

In New York we saw lots of sights,
And now my schedule's really tight.

Some spelling work, and a puppet show
Have made me feel so sad and low.

New York City's so much better,
I saw it all from the World Trade Center.

We smashed the Knicks and put them in their place,
And Now the Jazz are in the championship race.

I lost my head and forgot my work
And now I feel just like a jerk.

I got two incompletes right in a row
All I keep saying is, "Oh No! Oh No!"

I'm going to do my very best,
This will be a real test.

Houston Stockton
St Vincent De Paul School
Salt Lake City, UT
Grade 6

Scuba Divers
Diving down into the water
Seeing all the ocean's wonders
Crabs, starfish, and sharks galore
Blowfish, urchins, and many more
Watching fish swim rapidly
Followed by a shark pursuing happily
Spying otters at the top
Watching starfish and muscles plop
Squids flying by like a jet
Whales getting caught in a net
Octopi placing eggs
Many crabs walking with legs
Rushing up to get fresh air
I think I'd rather live down there.

Theo Kopff
Sacred Heart of Jesus School
Boulder, CO
Grade 5

Spring
Feel the rain fall on your head.
Hear the rain go ting-ting.
See the bears get out of bed.
That is Colorado in the spring.

Watch flowers spring from the ground.
Hear a bluebird sing.
Listen to all the sweet sounds.
That is Colorado in the spring.

Lisa Taylor
Larkspur Elementary School
Larkspur, CO
Grade 4

Basketball
In the bright light,
The thunder of feet sounded.
The crowd cheered loudly,
Excitement is in the air.
It is their last chance to score.

The ball looks like a globe.
It moves from end to end,
As fast as a bird.
The players run like jaguars,
They are hoping to win.

They take the shot,
And it bounces, then rolls
And swishes through the net.
The place explodes with cheers.
Life is a wonderful thing.

Will Parkin
St John the Baptist School
Draper, UT
Grade 4

Guitar
Guitar
fun, loud
jamming, banging, strumming
head banging while playing the guitar
Axe

Patrick McSweyn
Ecker Hill Middle School
Park City, UT
Grade 6

Star Trek
Spaceships traveling
Faster than the speed of light
Exploring new worlds.

Jordan Dutson
Kearns-St Ann School
Salt Lake City, UT
Grade 6

Sally
There once was a girl named Sally,
She went to a school called Malley,
All of the kids are great,
And the teachers are first rate,
So next time don't miss our rally.

Jacob Knuepfer
Malley Drive Elementary School
Northglenn, CO
Grade 5

Clouds
What are these white puffs I see?
This white puff floating in the sky's seas.
Its power to turn into anything.
They fly around the sky with soft wings.
With its unachievable beauty.
This wondrous beauty called clouds.

Matthew C. Brown
Ecker Hill Middle School
Park City, UT
Grade 6

Spring
Feel the melting mountain snow,
Feel the heat the sun will bring,
Hear the soft wind blow,
That's Colorado in the spring.

Hear the mountain rivers rush
Feel the coldness the moon will bring,
Feel the wet snowy slush,
That's Colorado in the spring.

Cara Yarman
Larkspur Elementary School
Larkspur, CO
Grade 4

My First Breath of Life
My first breath of life . . .
It seemed like just yesterday,
But it really was 10 years ago,
On the 10th of May!
My mom was playing baseball,
When from in her tummy,
She heard my call!
She smiled and said it was time,
Time, for that special day!
The special day when I would be born,
And she could watch me play!
And that she did,
When I was born,
And took a breath of air,
And after that,
I was held and hugged,
With lots of care!
And, still today I'm loved.
I'm healthy and I'm strong.
And I know I'll live a life that's,
Really, really long!

Kristina Swanson
Namaqua Elementary School
Loveland, CO
Grade 5

You Left Me All Alone
I loved it when you tickled me
you always made me laugh.
We sat beside the seashore
my fears were cut in half.
Then one night you left me there
standing in the dark.
You never knew that then and there
you had broken my heart.

Jackie Koehn
Colorado Academy
Denver, CO
Grade 4

The Mischievous Kitten
There once was a kitten I should say,
Who messed up the house that one day.
She knocked over the ant farm,
She tore off the doll's arm,
She knocked over the China cabinet,
It was quite a bad habit.
She ate the soup on the table,
And she chewed on the computer cable,
Then she swung on the chandelier,
We could hear that she was near,
Did you know my mom fainted?

Paige Haines Colton
Spring Creek Country Day School
Fort Collins, CO
Grade 4

Mountains

See the dancing ballerinas, pine trees gently sway in the air.
Hear the woodpecker peck constantly on them.
Smell the sweet smell of brightly, colored wildflowers.
Feel the rich green grass, wet with dew under your feet.
Taste the sweet, fresh air in your mouth like a mint lifesaver.
There is happiness all around you in the luscious mountains.

Rebecca Bachman
Larkspur Elementary School
Larkspur, CO
Grade 4

I Don't Like It

I don't like it when my sister hits me in the face
I don't like it when my sister keeps getting in my way
I don't like my sister when "no" is all she can say
I don't like my sister when she wants to play a dumb game.

My sister is kind of decent when she doesn't cry.
She's even kind of decent when she doesn't whine.
She can be sort of decent when her friend comes to our home.
She's kind of, sort of decent; that's why I'm writing this poem!

Hey, my sister's really nice, that is, when she has a toy
Hey, my sister's really nice, because I fill her full with joy!
Hey, my sister is pretty nice, when she wants to play,
She even shares her candy that she's had since last year May!

Michael Slywkanycz
Afflerbach Elementary School
Cheyenne, WY
Grade 5

Night

Look up at the dark night sky,
And you will see stars that fly high,
It's time for sleep for everyone,
Until we seek the morning sun.

In the beginning of a new day,
Bugs and critters come out to play.
It strikes one and the fun has begun,
For the beginning of a new day.

The mice come out to sing and dance,
The spiders come along to join the prance,
Time flies by as they're having fun,
But now their fun is done.

The alarm clocks ring as birds begin to sing,
The children awake from their parent's shake,
The night is done the morning has begun,
Until the night falls again, the bugs will keep cool
In the refreshing rain.

Morgan O'Donnell
St Vincent De Paul School
Salt Lake City, UT
Grade 6

Horses

Before my dad lived
with us,
he had a house up in Absarokee
When we used to go there,
he had a great big field behind his house.
There was a horse that
lived in that field,
but it wasn't my dads.
When the wind blew
the horses mane
blew
like the leaves blowing
in the fall.
When the horse ran he would run like he was wild and free.

Mandi Bulmer
Washington Terrace Elementary School
Ogden, UT
Grade 4

Compare

Some people think the mountains are for skiing in Vail
I go to the Rockies to hike up a trail
They ride on a ski-lift and speed down a slope
Unaware of the creatures, the deer, the antelope.

I hope that they realize that to nature it's home
God put it there just so animals could roam
Snow is not just for sliding, the trout need a stream
The elk need a drink, and the trees will turn green.

I wonder if people who play in the snow
Care about the land or the creatures I know
It is habitat and water and food for all kinds
We should respect it, revere it, and care in our minds.

Skiing looks fun, I can't wait to go
But I will always remember the creatures below
God gave us this beauty for all to share
But it will disappear if we don't take care

Stephen Hattendorf
Eisenhower Elementary School
Boulder, CO
Grade 5

Snow

The snow is falling slow and white
All through the day and all through the night
The children go quickly through the snow
On their skin the cold does blow
Against their skin the cold does bite
So the children bundle up so tight
Against the snow so soft and white

Sarah Setzer
Petersen Elementary School
Sunnyside, UT
Grade 5

Grocery List

Fruit
sweet juicy
eating reading playing
apples grapes carrots potatoes
munching crunching eating
delicious dark
vegetables

Jessica M. Cragun
Washington Terrace Elementary School
Ogden, UT
Grade 4

Going to Sleep

"Good night, Mom. Good night, Dad"
You say as your parents tuck you in.
You snuggle beneath the covers
And turn out the lights.

You lie in bed and listen
To the crickets and
The whisper of the leaves on the tree.
You listen to the dogs barking
And you watch the stars come out
And the moon go by.

You hear your parents talking
And your brother snoring.
You think about things.
Then you drift off into silent slumber
And dream.

Lelah Radostis
Heatherwood Elementary School
Boulder, CO
Grade 4

Hummingbird

Little bird,
divine bird.
When you fly, your wings flutter,
harmoniously.

When you fly from flower to flower,
your feathers glitter majestically.
The pollen on your head is your crown.

Now you disappear.
Gone forever,
with a flash.

Little bird,
divine bird,
adieu.

Alicia Harris
Laredo Middle School
Aurora, CO
Grade 6

Being in a Foster Home

As soon as you look at me,
My heart trembles with joy.
As soon as you inspire me,
My heart has faith.

You come closer and closer.
But walk right by.
Goodbye I say, goodbye.
My eyes fill with tears of sorrow.
My heart filled with bloody pain.
How it is so hard to be in a foster home.
Oh, how hard it is to be in a foster home.

The next person walks in and my heart drops in my empty stomach.
She comes and holds out her hand.
I am finally going home.
Home where the air is filled with love.
Where you can actually go to your family and hug them with love.
Where you know you will be loved forever.

Sarah Jones
Moore Elementary School
Silt, CO
Grade 5

Space Trip

Up, up and away I go up to the moon and beyond,
Where I can see the Milky Way into other galaxies and beyond.
The universe is neat if you don't cheat by teleporting and missing the sights.
Then we go down back to the Milky Way,
Down, down, down.
This time I go to see the planets
the red ones, the blue ones, and the green ones.
Then to the hot ones, then to the cold ones
but never too close to the sun.
Then I go down, back to home, planet Earth,
where I can eat a hot supper.
Oh what a trip,
I'll do it again, but not before I eat my hot supper.

Daniel Weidlein
Bixby School
Boulder, CO
Grade 4

I Like Winter

I like winter.
Soft snow standing frozen with strange beauty,
Christmas trees perched in every home decorated carefully for the holiday,
I like hot cocoa on the table after sledding all day,
And warm fires after building a snowman,
Presents for everyone to open on Christmas Day,
But the thing I like best is blankets,
Soft warm blankets to cover a cold body coming inside from the chill of winter.

Chris Knudsen
Lowell Elementary School
Salt Lake City, UT
Grade 6

The Eagle Above Lone Hill

Flying above Lone Hill,
Was a bird soaring in the early spring chill.
It wasn't a duck, because it had no bill,
That bird flying above Lone Hill.

Standing tall on Lone Hill,
Was an English man; paused in the early spring chill.
Looking, listening to the bird who sounded quite frill;
An eagle! An eagle above Lone Hill.

The man saw the eagle;
The creature was quite unlike the common beagle.
The eagle was proud to see the man.
He was the only Englishman in all the land.

The man came on a sailing ship;
Over the ocean that would rise and dip.

To this young man, this was a very new land.
He called the Redskins "Americans."
The Redskins were scared, but eager to make friends,
And the English soon like the "Americans."

But the man stood upon Lone Hill,
Watching a bird that sounded quite frill;
That eagle above Lone Hill.

Colter Huyler
Spring Creek Country Day School
Fort Collins, CO
Grade 6

Quiet

I have a quiet feeling
   A feeling that I only hear the sound of fingers on a keyboard.
   A feeling that I only hear a teacher calling a name.
   It doesn't sound quiet but in a way it is.

Danica Moore
Cherry Valley Elementary School
Franktown, CO
Grade 4

Dreamland

Tiny fairies all over the place
A princess awaits with a porcelain face
Fields of flowers sway like the ocean below
A waterfall of turquoise sparkles as it flows
Mermaids sing as they twist their long hair
If you stand on the hill, you can see the fun fair
A lion king with a golden mane
The sound of a whistle from a golden choo choo train
So much to see, but so little time
Day turns to night as the clock strikes nine.

Lindsay Jacobson
Ecker Hill Middle School
Park City, UT
Grade 6

Rain Falling Up

Rain falls down softly,
But falls up on the other side of the world,
Splash!

Elisha Reyes
Kearns-St Ann School
Salt Lake City, UT
Grade 6

A Sorrowful Good-Bye

I loved your hair.
You were always there.
You always smiled.
Your attitude was always mild.
You had a special gentle touch.
Your encouragement helped me much.
Your love was always true.
Now your face is cold and blue,
And all I can say is I miss you.

If only, if only, people weren't so...
You and Daddy wouldn't have had to go.
Now as I stand on the church steeple,
Should I jump and leave these cruel people?
To be with you in heaven above,
Where we can forever share our love.

I think of the life I might have led,
The children's mouths I might have fed.
But, you know how much I love you, Mom,
So, I won't make my life explode like a bomb.
I will always love and miss you!
Good-bye.

Heather Oertli
Shaffer Elementary School
Littleton, CO
Grade 6

Stuff About Me Austin Larsen

I used to live in Boise, Idaho,
   but now I live in Park City, Utah.
I used to like pizza,
   but now I like to eat sushi and crab.
I used to read short books when I was little,
   but now I read long books because I'm older.
I used to like apple pie and Puff Daddy,
   but now I like coconut cream pie and Drag-On
I used to play the violin,
   but now I play the cello.
I used to ski and have a CD player,
   but now I snowboard and have a stereo and a CD player.
I used to like to take pictures for a hobby,
   but now I like to play basketball.

Austin Larsen
Ecker Hill Middle School
Park City, UT
Grade 6

The Rumor

Guess what, guess what,
There's a rumor around,
Jimmy told Sarah,
and Sarah told Susie,
and Susie told Bobby,
and Bobby told Jake,
and Jake told Johnny,
and Johnny told Judi,
and Judi told me,
so guess what,
I forgot.

Charlie Rode
Ecker Hill Middle School
Park City, UT
Grade 6

Alligator

As it slithers to the swamp,
he watches his prey
closer, closer, CHOMP!

Danielle ValDez
Kearns-St Ann School
Salt Lake City, UT
Grade 6

Poem Making

One more poem
That's all I need.
Can you think of some words?
Can you give me a lead?
I just need a thought
To plant a seed,
To give me all the words I need.

Travis Smith
Nederland Elementary School
Nederland, CO
Grade 6

Cousin Sling

Yesterday,
my cousin came over,
we went in the backyard,
on our swing set,
got a blue pad,
wrapped her in it,
tied ropes,
and pulled,
she was,
up in the air,
like a,
bird.
"Weeeeeee"

Caitlin Anne Saal
Washington Terrace Elementary School
Ogden, UT
Grade 4

The Trail of Tears

The Long Walk
so painful to think about
I can see the sight
seeing the sight of my people
walk through the night
so hungry
so cold
so weak they are
only fate with them
but knowing death will come upon them
but knowing they will lose a loved one
on the trail of tears.

Kristin Begay
Cortez Middle School
Cortez, CO
Grade 6

Roller Skating

I get in the rink.
I'm flipping and flopping,
twisting and turning,
slipping and sliding,
zigging and zagging.

I'm having big falls
running into walls.

Now I have to give you some advice
don't put your roller skates on ice!

Ryan Wallace
Heatherwood Elementary School
Boulder, CO
Grade 4

Winter Is Like

Winter
Winter is a big beautiful white blanket
covering the earth.
A strong winter blizzard knocking
on your door.
A time of cold weather.
A white spot in time.
A sheep's wool.
A grandmother's hair.
A sheet of blank paper.
A time of joy.
Winter sounds like Styrofoam squeaking.
Winter tastes clean and fresh.
Winter smells of fresh pine needles.
Winter feels like a chill that won't go
away until spring.
Winter moves like a swift graceful dancer.

Seth Lamb
Crest Hill Elementary School
Casper, WY
Grade 6

Leaves

I see the leaves fall.
I can't hear them falling down—
But I know they are.

Amy Schmalz
Washington Terrace Elementary School
Ogden, UT
Grade 6

Dreams

Dreams,
Like growing beams,
Never ending,
God's always sending.

Kayla Dennis
Stein Elementary School
Lakewood, CO
Grade 4

The Alien World

In the Alien World

They have lots of things
That make "bong" sounds
And "boing" sounds
And lots of loud "bings"

Mechanical boats
That can pull a houseboat,
And lots of stuffed farmers
To tend all their goats.

Mechanical chairs
That can get up and walk,
And last but not least,
Small erasers that talk.

So remember the things
That they have in this place,
Because you will find
This location in space!

Amy Harr
Singing Hills Elementary School
Parker, CO
Grade 4

Dragon

Just before dawn
High up on his head
The Midnight Dragon
Carries the moon
And on his back
The twinkling stars

Isla Schanuel
Academy Charter School
Castle Rock, CO
Grade 6

Destruction

Swish, Boom!
Down goes the tree.
This was all caused by one man.
The tree didn't deserve this,
It can't cry, it can't yell.
VROOM goes the saw and down it fell.
It wishes and wishes this could not be.
It thinks and thinks, "Please don't hurt me."
Down and down it falls,
"Stop!" someone calls.
For a minute everything is paused.
The tree is a shooting star but stopped.
Then there is a flash,
The tree is standing as if nothing had happened.
This shows the power of wishes made by one person.

Paul Dominguez
Dos Rios Elementary School
Evans, CO
Grade 5

Apples

Apples are not disgusting
oh no they're really not.
They're green, red, and yellow and sometimes
they have spots.
They smell really sweet and fresh.
So why don't you have one?
They'll brighten up your day!

Sean Kenny
Pine Grove Elementary School
Parker, CO
Grade 4

A Knight

My sweat, the blood

The Bishop's praying in the cathedral,
While I am fighting in this war,
The wealthy count their riches,
Because I am a Knight.

I see a man fall to the ground.
I hear a wicked laugh, doth not the Scriptures say
"Thou shalt not kill a man?"

So why all this corruption?
Why all these wicked deeds?
Am I really keeping my honor,
Doing as they please?

I am a Knight.
I am a Knight.

Shimón Lidmark
Riverton Middle School
Riverton, WY
Grade 6

Skunk

I got out of bed and said
I'm going to stick my head in a skunk hole.
I did what I said just because I didn't want to go to bed.
Oh, I stuck my head in a skunk's hole
And the little skunk said
Bless you my soul.
Take it out! Remove it!
When I did not take it out,
The little skunk said, you better take it out or,
Or you will wish you were
DEAD!
Take it out! Take it out! Remove it!

I removed it...Ssssssssssssssssss. Too late!

Jerome Atkinson
Elkhart Elementary School
Aurora, CO
Grade 4

A Summer Night

It's a hot summer night,
Everyone's laughing in the house;
While outside the cover is coming off the water,
And the water is rippling;

We all run outside and jump into the water,
At first it is a bit cold;
We swim a little,
Laugh a little;

And the sun starts to go down,
As we all take one last swim;
We cover up the still water,
And the day is over.

Bobbi Seegmiller
Farmington Elementary School
Farmington, UT
Grade 6

The Hawk's Hunt

A hawk soars over his prey
That is eating up a farmer's hay
The hawk dives, he's gaining speed
While his prey keeps eating up its feed
The hawk hits with tremendous power
But doesn't start to devour
He takes his food to his favorite log
Where he feasts very quickly just like a hog
Very quickly the hawk eats his meal
To prevent another animal from making a steal
Once the hawk finishes its meat
He returns to sleep on his comfortable seat

Morgan Wichelhaus
Hudson Elementary School
Hudson, WY
Grade 6

Celestial Life

Born in dust
Die in fire
Living eons
Only to tire

Showing light
And might
Proclaimed to be a god
But only a fraud

Losing gas
While decreasing mass
It will not go alone
Sucking everything into an endless cone

Gregory Fein
Laredo Middle School
Aurora, CO
Grade 6

Grandpa

G randest man
R eady for anything
A lways has wonderful ideas
N ever sad always glad
D oes just about everything
P uts ideas in your head
A lways there for me

Brett Sabott
Franklin Elementary School
Pueblo, CO
Grade 5

Wolf

I creep about the tundra
a field of winter and ice
I hunt a sleek black crow
and little helpless mice

I go around in a pack
I baby-sit as they
hop on my back
They also chew on my ear

People hunt me
I escape them all
I'll run away from thee
safe and sound is me

I will not harm
therefore you
shall not alarm
for I am kind

Jenna Dixon
Woodman Elementary School
Lolo, MT
Grade 6

The Road of Life and Death

I woke up to go to school, although it was very early.
As I walked I found something very interesting,
a fork in the road, and on the right there was three signs
one said the road to the theme park, and the other one said the road to life,
and the last one said "DO NOT TAKE" this is the road to death,
at first I thought I better not take it, then I said to myself,
the road to death is just like the road to life, it's just so many people
are afraid to take it because they are afraid of death,
but why should they because they know sometime in their life they will die.
Right after I said that I woke up in my room crying,
so I went to my grandma's room so she could cheer me up,
but then I found that she was dead, but then I stopped
and remembered the road to death is the road to life.

Heather Searing
Ecker Hill Middle School
Park City, UT
Grade 6

My Choir

When I walk into the room, I see empty chairs.
I hear the echo of my feet walking through the hallway

I find a chair and it squeaks as I pull it up to convene in.
The room is empty, I hear nothing.

Finally, I hear footsteps coming towards me.
Soon the room is filled with laughter, ha, ha, ha
And never ending chatter.

We finally get started. I hear beautiful voices floating through the air.
It seems as if nothing could stop it but it's 6:25.

I walk outside. I hear cars swiftly going by– Honk, honk,
Doors opening and shutting, crickets noisily chirping, and I go home.
It's quiet. Shhh!

Kimber Kirwin
Shrine of St Anne School
Arvada, CO
Grade 6

Germany

I feel the jolt of the wheels as we land in Germany.
I hear the roaring engines of the plane slowly stopping.
I smell the syrupy smell of the food that was cooked for us earlier.
I can't wait to get rid of the perfume smell.
I see my grandparents waving at us out the window.
I hear the flight attendant announce that we can get off of the plane.
I taste the fresh air as we finally get out of the aircraft.
I feel people brushing past me trying to find their families.
We spot my grandparents and go over to them.
All of a sudden, I feel my grandparent's hugs crushing me as we find them.
We are together again.

Kira Vigil
Afflerbach Elementary School
Cheyenne, WY
Grade 5

Let Freedom Ring

Martin dreamed, and so did I
I dreamed that one day I would fly.
I'd fly over the USA,
And what I'd see is this I pray.

Oh Lord I pray that what I'll see
Is a land where no one disagrees.
A land where it's a guarantee
That no one needs a referee.

A land where life's a jamboree,
Of friendship, love, and family.
Yes what I'll see when I fly o'er all
Is a land of the free, and not one downfall.

My cry will be heard,
All over the earth,
"Oh yes this is a great rebirth!"
Our dreams were alike, Martin and me.

Both of us dreamed
That what we'd see,
Is a land of the free,
Of Liberty.

Hannah Geoffrion Radner
McClelland Center School
Pueblo, CO
Grade 4

Car Crash

When it rains it reminds me of the day my
Great Grandmother died,
The Thunder reminds me of the crash,
The Lightning reminds me of the ambulance lights,
The rain reminds me of the pain and suffering she went through.

Lance Lynn
Academy Charter School
Castle Rock, CO
Grade 6

Tide Pools

It's low tide, little pools of sparkling
blue water are filling up between big rocks.

Small sea urchins and starfish wash up on shore,
but find themselves trapped in a small tide pool.

Fish wash up on shore to visit,
but get trapped with the other prisoners.

Eight hours later it's high tide,
the prisoners are free.

Lauren Little
Heatherwood Elementary School
Boulder, CO
Grade 4

Watermelon

A cool summer treat, inside or out. A calm fresh feeling is
all about, when you bite into it, a fresh fruity feeling rivers
in your mouth. The luscious taste is incredible, exploding
with flavor. One little morsel will make you waver all over.
When you savor the melon, you'll relish it until the very
last second. You twist and turn with enchantment, and
ask for more. Oh how this fruit mumbles and jumbles
in your belly, the cold and crisp taste inside. Juices
dribbling down your mouth with pleasure, oh
how divine! Sitting there in the sun, with a
sensational fruit, sitting on the roof of
your mouth, you can't resist the
taste, the tangy tidbit of
watermelon.

Dannika Egan-Wright
Afflerbach Elementary School
Cheyenne, WY
Grade 6

My Dad

I remember that in October
My dad had moved to California
I remember that in October
My dad told me I could see him in the summer
I remember that in October
I told my dad, "I will miss you, Daddy."
I remember that in October
I told my dad, "I love you, Daddy."

Melissa Mangeri
Malley Drive Elementary School
Northglenn, CO
Grade 5

My Riddle

It's two antlers are on top.
I travel with it,
I talk with it.
It can eat and pop out square shaped things.
You may cry with it,
Or laugh with it,
Sometimes it hurts you in a way.
It does not need clothes or fresh air.
It cannot die.
It doesn't have feelings.
Your mother disapproves of it.
Your dad loves it,
And you like it.
It does not live in
Bowls, parks, or cages.
What is it?

Answer: A TV

Julie Melillo
Heatherwood Elementary School
Boulder, CO
Grade 4

Summer Fall Spring and Winter

In the summer bright and early
the sun comes out and shines on me

In the fall dark and quiet
you can hear all kinds of sounds

In the spring cool and noisy
you can feel the gentle breeze

In the winter light and cold
you can see kids playing in snow

Summer, fall, spring and winter
that is how I like it
Megan Ervin
Petersen Elementary School
Sunnyside, UT
Grade 4

Sorry

I'm really sorry I ruined your car,
I was only taking it for a short drive,
I thought I could warm it up for you,
I truly am sorry,
But I thought I should start practicing,
I mean I only have 5 more years left!
Kara Hiatt
Ecker Hill Middle School
Park City, UT
Grade 6

Good Bye*

Tears are shed
For this poor man who lay dead.
The family of him mourn greatly.
Wanting to hold him so badly
It makes them so sad;
They never wanted to let go;
It brings more pain to their woe.

They think, why he, not me?
He was so great,
Couldn't this death have been more late?
It's so hard to say good bye
Without the strong urge to cry.

To have the chance yet to say,
"Someday we will be together again
In love, no fear, and hope.
But for now, good bye."
Kristi L. McIntosh
Mary Blair Elementary School
Loveland, CO
Grade 5
In the most loving memory of George
Washington, the father of our Country

Snow

Snow, falling cold snow.
Falling from the sky
Cold in the morning and night.
Cameron Decker
Lomond View Elementary School
Ogden, UT
Grade 4

The Wonders of Winter

Isn't winter wonderful,
Pretty snowflakes fall,
There is a blanket of snow,
Covering our town,
This is the season of the snowman.
Rachel Freeman
Petersen Elementary School
Sunnyside, UT
Grade 4

Cake

There once was a man from Salt Lake,
And all he would eat was some cake.
He ate up his fill,
And felt good until,
His stomach, it started to ache!
Elizabeth Paxton
St Vincent De Paul School
Salt Lake City, UT
Grade 6

The Predator

In the forest a leopard waits,
to strike the tiny critter
who sits at the bottom of the tree
he has no idea he is the leopard's lunch.
Then leap, crunch. . .
The critter is gone and two yellow eyes
appear happy and satisfied at
the bottom of the tree.
Leela Nadler
Colorado Academy
Denver, CO
Grade 5

Bunny Eggs

Bunny
tall white
speeding delivering giving
eggs ears yolk chicken
coloring falling riding
bright round
Eggs
Katie Klema
Washington Terrace Elementary School
Ogden, UT
Grade 4

The Hand

The hand holds the pencil.
The pencil holds the words.
The words hold the feelings.
The feelings hold the brain.
The brain holds the power.
And the power holds the courage.
Linda Czechowicz
Clear Lake Middle School
Denver, CO
Grade 6

Winter Blizzard

The mountain over there has snow
like dust blowing across the top.
The trees are covered with snow
like white spiders on top of each other.
The ground all lumpy from the rocks
underneath the foot of snow.
The cliff with a blood curdling look
and sound shrills the ground beneath.
The freezing river like a cup of ice water
with the water making a path
for the fishes in the spring,
while the bushes and trees
huddle together to keep warm.
Molly Dawn Petersen
Farmington Elementary School
Farmington, UT
Grade 6

Books

Books.
So many different kinds of books:
Fantasy, novels and verses.
So many different authors of books:
Shakespeare, Lewis and Berry.
So many different books in the world,
And when you like to read
So many books you can read
But not all will be good!
Marina Manakova
First Presbyterian Church Academy
Las Vegas, NV
Grade 6

My Dad and I

My dad and I like to fish
We throw in the poles and they go swish!
We get a bite
Oh what a delight!
We reel it in
Only to throw it back again!
Britnee Miller Tenlen
Ashgrove Elementary School
Riverton, WY
Grade 4

Life

Life is a basket of fruit,
It can be sweet or rotten.
Things can be praised,
Or forgotten.

Life tastes like an orange,
Tangy, sweet, but delicious.
Life smells like a mango,
Different, but nutritious.

Life sounds like a banana in your mouth,
Mushy, gushy and busy.
Life feels like the smooth skin of an apple,
Bumpy, smooth or sometimes fuzzy!

So life is truly like a basket of fruit,
Life is different,
Fruit is different,
Life is a basket of fruit.

Jenny Beman
Afflerbach Elementary School
Cheyenne, WY
Grade 6

Backwards Poem

There is a man, who lives in town,
He never gets up, he always gets down,
This old man rakes leaves off the trees,
And bakes his cakes with antifreeze.
He never grows big he always grows small,
He's never felt what it's like to be tall,
This old man lives in backward town,
He never gets up, he always gets down.

Christian Lauber
Academy Charter School
Castle Rock, CO
Grade 6

Stars

They are cryptic,
Glimmering in the night sky,
Flashing, twinkling, sparkling, winking,
Why are they there, oh why?
With nothing to worry 'bout,
A large, round, inflamed mass of fire,
Flying around in empty space about,
Burning, pulsating, incandescent with desire,
Eventually, one day it will have to die,
It will solemnly burn out,
Falling down through the sky,
It is a fact not to doubt,
Do you know what they are?

Carol Tomanek
Afflerbach Elementary School
Cheyenne, WY
Grade 6

Water

What is this liquid that I see,
This liquid running into the sea?
Its quick white currents flying by,
when you touch its coolness, you say, "My, my!"
Its aquamarine color, oh so bright,
Shall I jump in? Well, I just might!
What is this liquid so full of color?
Why, it is the luscious and life giving water!

Kimberly Tosti
Ecker Hill Middle School
Park City, UT
Grade 6

Winter Trees

Winter trees singing their lonely song.
Reaching upward wanting to leap out
And soar with the wind.
Roots not wanting to let go.
Curly, gnarly feet and toes reaching downward.
Grabbing the earth, holding on tight.

Winter pine trees blowing in the wind,
Are girls in flip-flopping, jump-twirling dresses.
Dancing in the silver snow.

Lena Carroll
Rowland Hall-St Mark's School
Salt Lake City, UT
Grade 5

Discovery

I always do extraordinary things
each and every day.
I discovered France and Germany too,
and even the Hawaiian Islands
and exotic Timbuctoo
and everybody knew me
I was in the middle of my greatest discovery,
but Galileo came right in
and left me with no place.

Brady Ewell
Ecker Hill Middle School
Park City, UT
Grade 6

Colorado Winter

The wind starts to blow
The leaves fall, one by one, again and again
The tiny snowflakes grow cold among my cheeks
I shiver, I shake, the cold air cools my face
The grass dances tall above the snow blanket
My heart beats like a drum,
With a rhythm of a ending snowfall.

Marika F. McMeans
Boulder Community School of Integrated Studies
Boulder, CO
Grade 4

Light of my Life

The sun swept
beams caress
thy face
As beautiful as
the morning
dew
The winds blow
delicate as a
little lamb
And the suns
beautiful rays
hug us
Your eyes so
glassy blue
As blue as the
ocean and the
dew
You are the
light of my life

Tyler Archuletta
Academy Charter School
Castle Rock, CO
Grade 6

Winter Sky

I can feel the wet waterfall splashing.
I can smell the fresh air.
I can see the wet trees and berries.
I can taste all the blueberries.

Vinny Dipasquale
Buffalo Ridge Elementary
Castle Rock, CO
Grade 4

Boulder

We're going to see my sis that's older
She has an apartment up in Boulder

I'm sure it won't be boring
That means I won't be snoring

We'll stay up all night
I hope we don't fight

Be nice my mom told her
This is their first night in Boulder

I'll be up there for long
I hope I'm not wrong

If you need me
Boulder is where I'll be

Carli Valdez
Franklin Elementary School
Pueblo, CO
Grade 5

The Hurricane Is Coming

The hurricane is coming, the hurricane is coming.
People screaming, babies crying, and children scared.
What can we do to stop the furious beast?

Pilots roaring their jets to take off.
Firefighters have no use.
The police hiding behind their cars.
There is nothing we can do to this beast but pray for the weather.
We can't stop it, it's just going to go through.
The hurricane is coming
WHAT CAN WE DO?

Matthew Mozia
Colorado Academy
Denver, CO
Grade 5

A Winter Storm

As I peer at myself in the glass, glossy ice
A sparkling snowflake lands softly on my cheek.
A sharp, dripping icicle drops to the ground shattering to pieces
As I peer at myself in the glass, glossy ice.

As I skate on that glass, glossy ice
A small bird who's lost his way flies by.
Another sparkling snowflake lands on my cheek
As I skate on that glass, glossy ice.

As the glass, glossy ice gets covered with snow
A car gets covered with snow too,
And a snowman gets made
As that glass, glossy ice gets covered with snow.

As I sit inside drinking my steaming hot cocoa
A small bird lands on the glass, glossy ice that's covered with snow.
A chill of a blizzard zooms through the mountains
As I sit inside drinking my steaming hot cocoa.

Amethyst Rose Smith
Hawthorne Elementary School
Missoula, MT
Grade 5

Another Year

Another year has passed us, another year is done.
Another year has flown by, another year is gone.
And as we look back on our lives we think about the past.
We think about how the days could have faded so fast.
The day we stopped to smell a flower,
The day we felt we had the power, to make our lives worth something.
The day we felt just like a king.
But something we will not forget are the friendships we had set.
Yet the most important thing isn't we learned how to sing,
Isn't that we learned math, it's that *we* chose our path.

Courtney Blake
Bennett Middle School
Bennett, CO
Grade 6

Buzzy Number Thirty-Three

Cool, there is a snail on me
I will call him Buzzy Number Thirty-Three
I wonder if he flies high or digs low
I wonder if he runs fast or creeps slow.

All I know is I have a snail named Buzzy Number Thirty-Three
And he is still on me.

He is red and yellow and a slimy little fellow
I'll make him a bed of jello
And a pillow of marshmallow
In the morning he will rise and shine and I will say "hello."

I have a snail named Buzzy Number Thirty-Three
And Buzzy wants to stick with me.

Jimmy Gorrell
Marshdale Elementary School
Evergreen, CO
Grade 4

Spring Sensation

Spring is as happy and cheerful as can be.
All the colors fill me with glee,
And the bright sun, shining down on my eyes,
Nourishes the flowers of all different size.

During this season the trees start to bloom,
And all of us look towards summer real soon.
We enjoy the smell of cookie batter,
And the sound of children's laughter.

The crunches of snow have long gone away,
The mittens and gloves in their trunks will stay.
It is time to run and play in the sun,
And we are all so glad that winter is done.

Kiki Berrett
Challenger School
Sandy, UT
Grade 6

Open a Book

Open a book
If you're in for a bumpy ride
Open a book and see what's inside.
You can explore on the surface of the moon
Or even explore the heart of a typhoon.
There are a lot of things to explore
Like to the bottom of the ocean floor.
Another thing that would be grand
Is if you could see what is under the sand.
If you want a lot to learn
Just open a book and now it's your turn.

Jaimie Bloxham
Midland Elementary School
Roy, UT
Grade 6

Lightning Power

Lightning just rings with pure power
And feels like a nuclear bomb
And smells of the destroyed remains
Its color is a blinding white
With the crackling sound of electricity jumping the skies.

Spencer Harris
Farmington Elementary School
Farmington, UT
Grade 6

Our Nation's Flag

Our nation's flag
We should never let drag.
A beautiful flag have we;
From our flag, never should we flee.

Proud should we be of our flag;
Sometimes I have a tendency to brag.
To our flag we do salute.
Our flag is something we should never pollute.

Our flag shall soar high
In the gracious sky.
From thirteen to fifty went our stars;
We have stars instead of bars.

Our flag has changed much in many years
It has always received many cheers.
A vibrant flag our flag may be;
Our flag is a thing of majesty.

America is free
And a free flag our flag will always be!

Kristin Mary Scribner
Mary Blair Elementary School
Loveland, CO
Grade 5

Eagles

Flying   Soaring
    Watching   Waiting
        Looking   Seeing
            Listening   Hearing
                Diving Faster
                Ever Faster
                Never Stopping
                Nor Hesitating
                A Dream of Freedom
                    In the Air—
                Only to Start
        His   Soaring
    Once   Again.

Sam Bleckley
Laredo Middle School
Aurora, CO
Grade 6

Patience

Patience is
the lavender on the ocean surface
right before the sun comes up.

It is
a large eagle soaring across
a full moon at midnight.

Patience is
the large mountains
with the clean white snow
in the winter.

Patience is *beautiful*.

Kenley Turville
Morningside Elementary School
Salt Lake City, UT
Grade 6

Fear

the place i fear most is here.
it is a place
where you won't know
where
to come back to.
even though
i wait for you,
i know that
although
you say
you know the way,
you'll never
be back.
no one knows
if I'm still here,
and if
i truly am,
why
no one else
sees.

Allison Hubbell
University Lab School
Laramie, WY
Grade 6

Butterfly

Oh so delicate
wing with woven lace.
With so many colors
that are out of this world.
It seems like you could
fly to the heavens.

Rory Fry
Colorado Academy
Denver, CO
Grade 4

Nature

The bird sings beautiful songs
The wind blows in the trees
The leaves rustle under my feet
The flowers bloom in mid spring
As I walk through the valley of life

Joseph Sanchez
Academy Charter School
Castle Rock, CO
Grade 6

Peace and Quiet

The snow on the mountain top
And the water down below
And small and large rocks
Tall and short rocks
Fat and skinny rocks
Strange and normal rocks
But the mountain is not alone
Something is there
It's not a person
It's not a plant
It's peace and quiet

Brooks Van Orden
Farmington Elementary School
Farmington, UT
Grade 6

Callie

Black and gold,
Brown and white,
When you see her
You'll say she's quite a sight!

She's beautiful
No doubting that,
She's very small,
She's my favorite cat!

What's her name?
Her name is Callie.
You'll find her anywhere,
Except for an alley!

Well, that's not all
I can tell about her,
She's very smart
And has soft fur.

I love it when she cuddles with me.
I pet her and she purrs out loud
She'll always be in the family tree.
To own her, I am very proud.

Erin Gorsett
Roy Moore Elementary School
Silt, CO
Grade 4

Gorillas

Deep in the forest
The most graceful among all
Sadly almost gone.

Chelsie Anton
Kearns-St Ann School
Salt Lake City, UT
Grade 6

Haunted House

There's a house at the end of the street
That everyone says is *haunted*

Its paint is worn and peeling off
The shingles on the roof, old and fragile,
Fly away when the cruel wind blows.
The shutters bang and creak,
Bang and creak all day long.

Some leafless trees in the front yard
Are like monsters
With their long arms and sharp claws
Reaching in the dark

There's an eerie glow
In the attic window
I think I'll see if anyone's home

Marissa Masihdas
Morningside Elementary School
Salt Lake City, UT
Grade 6

Hawaii

Summer
Can be a bummer

But not for me
I'm going to Maui

We have some loot
I think I'll buy a new swimsuit

I'm sure I'll go swimming
I race and I love winning

My mom said we'd see dolphins
And maybe a whale with big fins

We're staying at the Marriott
It's a great spot

I'm so happy I could do a back bend.
The end.

Deandra McCain
Franklin Elementary School
Pueblo, CO
Grade 5

Happiness

Happiness looks like summer rain.
Happiness smells like a bright red rose.
Happiness sounds like kids playing on the streets.
Happiness tastes like hot Campbell soup.
Happiness feels like the deep blue sea.
Happiness is wonderful!

Tyler Chapman
Roy Moore Elementary School
Silt, CO
Grade 4

A Stroll in the Park

One day I took a stroll in the park.
There were many sights to see.
I looked and looked all around.
Dogs, trees, and bumble bees.

I saw people having a picnic.
There were kids tossing a Frisbee.
Some kids were playing at a playground.
Others on the swings were going "WEEE."

I saw a group of strong-looking boys.
Playing a game of hard-hitting baseball.
They were smacking balls with bats.
Balls flying into walls as the umpire made his calls.

Kids were flying kites up in the soaring wind.
Parents were having cake and pie.
I was preparing to leave the park
I took one last look at the sky and said bye-bye!

I went back home to my house.
I got ready to go to the park again,
But before I went back to the park,
I fell asleep as I counted to ten in my den.

Kyle Van Cure
St Vincent De Paul School
Salt Lake City, UT
Grade 6

Rain

Rain is music
as it beats on my umbrella
in a wonderful tune
I sing along
I love to listen to the rain beat
on my roof at night; it sings me to sleep
Rain is music
some may see wet, others see horrible gray
but I see music
Rain is music and I love the rain

Mandi Bauer
Woodman Elementary School
Lolo, MT
Grade 6

George Washington

George Washington was wonderful and great.
He led an army through a war.
To be a good president was his fate.
His spirit lives on forever more.

George was a farmer, and a surveyor too
And loved to ride horses every chance he got.
He learned many lessons, but one thing he knew
Farming was fun, but you worked a lot.

One day he rode through the snow;
Cold and wet it was
As the wind gave a mighty blow.
When he got inside, everything became a fuzz.

Ashlyn Rhule
Mary Blair Elementary School
Loveland, CO
Grade 5

My Best Foot

My mom always tells me to put my best foot forward.
But I only have a right and a left foot.
So which is my best foot?
Do I have a worst foot?
Do I even have a best foot?
Does it look like a normal foot?
Or does it look like an alien foot?
Is it even a foot or do they just call it a foot?
Oh well, I guess I'll never know.
By the way, do you know?

Julia Carlson
Colorado Academy
Denver, CO
Grade 4

Footprints

Every day at recess, I see footprints
Whether they are small medium or large
They always seem to be special in a different way

When I go outside, I always see footprints
They're all slushy or snow-covered
But they're all unique in their own way

I love FOOTPRINTS
They are peaceful
As I look at them, it makes me feel joyful
Sometimes they have frost on them
And sometimes they are smooth
And sometimes they are bumpy
I don't really care if they are destroyed
But I love FOOTPRINTS!

Richelle Barba
Hawthorne Elementary School
Missoula, MT
Grade 5

Golf

Golf
Fun, frustrating
Putting, chipping, driving
Onto the green
Hole-in-one

Katie Cummings
St Vincent De Paul School
Salt Lake City, UT
Grade 6

Ducks

Ducks
Small, Furry
Waddling, Swimming, Diving
Fun to watch
Quacker

Randy Pankow
Ecker Hill Middle School
Park City, UT
Grade 6

Pine Tree

Nothing is as faithful as a pine tree
Its loyal green needles I can always see
It stands so proud,
Its tip in the clouds.

Chloe Hansen
Sacred Heart of Jesus School
Boulder, CO
Grade 5

Imagination

As a shadow moves past me
  I see the misty glow
I say to myself
  What was it?
Sometimes I think it was my
IMAGINATION.

I see this once again
  It is a simple shape
The color is so simple
  What was it?
Many times I think it was my
IMAGINATION.

I see this shadow only once more
  It whistles while it passes
Moving past the trees
  What was it?
Many times I think it was my
IMAGINATION.

Lee Burkett
Colorado Academy
Denver, CO
Grade 5

Memories

In the dictionary a memory is
the mental capacity or faculty of retaining or recalling,
events, impressions, or previous experiences.

But to me a memory is...

Tubing on the cold, icy water with the mist rushing past my face in Lake Powell
or the long painful surgery I had on my feet.

Remembering that my granddad died on Thanksgiving
or remembering holidays like Christmas, when I was too excited to sleep.

Easter when I laughed seeing a friend in an Easter Bunny costume
or the funny moments at birthday parties, like the relay race.
Watching everyone made me laugh.

But then the memories of moments with family and friends...
with friends, it's laughing, watching the plays we did,
and then more laughing.

And, with family it's laughing, crying, talking, wishing, and hoping.

But of course, these are just my memories.

Ali Goldsmith
Morningside Elementary School
Salt Lake City, UT
Grade 6

Freedom

Working in the cotton fields, it wouldn't be someone's dream.
A nightmare would be more precise, a dream to some whites or so it seems.
A life of deep darkness on the inside and out.
Life is awful. It has many doubts.
Being sold from one white to another and to another.
They don't care if there's separation between sisters and brothers.
It doesn't matter if my skin is different from the rest,
So why do you treat whites like they're the best?
So maybe a white's dream is to have slaves in their fields
But our dream is to be free. We want freedom!

Sydney Emmitt Morauer
Jamestown Elementary School
Jamestown, CO
Grade 5

I Like Bugs

I like bugs,
Slimy, sloppy bugs with seven legs,
Scary, stinky bugs with stretched antennae,
I like creepy, crawly bugs that live in dark corners,
And slinky, scuttly bugs that crawl and creep through your house at night,
But the bugs I like best are computer bugs that are invisible to your eye,
And eat away your computer chip, stealthily.

Shayne Metos
Lowell Elementary School
Salt Lake City, UT
Grade 6

America

America is a place of great beauty,
And wonderful things.
All the land is getting built on,
Only so we can house more traffic.
It's bad enough as it is,
Let alone twenty years from now.
I hope that someone, somewhere, sometime
Will decide to stop all the building,
And reserve all the beauty of this country.

Alex Seifert
Academy Charter School
Castle Rock, CO
Grade 6

Hockey

Hockey fun fast.
Hockey skating on an uncontrollable surface.
Hockey rough tough, and mean.
Hockey heavy hard hits, glass shatters.
Hockey traveling to different states.
Hockey very strict refs.
Hockey

Brendon Olson
Heatherwood Elementary School
Boulder, CO
Grade 4

The Perfect Game

One day I went bowling,
But it wasn't my turn,
So I sat and watched the bright green ball rolling.
Quicker and quicker down the lane,
I could tell that the pins were expecting pain.

Then it was my turn,
I threw down the ball.
And I watched the pins fall, "That had to burn."
I got a strike my dad said, "Good shot."
I said, "That you could not dislike."

I'm in frame five,
I've gotten only strikes,
"I know I will survive."
I'm on my way to getting a 300.
And all the others are falling behind,
Even though I'm just a kid.

Now it's the tenth frame,
I walked up to bowl.
The ball went down the middle,
I had perfect aim.
And that's how I got my perfect game.

Ryan Hornacek
St Vincent De Paul School
Salt Lake City, UT
Grade 6

Travis Cartwright

Travis
who is short, outspoken, humorous and skinny
child of Konnie and Tracy
lover of basketball, Playstation, and cake
who feels hyper, bored, and hungry
who needs sports, sugar, and Mountain Dew
who gives headaches, laughter, and time
who fears jail, drugs, and robbers
who would like to see Canada, Europe, and Japan
resident of Aurora, Colorado
Cartwright

Travis Cartwright
Most Precious Blood School
Denver, CO
Grade 5

Ottie

My dog is a black lab,
And some days he looks sad,
But when he sees my dad,
He is very glad.

When Ottie is really glad,
He doesn't look sad,
He jumps on my dad,
And my brother gets real mad.

When my brother is real mad,
Ottie gets so sad!!!
He goes over to my dad,
And then gets very glad.

So when Ottie's glad, and Orrie's sad,
My dad is so glad!!!
He brings out a sack,
Boy, Ottie wonders, what's behind his back,
Guess what?
It's a sack full of snacks.

Ashton Gondeiro
Fort Shaw Elementary School
Fort Shaw, MT
Grade 5

Lingering Lovers

In a small café,
Two, romantic lovers linger over tea
Sharing secrets and English cakes dipped in cream
After moonlight turns
Their fingers gold
"Bliss" says he
"Decay" says she
The light cannot hold any longer

Nicole Westerman
Franklin Elementary School
Pueblo, CO
Grade 5

River

River flows down the mountain.
It flows down very slowly
Flow, flow down down down...
Ashlie Boehme
Lomond View Elementary School
Ogden, UT
Grade 4

Summer Leaves

Summer leaves
Remind you of the hot scorching sun

Summer leaves
Remind you of picking food
From the garden you grew

Summer leaves
Remind you of the cool splash
From the swimming pool

Summer leaves
Remind you of the adventures
You have in your back yard

I wish it were summer
But right now
I *have* to be in school.
Wesley Burningham
Morningside Elementary School
Salt Lake City, UT
Grade 6

Kittens Are...

Kittens are cute,
And kittens are lovable,
You can tell if you see one.

Kittens are fluffy,
And kittens are soft,
You can tell if you pet one.

Kittens are smelly,
Because they don't wash,
You can tell if you smell one.

Kittens go meow,
And kittens go mew,
You can tell if you hear one.

Kittens like tuna fish,
And kittens like to play,
You can tell if you own one!
Devan Carter
St John the Baptist School
Draper, UT
Grade 4

Greece

Parthenon crumbling
Lemon Chicken Soup aromas
Fill the room
Olives growing
Horns honking in Athens
Go to the shores
The markets are busy
In Greece
Dorian Shockley
Colorado Academy
Denver, CO
Grade 4

My Sister Kelsey

My sister Kelsey is bigger than me
and lifts me up quite easily.
I can't lift her—
I've tried and tried,
She must have something
heavy inside.
Samantha Waller
Pioneer Elementary School
Billings, MT
Grade 6

Holly

dependable
trustworthy
loving
Wishes to become famous
Dreams of becoming rich
Wants to be a dentist
Who wonders about stars
Who fears war
Who likes boys
Who believes in God
Who loves basketball
Who plans to live a happy life
Whose final destination is heaven.
Holly Cook
Franklin Elementary School
Pueblo, CO
Grade 5

Day/Night

Day
Sun, hot
Morning, sunny, Light
Hot, warm, fireflies, chilly
Dark, star, moon
Cold, draft
Night
Josh Lee
Ecker Hill Middle School
Park City, UT
Grade 6

Hale-Bopp

A silent sky,
with speckles of stars,
scattered.

Evergreens sway,
casting their shadows,
on darkness.

Then suddenly,
a flash erupts,
parting the heavens with its flaming tail.

It disappears,
leaving the silence,
where evergreens sway.
Rabah Kamal
Laredo Middle School
Aurora, CO
Grade 6

Columbine Thirteen

Thirteen tears wept so bitterly,
On an annual occasion.
One for every soul that left
This world so cold and quickly.

Thirteen scars made so harshly,
On a face so fair and true.
Those wounds will always pain
Colorado's grieving body.

Thirteen not just an lucky number,
But a memorial to remember.
Veronique Van Pelt
Cherry Valley Elementary School
Franktown, CO
Grade 5

Lunch

Peanut butter and rock jelly
Old rotten cheese from the Deli
Green ugly potato chips
Purple colored slimy dip

A hot dog a million years old
Black hot pockets that are cold

An apple that's been chewed by a worm
An orange that's hard and firm

I think I'll bring my own lunch
Or I'll be sick a whole bunch
Elisabeth Farmer
Heatherwood Elementary School
Boulder, CO
Grade 4

Scrapbook

Scrapbook
Memories forever told,
To treasure always till we're old.
My mom, my dad, my dogs and me,
Pictures of swimming, eating, and going to ski.

My dad has a picture of him and a fish,
My mom has a picture with her making a dish.
My dogs, they just slobber from January to November,
And me, I have pictures I don't want to remember!

Joshua S. Carroll
Afflerbach Elementary School
Cheyenne, WY
Grade 6

Gold

Samuel Smith he was told
That in the desert he'd find gold
So Samuel left in the bright sunlight
Then he figured he'd been traveling from dawn till night
As he stooped in the plain
He felt a little drop of rain
And then in the night
He saw a beautiful sight
It was the gold like he'd been told

Alyssa Scott
Mound Valley Rural School
Elko, NV
Grade 4

The Glistening Sunset

I was sitting with a light blue blanket,
Listening to the waves crash against the shore,
Each time bringing more beautiful and unusual seashells.

I began to stand up in the soothing, but unbearably soft sand,
When the cool breeze skimmed my neck.
It seemed to be giving me a sign,
Not knowing what to do, I ran to the shore.

The seagulls were talking back to the breathing ocean,
The wind blew again,
This time it seemed to carry me somewhere.

I was staring at the glistening sun from the highest hill top,
Still with the blanket.
I seemed to be dreaming,
But I was aimlessly thinking.

I was being carried to a sparkling far off place as the sun set,
I wondered, I just wondered.
I was, was thinking, but not really thinking.

Johanna Blumenthal
Broomfield Heights Middle School
Broomfield, CO
Grade 6

The Dog Run

My dogs run out before me
My dogs lead my sled through the tundra
My dogs have taken me on unforgettable journeys
My dogs are the spirits of the wild
The spirits of my dogs are mild but strong
The hearts of my dogs are wild and free
With a loud whistle the dogs are off
When I yell gee they turn right
When I yell haw they turn left with grace,
After days on the trail, I spot the finish line
Everyone watches as I cross the finish line with much joy
And that is when I know, the medal is mine.

Jayson Collins
Hudson Elementary School
Hudson, WY
Grade 6

I Like Football

I like football
Tough, towering tacklers try to eliminate their enemies,
Enormous players hit each other's helmets in celebration,
Speedy runners who are loaded with heavy equipment,
Running toward the end zone.
I like linebackers who hit hard enough to make you bleed,
Tiny quarterbacks who throw long passes to receivers,
But the players I like best are receivers
Who make diving, one-handed catches in the air for a first down.

Chase Nelson
Lowell Elementary School
Salt Lake City, UT
Grade 6

The Park

Here I walk by the park
Watching children play.
Maybe I'll bring my children here tomorrow.
They would love it here!

Children play, on the wood,
Going down the slide.
Children play, in the tunnel,
Going down the pole.

Here I smell the morning dew,
Floating at my side.
Seeing children laugh and play,
That's what my children would do!

Here I smell, the pink roses in summer,
Sometimes red, sometimes green.
But here, it all ends up to be,
One big fantasy come true!

Olivia Wee
St John the Baptist School
Draper, UT
Grade 4

Lacrosse

When the ball goes in the net,
the crowd goes wild
as you win the game.

Mike Ritucci
Kearns-St Ann School
Salt Lake City, UT
Grade 6

Small-Footed, Stomping Centipedes

Coming from afar
With too many legs to count
It just stomps about!

Nick Koning
Kearns-St Ann School
Salt Lake City, UT
Grade 6

The Night Sky

The night drifted across the sky,
She pushed the sun, the clouds, the blue
Out of the way.
She hushed the world with a
Silent breeze,
She put on her starry robe and
Her moon cap.
Then she left.

Tai Ventrella
Nederland Elementary School
Nederland, CO
Grade 6

Wolf Cry

There is a wolf cry in the
    distance.
Under the trees below.
The wolf is telling everyone the
    coming of winter snow.
The air is as crisp as peppermint,
    fresh and clean.
The snowy mountains fresh and
    white makes a beautiful
    winter scene.
The wind whistles a song of an
    icy winter night.
And the moon shines on everything
    making dark things bright.
And if you like these winter scenes
    listen under the trees below.
To a wolf cry in the distance
    telling the coming of
    winter snow.

Kate Faulk
Sacred Heart of Jesus School
Boulder, CO
Grade 5

Sunrise

He wakes up
At the crack of dawn
His arms of red, orange, and yellow
Shining brightly
Stretch down to the ground
Awakening the world

He is a fireball
Slowly shooting upwards
Covering up night
For it is his job
To begin a new day

Rohini Muralidharan
Laredo Middle School
Aurora, CO
Grade 6

Diary

I came across your diary
and accidentally read it.
I know it had all the secrets
and crushes you have ever had.
I'm sorry that I read it,
and will you please forgive me?
I was just really bored so I read it.
By the way, I can't believe
that you liked the dorkiest kids.

Jenna Innis
Ecker Hill Middle School
Park City, UT
Grade 6

Golf Course

Splash! Splash! In the pond
cart paths here and there
on the peaceful, calm golf course

Andrew Rasmussen
Kearns-St Ann School
Salt Lake City, UT
Grade 6

Annie

She is tiny but mighty
Is small but can jump high
Over the fence and touch the sky.
She eats very little that's why she's small.
She's fast and playful and a doll.
She loves to cuddle under the blanket
    with you or others.
She's my dog I love her so!
Annie

Maggie Heimbichner
Pioneer Elementary School
Billings, MT
Grade 6

In Case You Didn't Notice...

I ruined your new vest,
The one you got from Grandpa,
that one was your best,
Please, please forgive me,
I thought it was a tablecloth,
and I spilled my grape juice on it.
I know you must be mad,
but if you dyed it yellow-green,
then it wouldn't look half bad!

Tom McCosh
Ecker Hill Middle School
Park City, UT
Grade 6

Sights of Seasons

The sight of a wolf,
on a warm summer night

The sight of an elk,
on a cool fall afternoon

Or the sight of a coyote,
on a cold winter day

Or the sight of a bobcat,
on a warm spring morning

Justin Robison
Hudson Elementary School
Hudson, WY
Grade 5

Something Up

dark as a black hole
is prettier than a rose
the sky was crying comets
brighter than a candle in darkness
sky went by my house tonight
stars are cars driving through night
was darker than a bottomless pit
whoosh! goes the falling star

Colin McClure
Dos Rios Elementary School
Evans, CO
Grade 5

Tiger

Tiger
Ferocious, hunter
Killing, biting, purring
Protecting her new cubs
Feline

Aldo Arnone
Ecker Hill Middle School
Park City, UT
Grade 6

Friends

Friends never part unless they get in a fight
Friends bring joy but some bring hatred
Friends are like family, well some are
Friends are pleasant a lot of the time
Friends are there when you need them most of the time
Friends can be ridiculous
And make you laugh when you are feeling blue

Shellie K. Swinney
Broadwater Elementary School
Billings, MT
Grade 6

Candles

The soft candle light misting the room
With sprinkled light throughout the chair I sat in.
Dripped wax along the side.
A drop of light turns into a flame,
Bouncing off the walls and bookshelves.
The flow of the spark sneaks it's way to the space I sat.
Then when the clock strikes 12
A gust of wind blows the flicker away.

Francesca Dreith
Foothills Academy
Wheat Ridge, CO
Grade 5

Oh, Thunderstorm

Oh, thunderstorm, so dark like night,
You scare some people with all your might.

But me, you storm, you'll never scare,
For I'm inside and you're out there!

While you are pouring and blocking the sun,
I'm inside having lots of fun!

And if you really howl and shriek,
I might come out and take a peek.

And then you will see, if you even once went to school,
That I, my friend, am no fool!

Lindsay Snyder
Campus Middle School
Englewood, CO
Grade 6

Missy

There was once a cat and her name was Missy
She was always very angry and always quite hissy
And she always would burst
When she couldn't be first
And her mother would always call her a sissy

Andy Cornia
Washington Terrace Elementary School
Ogden, UT
Grade 4

Rain Forest

The rain forest is bright and beautiful,
With no darkness until night, with almost every animal
And reptile living in one home.
Only to part, when one is hungry.
But never will there be just one.

Meagan Slater
Colorado Academy
Denver, CO
Grade 5

The Substitute

We had a substitute today
She was mean in every way.

She was a Russian lady
Her voice was very faded.

Finally it was time to go,
Only out for recess though,

Recess was way too short.
I think it's time to port.

Thank you, lunch.
We got away from the bunch.

Lunch wasn't good.
I stand under my hood,
Because I don't feel good.

Leaving,
  I wish I could.
We all would.

The afternoon was mixed-up
We need another back-up
Thank you.
  The day is DONE!
  It wasn't fun.

Alex Patterson
Heatherwood Elementary School
Boulder, CO
Grade 4

Babies

God put them here for many reasons.
To be loved
To be cared for
To be blessed with God's wishes
How the angels play with your feet
As you sleep and dream of all the angels and God
Looking down on you

Christina Martinez
South Elementary School
Brighton, CO
Grade 5

Castles in the Air

Flying with a prayer,
To castles in the air,
Singing a sweet tune,
With sky blacker than a loon.

Stars play with clouds in the sky,
While rainbows dance way up high,
Magic always happens there,
There, where there are castles in the air.

But sadly as I fly away,
I'll dream of where I flew today,
There, where I fly with a prayer,
Away, to castles in the air.

Liz Rader
Afflerbach Elementary School
Cheyenne, WY
Grade 6

Mr. Pencil

Hello Mr. Pencil
How are you today?
I've got to write a poem
Can you help this way?

Have you any good ideas
You could help me create.
I'm having trouble thinking!
Let's plan a study date.

We could meet tomorrow
In the study hall.
Bring with you your writing charm
We will have a ball!

And I will bring Miss Paper
A sheet or two about.
She is very receptive
To pencil lead I've found out.

Riley Calvillo
Cortez Middle School
Cortez, CO
Grade 6

Dragons

I am charging at the dragon,
Yet I am not the dragon slayer.
I am getting chased by the dragon,
Yet I am not its prey.
I am sleeping in the dragon's lair,
Yet I am not a prisoner.
I am a guest in my dream of dragons.

Kelly Andrews
Woodland Park Middle School
Woodland Park, CO
Grade 6

Friends Forever

You were always there when I came to cry.
You were always there when I came to complain.
You were always the gentle shoulder when everything went wrong.
You always knew just what to say when the world came crashing down on me.
This is what a friend is
And this is what you are.

Cierra Cummins
Marshdale Elementary School
Evergreen, CO
Grade 4

Time, the Morning

I got out of bed at half past eight
Threw on my clothes and said "can't be late!"
I grabbed a bite to eat and then went to brush my teeth
I slipped out the door but my shoe caught underneath
"Aha!" I said as I got up very slow,
It was my shoelace that had done it and I didn't even know.
Well, I got up and continued down the steps of the stairs
While I watched all of the other kids playing lions, tigers, and bears.
I opened the garage door to get to my bike...
Because I had tripped I didn't feel like a hike.
So I got on my bike and strapped on my helmet real tight
I started my ride down the hill, and in no time my house was out of sight.

Anthony Carter
Afflerbach Elementary School
Cheyenne, WY
Grade 6

Friends

F riends are always there for you when you need somebody to talk to.
R iding bikes, playing Barbie's, no matter what, they are there.
I n the dark of the night, they comfort you.
E ven when you have the flu, they call and talk.
N o one can have better friends than I do.
D oesn't matter whether girl or boy.
S weet, kind, caring. That's what friends are.

Shawna Wolfe
Shaffer Elementary School
Littleton, CO
Grade 6

Emotions

Emotions are something you feel with your heart and soul
You cannot predict or keep them shut up inside
They change day by day no matter what the circumstance
If the earth had no emotion it would be an awfully dull and boring place
Your emotion may be shown by what you do,
What you wear, and how your eyes look
Love is an emotion of true happiness and roses
Sad is an emotion of mourning and black
Emotions are different in many beautiful ways.

Lily Alasia Schamp
Ashgrove Elementary School
Riverton, WY
Grade 4

Planning Ahead

The party is this date!
The party is this date, I say!
There'll be prizes and food
And puppy dogs, too!
And will you be there as well?

My mom will take care of the balloons,
Dad'll be in charge of the cake,
I'll take care of the pink baboons.
And sis' will take care of the lake.
And will you be there as well?

We're going to have 100 swans sitting in the lake
400 gallons of punch we'll have
And we'll also have 300 cakes
100 presents will be unwrapped
And will you be there as well?

The party will be at my house
1,000 people there
Don't forget your children and spouse
Oh, I can't wait 'til next year.
I hope you will be there.

Angela Alley
Farmington Elementary School
Farmington, UT
Grade 6

A History Hobby

They have been through war, they have been through death,
they have been through the worst of Earth.

They've seen the things that doctors have seen,
and all the screams they've heard.

Through bloody fields, through times of yield,
and a lot of shells and bolts.

They left their lives, their children and wives,
and only spoke by notes.

Now their stories are written in books and on pads,
and read for the adventures they told.

They are dressed in green, are strong and mean,
and are also brave and bold.

And now to this day they join the brigade,
and a hobby this is to me.

In the army I'll be when the time comes to me,
and my hobby will soon be a dream.

Joseph Branecky
Sargent Elementary School
Monte Vista, CO
Grade 6

Your House Was Not There

I was lighting a candle on the table.
The candle lost its balance and fell on the floor.
Your house was not there in about five minutes.
I did not mean to.
It happened so fast, I don't know what to say.
But will you forgive me.
It won't happen again.
So once again, will you forgive me.

Alex Reigelsperger
Ecker Hill Middle School
Park City, UT
Grade 6

Boston Tea Party

The Boston Tea Party is as famous as can be
The people didn't want to pay taxes on tea
Men dressed up like Indians and went to the ships
And into the harbor the tea they tipped

Then came a man named Paul Revere
Who rode on his horse without any fear
He rode through the night like an eagle in flight
Shouting and screaming the British are here

Then came the war–people fought for their country
Sometimes going without sleep and going hungry
We're sad that they died and we're glad many lived
We should always remember the brave things they did

Tayler Deamer
North Ogden Elementary School
Ogden, UT
Grade 5

I Can Be...

I can be your lion that roars so wildly.
I can be your sloth that swings so quietly.
I can be your hero that keeps you safe from harm.
I can be your fire that keeps you feeling warm.
But, most of all I'd rather be your best friend 'cause
it's plain to see that I'm just plain ole me.

Heather Raitt
Lomond View Elementary School
Ogden, UT
Grade 4

War

War, no one wants to go.
War, the goriest place to be.
War, gunshots and screams.
War, the place where horror becomes reality.
War, like a death sentence.
War?

AJ Jackson
Malley Drive Elementary School
Northglenn, CO
Grade 5

Now Isn't This the Life

A stream flows gently by,
and twists and bends and pools,
the fish swim by and think,
"Now isn't this the life?"

And then the stream goes on its way,
twisting and turning and bending,
the grass and trees and bushes think,
"Now isn't this the life?"

Then the stream flows past some deer,
as they drink contentedly,
then they think without much care,
"Now isn't this the life?"

As the stream goes on its way,
it splits around an isle,
and flows past playful cubs who think,
"Now isn't this the life?"

Now the stream goes out to the sea,
and trickles slower, silently,
slower now, the stream thinks to itself,
"Now isn't this the life?"

Corey Furney
Connect Charter School
Pueblo, CO
Grade 6

Spring

Cloud
puffy, white
moving, gliding, soaring
fat, fluffy, colorful, thin
sitting, fading, melting
bright, misty
rainbow

Emily Cohn
Ecker Hill Middle School
Park City, UT
Grade 6

California

California is my favorite place to go.
But I'm stuck here in Pueblo!

I lived in California a long time, 8 years
When we moved I had lots of tears.

We go back every spring break.
All we have to fear is an earthquake!

Amy Liptak
Franklin Elementary School
Pueblo, CO
Grade 5

Cat

I am a cat
lying down, falling asleep
dreaming:
I am in a forest
creeping, listening, alert, and cautious
Did I hear something?
Is there something there behind me?
I am a cat
sleek, soft, and afraid.
Can you hear?
There is something there?
Creeping
my heart is pounding
Should I attack?
But I am a cat
it is something bigger.
It's getting dark
too dark for it but not for me.
I am a cat
I have eyes for darkness
not it, not anymore, not anyone.

Shannon Troy
Colorado Academy
Denver, CO
Grade 4

Useless Things

A smile without a face,
A shoe without a lace,
A board without chalk,
A key without a lock,

A cow without a spot,
A flower without a pot,
A car without a wheel,
A ziplock bag without a seal,

A boat without a sail,
A shovel without a pail,
A car without a beep,
A frog without a leap,

A cave without a bat,
A door without a mat,
A ball without a glove,
A heart without love,

A buzz without a bee,
A leg without a knee,
A clock without time,
A poem without a rhyme.

Breanna Kreager
Walt Clark Middle School
Loveland, CO
Grade 6

Colorado

Colorado in the fall,
Hear the leaves crack,
See them fall,
Smell the air in the fall,
Colorado in the fall,
See the rain from the sky,
See the birds fly south for the winter,
That's Colorado in the fall.

Miriam Moller
Larkspur Elementary School
Larkspur, CO
Grade 4

How Bright Is It?

The light is as bright as the sun
Almost woke up the whole town
Every time you look at the light . . .
You need sunglasses
It lighted up everything in sight
The light glowed in the house
You can see the light from state to state
The light was still going . . .
Until it burned out!!!

Rose Sena
Dos Rios Elementary School
Evans, CO
Grade 5

The Cherry Fairy

My cheeks as red as cherries,
Unlike the other fairies,
I have a twinkle in my eye,
Oh wait that's a fly,
Shoo away fly, I have work to be done;
I have to carry a message to the sun:
"My cherries are in pain,
From all this rain.
So please come out sun,
So the children can have fun."

Natalie Vogan
Cherry Valley Elementary School
Franktown, CO
Grade 5

Breckenridge

fun, fantastic
skiing, biking, swimming
majestic, beautiful, ski peaks
snowboarding, lift riding
lovely, cool
ski town

Garrett B. Boothe
Larkspur Elementary School
Larkspur, CO
Grade 4

Love

Love can be your destiny.
Love can be your fantasy.
Love is a thing that comes and goes.
Love is a thing that lasts long.
Love is a puzzle.
Love is a maze that you can't get out of.
Love is a thing that could burn a hole in your heart.
Love is love, but love can be a great thing until you let it go.

Tanisha Dews
Montview Elementary School
Aurora, CO
Grade 5

In My Dreams

As I look into the first sunlight of the day,
I wish I could fall back to sleep to see you face to face.
I want to touch you so that you know I am here.
I want you to know that I am real,
Because I know that you are.
When I am away I want to be with you,
I like how you always stand up for me.
I like when you really understand how I feel.

Ashleigh Ter Maat
Riverview Elementary School
Durango, CO
Grade 4

Why?

I do not understand why,
people have to die,
I do not understand why there is death and decay,
I just don't understand why things work this way,
I do not understand why there is war,
and blood, guts and gore.
I don't understand why people are so greedy,
they just seem to be so needy,
but the one things I know most,
is a ghost a person who had to die, but I'm not sure why.

Kale Crowder
Pioneer Elementary School
Billings, MT
Grade 6

I Like Christmas

I like Christmas,
Cozy, a white-powder-snow Christmas,
A Christmas with flocked trees full of joy,
A Christmas full of snowmen and igloos,
A Christmas with happy and healthy families,
But the Christmas I like best, is a Christmas,
Full of presents, warmness, and hot chocolate,
A house full of happiness

Demetri Roumpos
Lowell Elementary School
Salt Lake City, UT
Grade 6

Home

Is not just a place, it's a feeling you get when you're there
When you're happy, when you're sad,
it holds your heart close, even when you're not there.
It welcomes you,
And it holds all the keys to life.
Home

Spenser Bomholt
Pine Grove Elementary School
Parker, CO
Grade 4

The Forest

I see the trees around me,
I hear the stream softly flowing,
I smell the fresh clean air,
I feel the mosquitoes scratching at my skin.
I taste the dew on the flowers and leaves.

Ryan Selby
Afflerbach Elementary School
Cheyenne, WY
Grade 5

Anything Is Possible

You could be an Astronaut, that flies into space,
or be in the Olympics, and win the big race.

Anything is Possible

You could be an Artist, like Monet,
or be the Director of a famous play.

Anything is Possible

You could be a Chef, and make fancy cuisine,
or be a Chauffeur, and drive a limousine.

Anything is Possible

You could be an Explorer, and travel to Rome,
or you could be a Homemaker, and stay all day at home.

Anything is Possible

You could be a Pilot, and fly an airplane,
or a Meteorologist, and forecast the rain.

Anything is Possible

You can do Anything, if you work hard and plan
If you never give up and believe that you can.

Anything is Possible

Sarah Frederiksen
Midland Elementary School
Roy, UT
Grade 6

Sunrise

The sun is going up now
The light is shimmering gold
It reflects on me.

Chelsea Waterfall
Lomond View Elementary School
Ogden, UT
Grade 4

The Wolf

The wolf is beautiful
So strong and proud
Moving silently
As a cloud
By the light of the moon
He howled,
Calling the others
To join the fight
The fight for survival,
The fight to live
Taking what nature has to give.
The black wolf is rare
A beauty to see,
So wild
So free...

Levi Millican
Cortez Middle School
Cortez, CO
Grade 6

Always a Place

As the wind blows,
as the trees grow,
I hear a voice calling my name.
I know there is always a place
that will welcome me in
and treat me like a friend.
Then as I grow old
I'll remember this place
over
and
over
again!

Kimberly Janson
Singing Hills Elementary School
Parker, CO
Grade 4

Wind

A bullet
Blowing, crashing, stopping
Strong blow of impatience
Nature

Shalee Lyn Cary
Christ Lutheran School
Murray, UT
Grade 5

Little

"Being little ain't so bad," said my mother to my brother.
"But, I can't touch the ceiling, only the floor, I can't even touch the top of the door!"
"You won't be little forever," said mother.
"How long until forever?" asked brother.
"Oh, don't be mad about your height!"
"No one can see everything insight."
"I am already five and only three feet tall."
"All my friends say I am way too small!"
"How come I am so small, but you are so tall?"
"Because, that is the way it sometimes works, honey."
"But, some kids say I am so short I resemble a bunny!"
"Now honey please don't be so funny!"
"Who is being funny, mummy."
"Name one thing I can do, that doesn't require being tall like you."
"There are millions of things you can do, like crawl under a bed to get a lost shoe."

The next morning when my brother awoke
He had had a strange dream he thought was a joke.
He grew five more feet,
And couldn't get through a door,
So now he's content to not wish anymore!

Erin Trapletti
St Vincent De Paul School
Salt Lake City, UT
Grade 6

Holocaust

One yell echoes into thousands
One scream morphs into millions
A simple shower turns into puddles of death
Many men constructed the Gestapo under Hitler's rule
Like bees forming a hive under the Queen's orders
Being perfect was no longer being yourself
Freedom of religion was now only a dream
Living life to its fullest transformed into hiding out
A presumably flawless plan turned into dictatorship
"One state, one nation, one leader" turned into a promise long forgotten
And individuality turned into nothing more than a legend of the past

Stephanie Georges
Las Vegas Day School
Las Vegas, NV
Grade 6

Colorado Mountains

See the blanket of white snow covering the mountains,
Hear the wild geese call as they fly over the apex,
Smell the pine trees' minty needles,
Feel the soft touch of a mountain goat's beard,
Taste the mountain spring water as it runs down the side of the peaks,
Feel the wind as it lashes against your face,
Hear the mountain lions' roar
This is the happiness in the mountains.

Bea Sanders
Larkspur Elementary School
Larkspur, CO
Grade 4

Hiking with My Eyes Closed

"Crunch, crunch" under your feet, sounds so sweet.
"Chirp, chirp" from a nearby nest in a Blue Spruce tree.
"Chitter, chitter" from a squirrel high in a Scrub Oak.

"Rushing water" near the rock where you sat last night.
"Plants rustle" from a small raccoon passing by.
"Shish, shish" from the passing wind through the leaves.

Other hikers "chatter" away as they please.
"Crackle, crackle" from their campfire.
The peace and quiet allows you to hear yourself "breathe."

So listen closely on your next hike
And make that journey
A Hearing Hike

Alina Szabo
Shrine of St Anne School
Arvada, CO
Grade 6

Horses

Horses are beautiful all throughout,
Some are tall and some are stout.
Most everyone loves and cares about them,
As if each one was a gem.
When galloping through the open field,
Their true stamina is revealed.
Their silken coats beautifully shine,
As they canter through the woods of pine.
Most of these animals are wild and free,
Because they truly are very carefree.
These are animals of true grace,
Only one wins in a horse race.
They are so extremely gentle,
But they can be temperamental!
They are animals of such youth,
And that is surely the truth!

Kelsey Shepard
Buffalo Ridge Elementary
Castle Rock, CO
Grade 5

A Kitten in My Mitten

There's a kitten in my mitten and he looked very cold.
He was just a little tyke not even six weeks old.
When I warmed him up he was very active;
he was also quite attractive.
My so-called kitten loved mint
and when he played in my clothes he came out in lint.
I like painting with colors that have some tint,
it seems like he wants to paint with me, hint, hint.

Brianne VanCleave
Bennett Middle School
Bennett, CO
Grade 6

Scared

Water is flying in the air,
Soldiers talking without a care,
I load my rifle to act ready.
Even though I'm not steady,
I'm scared about going on the beach,
Because the Nazis are on the beach,
The captain yells "30 seconds, good luck"
Because he knows we are each as dead as a duck,
We wait for the door to drop, breathing slow,
We all look like we are ready to go,
The door drops and we all start running,
The Nazis fired and people start dying,
I dug a hole on the beach, and screamed crying,
"Please end the battle because we are dying."

Matt Kunkel
Ecker Hill Middle School
Park City, UT
Grade 6

Summer Is Fun

S ummer is fun.
U nderwater is fun for summer.
M any kids go out and play.
M any go to the pool.
E very summer is hot!
R emember the fun and do it again next year!

Alex Winckler
Crest Hill Elementary School
Casper, WY
Grade 6

Sunset

As the fiery, golden orb descends,
I wish this scene would never end.
When it's nearly half way gone,
A symphony of colors streaks the sky,

I watch,
With nothing to say,
As my light,
My warmth,
Fades away.
When it's but a sliver,
My friend,
My foe,
Turns to me with nothing but a desperate plea,
And jumps up once more to kiss the sky,
Before it descends,
Descends,
And a blanket of darkness,
Covers the sky.

Danara Pollitt
Laredo Middle School
Aurora, CO
Grade 6

The Shot

He passed me the ball
I could feel it in my hands
I looked out and could see
The crowd waiting in the stands
I dribbled left
Then I dribbled right
I passed the half line
I psyched the other guy out
Time was running down
I had to do something quick
I took a look around
No one was open
I dribbled to the 3-point line
I jumped in the air
I was out of my mind
I let the ball go out of my hands
It sunk in the hole
The buzzer rang
I made my goal

Jake Haag
Reedpoint Jr/Sr High School
Reedpoint, MT
Grade 6

The Family Get Together

Our family makes cookies,
Oh so fun.
Mix up the ingredients,
Pitch in everyone.
Before we bake the cookies,
Let's have some cookie dough.
Then we'll all go outside and yell,
Yo-Ho-Ho!

Tyson Benard
Centerville Elementary School
Centerville, UT
Grade 4

Dragons

Dragons, large and fierce
Fly high in the sky growling
Blowing large red flames

Josh Sandoval
Kearns-St Ann School
Salt Lake City, UT
Grade 6

Snow

Small white confetti
Frozen little drops of rain
White fluffy clusters.

Shannon Quinn
Sacred Heart of Jesus School
Boulder, CO
Grade 5

Home

Home.
Cozy, warm.
Family.
Safe place to be.
Stay.

Ryan Kelleher
Washington Terrace Elementary School
Ogden, UT
Grade 6

Day and Night

The sun is yellow,
The moon is white,
When I see,
It's a really bright sight.
Thunder is loud,
Lightning is bright,
When I see,
It's a frightening sight.
Day is light,
Night is dark,
I'd hate to say
Good night.

Skyler Lien
Cottonwood Plains Elementary School
Fort Collins, CO
Grade 4

Yellow

Y ellow is my favorite color.
E ven more than green.
L ight lime
L emon yellow
O utstanding
W onderful color.

Liz Seegmiller
St Vincent De Paul School
Salt Lake City, UT
Grade 6

My Cat Bee

My cat Bee,
Ran round a tree.
She stopped to look,
At a chapter book.
I didn't know,
That she could read.
So I guess I need,
To learn more about
My mellow yellow
Cat named Bee.

Caroline Schubert
Most Precious Blood School
Denver, CO
Grade 5

Peace

Peace is like a stream of love
chanting songs of freedom.
Sometimes there is no peace
and it is cold, lonely, sad, and dark.
When there is peace,
birds whistle
and clouds float by in tie-dyed colors.
There is peace on earth now
but will there be forever . . .

Adrienne Koch
Heatherwood Elementary School
Boulder, CO
Grade 4

Sleek Submarines

I'd like to peek underneath me
To see a sleek submarine.
They don't exactly have a good history
But I still think them interesting.

They did sink ships.
That's okay, they got sunk someday.
Now they protect us.
They don't fight wars.

I think they're cool, quick, and keen.
That's why I like sleek submarines.

David Jepson
Holy Trinity School
Westminster, CO
Grade 4

Computer Bug

My teachers and family
Are all continuously talking
About a computer bug
I pictured a six legged
Creature walking
Some sort of creepy thug
Does he have two or four eyes?
Is he mean or nice?
Is he blue, purple, or green?
Well, Dad said that computer bug
Has been taken care of
It wasn't quite so mean
But now I think we have a virus
It's another problem for us
Our computer has gone askew

A virus? Hmmmm
Chicken Pox?

Julia Almond
New Life Academy
Durango, CO
Grade 6

Cross Country Skiing

I see the snow covered ground with rocks occasionally
piercing out of it, and the evergreen trees shooting out of
the snow towards the sky that the snow darts from.
 I hear the wind gusting through the trees high above
and the soft powdery snow gliding by softly under my skis.
 I feel snowflakes dotting my head and hands and the
sweat from all this hard work going down my forehead.
 I smell the fresh pine trees that shake under their
newly acquired snowdrifts.
 I taste the cool crisp air with an occasional hard candy
or drink of cold water.

Philip H. Michael
Afflerbach Elementary School
Cheyenne, WY
Grade 6

The Book

My parents told me to put it away.
They said it was always in my way.
They tried coaxing and a stern voice.
Then they said I had no choice.

Since I was little it was always my book.
Every once in a while I would give it a look.
When I got older I grew less attached,
that old book of mine was now under a latch.

I've so many books, but I still remember
that book I put away on a cold December.
Reading it still gives me much pleasure,
so now In my heart it will always be a treasure.

Bianca Hernandez
Challenger School
Sandy, UT
Grade 6

My Favorite Pet

My favorite pet was a dog,
She loved to play and run,
She always went with me for a walk,
And sometimes I felt a lot better.

Her fur was golden like the sun,
Her eyes were dark as the night,
Her nose was always wet,
It looked just like a Junior Mint.

Although she is not with me anymore,
I still remember her really well,
I always knew we had a strange communion,
That is why she is my favorite pet.

Nadia Covarrubias
Orr Middle School
Las Vegas, NV
Grade 6

The Old Hat

When they gave me that hat,
 It was from my grandfather.
 As the years rolled by,
 My parents thought it a bother.

The hat in itself was very dark and black,
 And it was very torn and tattered.
 My parents told me to throw it away,
 But its sentiment was, to me, what mattered.

When I have grown old,
 I hope that it will stay, in my study
On the very top shelf next to journals,
 And it shall be like a buddy.

Now that I am dying,
 I have given that old hat away,
To my daughter who keeps it inside of her study,
 And there I hope it will stay.

Wade Clark
Challenger School
Sandy, UT
Grade 6

Is It Okay to Dance in the Grocery Store?

Is it okay to dance in the grocery store?
It is one of the questions I have.
Maybe if I do I will become famous.
If I am lucky a director will
just happen to be in the store.
He will need a good, no, *great*
dancer for his next movie.
He will comb my hair
and put cool sunglasses on me.
He will put me on a big plane
and fly me all the way to Hollywood.
Soon I will be signing
autographs for everyone.
Or maybe I will just
be embarrassed?

Hillary Hoffer
Colorado Academy
Denver, CO
Grade 4

Joy

I hear aspen leaves rustling in the breeze.
I smell spring flowers and greenery.
I feel the soft fur of the mini lop rabbit.
I think of the taste of sugar, because he is so sweet.
I see pure joy.

Kelsey Matson
Afflerbach Elementary School
Cheyenne, WY
Grade 5

Snorkeling

Turquoise water
Yellow tang
Nothing ever looks the same.

Green turtles
Pink fish
To snorkel all day long, I wish.

Black rocks
Golden sand
Swimming longer than we planned.

Purple urchins
Orange fins
Palm trees blowing in the winds.

Silver reflections
Blue skies
What beautiful things I see with my eyes!

Brady Samuelson
Ashgrove Elementary School
Riverton, WY
Grade 4

Two Seasons

Summer
Hot, warm
Swimming, biking, running
Soccer, camping, sled, snowboard
Skiing, ice skating, ice fishing
Cold, snow
Winter

Ira Kersten-Wines
Jacks Valley Elementary School
Minden, NV
Grade 4

Waterfalls

Sparkling water cascades down,
Forming mists of white-pearled lace,
Shimmering with a roaring sound,
Oh, how I love this special place!

Creatures come with leaps and bounds
To enjoy the beauty of the pool,
Rainbows glitter all around
The lake that glistens like a jewel.

Dark, black boulders shine with dew,
The river roaring with great speed,
The depths of the pool a secret blue,
Waterfalls seem a forest need.

Aubrie Taylor
Challenger School
Sandy, UT
Grade 6

Blustery Night

The moon glistens like silver shining over a deep gleaming river.
The clouds that swirl around it are like angels with their great and mighty wings
blustering over the trees.
The stars that glimmer over the clouds are like little Christmas lights,
forever lighting the sky.
The leaves that try to cover up the stars are like a kite swiveling together
to form something great.
The bare trees that the blustery leaves come from are like limp snowmen,
with their bare arms sticking out.
And the bird nest that rests in the tree that hangs on by a single limb,
is like an icicle at the end of its time on a sunny day.
The feathers in the bird nest are like signs from above,
telling us that they are always watching us.

Rachel Bouzis
Crest Hill Elementary School
Casper, WY
Grade 6

Colorado's River

See the rushing rivers flow on the shiny rocks,
Hear the soft sound of a calm rapid,
Smell the fresh spring air,
Feel the weeds crunch on your feet *crunch*!
Taste the clear, cool water when you swim in it,
The rivers are like a roaring waterfall
When the hard rapids hit the bottom surface,
See the calm river pool, a reflecting mirror,
A river makes me feel peaceful and cool when I walk in the water.

Emily Wagner
Larkspur Elementary School
Larkspur, CO
Grade 4

The Battle of Trenton

For Washington and his army the war was going badly
They were hungry, sick, and tired, and many had died sadly.

Washington was determined to change the war around
He said, "Attack the Hessians while they are sleeping sound."

Across the Delaware River on that icy Christmas day
They rowed through cold and darkness trying to beat the sun's first ray.

The crossing took much longer than the generals planned
But they found the Hessian's guard house with six sentries undermanned.

They snuck into the Hessian's camp and got everything in place
It took a lot of courage to meet the Hessians face to face.

The attack surprised the enemy, they couldn't get in formation.
The Americans won the battle and saved the hopes of our nation.

Sam Pacheco
North Ogden Elementary School
Ogden, UT
Grade 5

Dogs and Butterfly

Pugs
playful funny
jumping playing running
pugs labs bug dragonfly
flying soaring dancing
fly pretty
butterfly

Jessica Gross
Washington Terrace Elementary School
Ogden, UT
Grade 4

A Drop of Hope

In the dead of autumn brown leaves fall and wrinkle into dust.
Letting the cold frost bitten wind pick them aloft,
tossing them around like a reckless tornado.

As I walk down a dusty path
I cringe as the branches of my spine,
are chilled by the cool crisp air.
My long dirty beard is beginning to form discolored icicles.
My skin is tough and dirt stained from all the work.
My bones are scrawny and weak,
the only thing that keeps me going
is a small flickering candle.

These men, the Nazis,
are blind to all around them.
My people pay for their stupidity.
Freedom seems distant,
but I can't give up hope,
I must bring hope to others.
I've fought for everything I have
I won't let these evil camps tear me apart.

The Americans will come, they will come.

Eli Berenbeim
Foothills Academy
Wheat Ridge, CO
Grade 5

Basketball

Basketball is a wonderful sport,
When you're dribbling down the basketball court.
The feeling of leather in your hands,
When you shoot the ball, where will it land?

The great feeling when you make a hoop
Or when you do a loop-de-loop.
When the other team has the ball,
You get a steal and then you haul!

Daniel Maxwell
Farmington Elementary School
Farmington, UT
Grade 6

Nobody

Nobody knows what I go through
Nobody, nobody, except you!
I left all my friends and you were there
Standing right behind me, in the air
I met new friends but they weren't the same
I invited them over, but they never came.
They think I'm not cool,
Just a fool.
I play soccer but that's not enough
To keep them from thinking I'm not tough.
Nobody knows what I go through
Nobody, nobody, except you!

Lisa Hammitt
Lewis-Palmer Elementary School
Monument, CO
Grade 5

Friendship

Friendship looks like a cool winter day.

Friendship smells like the rain forest filled with
beautiful blooming flowers.

Friendship sounds like rain drops landing on the leaves.
Friendship tastes like hot creamy cocoa melting in my mouth.

Friendship feels like brown and sparkling reindeer dancing
in the moonlight.

Friendship is a glittery star in the dark blue sky.

Stephany Faber
Moore Elementary School
Silt, CO
Grade 4

Love

Love is something everyone needs,
Even the animals that my dad feeds,
Some show love by giving their loved one
Something that looks like flowers but are actually weeds,
Others show it by giving a necklace with beads.

Love should last a lifetime,
It's worth more than a dime,
It wasn't created so you can drink wine,
Nor to pretend like you're on grape vine!

Love comes from the heart,
It doesn't matter what part,
Some people dream of its start,
Now days, instead of arrows, Cupid uses darts!

Jessica Nusbaum
Pawnee Jr-Sr High School
Grover, CO
Grade 6

Many Things of Death

Many things of death
Dying today
Feels like something
is slithering out of my soul.

It has the feeling of happiness,
the feeling of loneliness
and the feeling of wonder

What will happen from now,
from here
Will I go
or will I stay?

Death.
Say that aloud.
Death.

It has the emotions of
wonder
loneliness, fear
forgetfulness
and finally sadness

Good-bye my friend.
Good-bye.

Nicole Wilson
Rowland Hall-St Mark's School
Salt Lake City, UT
Grade 5

The Race

We lined up at the starting line;
Ready to run at the sign.
The flag went up; the whistle blew.
We all knew what we had to do.

To win the race, to win the race,
And now we had to get a pace.
To win or lose; it's only a game;
Yet, we were thinking just the same.

The finish line, the finish line,
If we were there, all would be fine.
We run so hard; we almost burst;
Till I crossed the line the first.

Run with will and determination;
You will find it a sensation.
So keep on going, and hold on,
Never give up; it won't be long.

Jeffrey Chen
Challenger School
Sandy, UT
Grade 6

Morning Comes

Morning comes
Shining,
In the clouds.
Shine comes
Sparkling.
Sun comes
Peeking.
Yellow-shine.
Who is
Running,
Jumping,
Hiding?
Who has fun
In the day?
That's me.

Bethany McHugh
South Elementary School
Brighton, CO
Grade 5

The Bee

Something comes buzzing,
It's a bee coming by me,
And then it landed on me.

Amber Saxton
Lomond View Elementary School
Ogden, UT
Grade 4

Spring

Spring, it comes, it goes
Spring, the flowers grow beneath my toes
Spring, the beauty and it shows
Spring, as lovely as a rose
Spring, the smell goes up my nose
Spring, a time when everything grows
Spring, with many birds and crows
Spring, it comes and it goes

Doug Clark
Farmington Elementary School
Farmington, UT
Grade 6

Mountains/Beach

Mountains
Snowy, white
Skiing, smoked, hiking
Wind, wolf, sand, water
Playing, digging, boating
Bright, noisy
Beach

Alexandra Stephens
St John the Baptist School
Draper, UT
Grade 4

The T-Rex

What's in the leaves.
Wait! Look up in the trees.
Something big,
something green.
It makes sounds like
roar
slash
growl
roar
slash
growl.
If you think it's a bird
take a hike.
It's
it's
T-Rex.

Derick Mathew
Laura Mason Christian Academy
Cheyenne, WY
Grade 4

Pencil Stealer

Don't lay it down in plain sight
If you do, I just might
Pick it up and use it to write.
I have plenty, I know it's not right
But I'll pick it up out of spite.
I specially like it if it is bright
Or if it's neon, you can see it at night.
Sometimes these also I may bite
Out of nervousness or out of fright.
So if you want to keep your pencils right
Keep your pencils out of my sight!

Jesse Hovis
McClelland Center School
Pueblo, CO
Grade 5

A Baby

That giggle is so sweet,
Like the drop of rain soft and gentle.
Those toes,
Those tiny wiggle toes.
Those hands,
That grabs my hair to play.
Do you know...
That the thing that giggles,
That has the toes,
That has the grip
Is...
A BABY

Felisha Castorena
South Elementary School
Brighton, CO
Grade 5

A Storm

A storm is coming.
Wind blows through the trees like an out-of-tune whistle.
Waves crash against the shore like a watery battering ram.
Then the hail comes down.
First as soft as a baby's touch.
Then harder, and harder,
Until the whole shore is getting pelted by hail
As hard as bullets.
Then, as suddenly as it began,
The wind stops its cursing and shouting,
The waves stop ramming, and the hail stops pelting.
Then the clouds clear up and the storm goes away,
Leaving behind it, a fresh new day.

Caitlin Jean Agawa Robinson
Bixby School
Boulder, CO
Grade 5

Freedom

Freedom.
A word so precious that people would give their lives
if that was what it took.
Like the war heroes from the Revolutionary War.
Or the brave slaves from the Civil war?
What do you think they were fighting for?
Land?
Money?
No.
Freedom.
Freedom of the chains that bound them so.
Freedom of the pain.
Freedom.

Kathryn Cammack
Academy Charter School
Castle Rock, CO
Grade 6

The Deep Woods

In the deep woods, there is a sudden stir,
a chipmunk scurries back to its hole, another move,
and a black bear cub climbs a tree,
a white horse appears and reappears deeper in the wood,
as you walk the leaves crunch crisply under your feet,
a breeze ruffles your hair and rises your hopes,
soon it is dark,
and the trees start to surround you,
getting closer and closer,
finally you scream and wake up,
in your own bed,
sweating and breathing deeply,
you fall back to sleep.

Megan Kearl
Hudson Elementary School
Hudson, WY
Grade 6

Inside the Computer

Inside the computer it must be pretty weird
with wires and gizmos and things like that.
Inside the computer there must be
a very good painter to paint the screen
and make the mouse move around.

Pierce Martin
Bixby School
Boulder, CO
Grade 4

Traveling

Traveling, Traveling, oh so far.
To Greece, To Paris
England, Italy, and Ireland too
Or Asia or Africa, some place different or new
Actually just anywhere with a mall will
Do!

Shae Orrick
New Life Academy
Durango, CO
Grade 6

Friends

Friends are very fun at school.
On the weekend, you can go swimming in a pool.
Friends are there to play with you
And can do fun things with you,
Like going to the zoo.
Friends can be in girls or boys,
And when you are little you usually play with toys.
Although sometimes you may get in a fight,
Friends are always going to be there to make things right.

Ashley Magurany
Sacred Heart of Jesus School
Boulder, CO
Grade 5

My Piano

My piano is my favorite friend to play with,
I love to play, Broken Record Boogie...
After a while we will play a different song.

We will drown out other noise together,
As the piano rings throughout the house.

The hammers hit the strings with care inside its wooden body
We will play soft tunes together and then learn a new song.

Some music touches my soul,
Some music makes me ROCK AND ROLL!

Katy Evezich
Parmalee Elementary School
Indian Hills, CO
Grade 4

Cheetah Kill Everything

Cheetah kill deer
eat for lunch dinner and breakfast
Cheetah kill water buffalo
eat for lunch dinner and breakfast
Cheetah kill elk
eat for lunch dinner and breakfast
Cheetah kill everything
no more food
Cheetah get old and die

Alex Duersch
Washington Terrace Elementary School
Ogden, UT
Grade 4

Broccoli is Evil
Celery is Demented
Mushrooms Insane

Broccoli is evil like a tree.
Evil in butter.
Evil in ranch.
Evil plain.
Evil cooked.
Celery is awful too!
Celery is evil.
It's all stringy.
It's out to get me.
Ahhhh!
Help me!
Eat your vegetables!

Drew von Gunten
Colorado Academy
Denver, CO
Grade 4

Do You Want to Race Me?

Want to race me?
Don't be hasty
You'll never beat me
I drive a dragster
I am the master
Of the dragster

My car is Jaws Jr.
Hear it roar
I'll get there sooner
Before you put the pedal to the floor

Now that I see that I won
I turn around and smile
That I remember it was just for fun
'Cause I just went 1/8th of a mile

Brent J. Singleton
Washington Terrace Elementary School
Ogden, UT
Grade 6

Two Children at Play

Two children at play.
What do they say?
Play play play!
All through the night,
All through the day,
All through the noon,
But when morning comes again
They sleep.

Derick Secrist
Washington Terrace Elementary School
Ogden, UT
Grade 4

Predator, Prey

Predator
Dangerous, quick
Eating, prowling, stalking
Hunter, carnivore, food, herbivore
Running, scared, hunted
Awake, fast
Prey

Aaron Ptacek
St John the Baptist School
Draper, UT
Grade 4

No Love

When I cry,
I wonder why
Nobody comforts me.
I want some love,
And kindness, too,
They treat me like I'm three.
I don't understand,
And I don't want to, either,
But when people say,
"I get no love!"
Then I say,
"Me neither!"

Emily Peterson
Most Precious Blood School
Denver, CO
Grade 5

Pencil

My pencil
has lots of
words in it.
It even has
words that
are unknown.

Tyler Aronstein
Colorado Academy
Denver, CO
Grade 4

Flowers

Flowers
colors bright
blooming planting watering
seed leaves water puddle
wetting falling watering
wet drippy
rain

Jordan Berkenpas
Washington Terrace Elementary School
Ogden, UT
Grade 4

Mice

Mice are cute and mice are cool
But my mom always screams
When there are mice in a pool.

They hide in your bathtub
They hide in your sink
But when they die
They really start to stink!

Daniel Mitchell
Pioneer Elementary School
Billings, MT
Grade 6

Racing My Four-Wheeler

Racing my four-wheeler
As I fly through the air.
My mother is squealing
And gives me a stare.

My dad says,
"Courtney, you go faster"
So I hit the gas,
And become the master blaster.

Over the whoops and
Across the table top,
I cleared the triple
With one great big ker-plop.

I head down the straight away,
As I zoom the top rider.
I turn the sharp corner,
Ever so tighter.

I see the checkered flag,
For this race I have won.
So I do one more lap,
Just for pure fun!

Courtney Porter
Ashgrove Elementary School
Riverton, WY
Grade 4

Pasta

Pasta, a favorite meal of mine
to me it is really, really divine.

Fettucine Alfredo, add a little cream
going to Olive Garden is supreme.

Shapes and sizes of all different kinds
carbohydrates they say are good for your mind.

Macaroni, spaghetti, and even bow tie
I really prefer over chocolate cream pie.

Pasta salad full of veggies galore,
I eat it and eat it and eat it some more.

Linguine is fine when you don't add the clams
but sea shell salad must have bits of ham.

Curly noodles with butter and salt
I slurp them up it's not my fault

Oodles of noodles with lots of sauce
I need them right now so I won't be cross.

I have to admit pasta is the best,
if you don't agree put it to the test.

Emily Petersen
Morningside Elementary School
Salt Lake City, UT
Grade 6

Courage of the Bored One

One day in the fifth grade,
The teacher was talking
About the First Crusade.

His voice was so flat,
And his speech was boring,
That all the kids wanted to sleep 'til next morning!

After ten minutes,
They had had enough.
Then up stood the little boy called Scruff.

He told the boring teacher
Just how they all felt,
And how they thought they were gonna melt.

And then the teacher stopped his speech
And took them outside to play,
All because of the courage little Scruff had that day.

John Fenton III
Academy Charter School
Castle Rock, CO
Grade 5

Look into a Book

Whenever I take a look,
At what to me seems like a good book,
To the place the story is in,
It takes my mind, but leaves my skin.

I think books are great!
Do they leave your skin but your mind take?
I love books, I really do,
And I know lots of people love books too.

Lauren Russell
Marshdale Elementary School
Evergreen, CO
Grade 4

Mirrors

When I look into a mirror,
I see something weird,
It's a person like me.
It can do the same things I can do.

I jump, it jumps
I kick, hop, run, walk and even spit
It does it back as if I did.

This makes me mad,
I think I will just tell it I don't want to play.
But it says it right back.

Oh, oh, what am I going to do?
How am I going to get it to go away?
Oh, oh, oh, what am I going to do?

Kelsi Bodily
Centerville Elementary School
Centerville, UT
Grade 4

Beautiful Sights

When I wake up I hear the birds sing.
Just as well as I hear the bells ring.
When I hear these, my heart fills with joy,
And as my sister says, "Oh boy! Oh boy!"

When we run out to see the bells cling,
I find the urge that my heart wants to sing.
Suddenly something catches my eye,
Believe me it's no lie.

What it appears to be is a bird,
You can trust my every word.
It's a bright blue one!
Boy is this fun!

Elizabeth Peil
Ashgrove Elementary School
Riverton, WY
Grade 4

The Hawk's Cry

The soaring hawk's cry
A beautiful hawk.
Its cry, so sad, so lonely.

Theresa Malley
Kearns-St Ann School
Salt Lake City, UT
Grade 6

Grandma

Grandma, as beautiful as the snow.
Her hair blew through the wind,
as trees do in the breeze.
I cry in the nights.
I miss her more than gold is worth.
Oh, the pain and agony.
I know I'm wrong,
but I'll be strong.
Why December 23rd,
Why so close? So soon, so near.
Was this my present for the year?
Why did she die so close to Christmas?
MERRY CHRISTMAS (yeah, right!)

Bryan Poulsen
Hurricane Elementary School
Hurricane, UT
Grade 6

Best Friends

My best friend is mad
My best friend is sad
What's this you say you're glad
Whoopee, hurray lets go play.

Mary Kihorany
Riverdale Elementary School
Denver, CO
Grade 4

Foods I Like and Dislike

I used to eat sardines,
but now I don't like seafood.
I used to drink soda,
but now I don't drink fizzy drinks.
I used to like steak,
but now I don't.
I used to hate cooked ham,
but now I love it.
I used to like ham sandwiches,
but now I like turkey.
I used to eat less candy,
but now I am addicted.
I used to like to eat,
but now I think it's a waste of time.

Megan McJames
Ecker Hill Middle School
Park City, UT
Grade 6

Horses

Horses are wonderful
You can go riding off into the orange sunset looking like a flower,
they go by your command,
with a kick in their side they'll run.
With a tug on the reins they'll stop.
I have my own horse,
Prince Decus.
My friend and I always go riding on him.
He is very gentle!

Marie Cook
Washington Terrace Elementary School
Ogden, UT
Grade 4

The Girl Without a Face

Once there was a girl. Her name was never known.
She was just a plain girl. Nobody recognized her
not her teachers, parents, or schoolmates.
She was just a face in the crowd.
At home she liked to have fun with her family.
Yet they didn't always see her.
Sometimes making her do things she simply couldn't do.
Making her do things that were other people's chores.
There were always times when she felt unhappy and insecure.
Even though she knew her parents cared for her,
she sometimes wanted to scream.
She wanted to be a free spirit.
Wherever she could go, traveling all over,
Always being kept in. Supposed to be innocent and sweet.
She wanted to shine like the sun, and beam at everyone she liked.
But she had to do as she was told, just a girl who people never knew.
She was just the girl without a face.

Riena Long
Widefield Elementary School
Colorado Springs, CO
Grade 6

Brilliant Snow

As I walked outside brilliant snow covers my eyes
I feel like jumping into the snow cause it looks so beautiful

    I go to the shack and get my sled
    I slide down the glistening hill and fall into the freezing snow

I run on the chilly snow and jump in it to make a snow angel
It looks so beautiful in the glossy snow
As I look at it, I feel like making ten more

    Then I found some ice
    I got on it to glide
    I feel like gliding more as I walk to my warm home

Alina Maslo
Hawthorne Elementary School
Missoula, MT
Grade 5

Girls

I hate girls.
They're picky and slow,
They never do chores like shoveling snow.
They can't keep secrets, especially mine,
They always tie up the telephone line.
They're tattle-tales and bullies,
They smell like cats,
And have boring stories.
They're oww!— With the exception of you!

Jake Sagaser
Marshdale Elementary School
Evergreen, CO
Grade 4

My Little Goosey

I caught you little goosey at the rodeo
I fed and watered you so that you would grow

Your baby feathers turned from yellow to gray
In just a matter of a few days

You turned out to be a fine young hen
I had to build you a great big pen

In just a few years I could see
that you were in need of some company

I looked around for other geese
So I could fulfill all your needs

I loved you so much, so you see
I decided to set you free

John Naylor
Petersen Elementary School
Sunnyside, UT
Grade 5

War and Peace

What is the difference between war and peace?
People think that you need to be more brave
to go into war.
That is not true.
Peace takes more bravery.

Peace takes bravery,
peace is to stand up for what is right.
People are too afraid to do that.

War is hatred and madness.
Peace is love and caring.
That is the difference.

Adam Sammakia
Heatherwood Elementary School
Boulder, CO
Grade 4

Mountains

See the giant pine trees almost touching the sky,
Feel the rivers' water slip through your hands,
Smell the fresh pine needles,
Taste the pure river water in your mouth,
Hear the blue birds chirp and sing their cheerful songs,
You can feel the dirt in your hands, rougher than a rock.
You can hear birds sing as if they were singing for summer.
You can see the midnight stars glare at you in the mist.

Kallie Rose Mock
Larkspur Elementary School
Larkspur, CO
Grade 4

Night

The day is done.
Night has crawled on the sky making darkness
but the full moon lights your way.
You hear the crickets sing their night song.
The wind whistles in your ears.
You walk to fields of dancing grass.
You sit and listen.
You start to dance with the grass.
You are tired.
You fall down and sleep.

Your dad goes out
to where the night has crawled on the sky
and the moon lights the way
and the crickets sing their night song
and the grass dances.
He picks you up.
He brings you to your bed.
You sleep.

Gavin Patt
Heatherwood Elementary School
Boulder, CO
Grade 4

I Am a Mountain

I am a mountain,
I'm so happy because
I can see the whole lake.
I am very tall, and some people
build their houses on me most of the
time. I'm pretty cold, because I'm so
high up. Snowflakes fall on me in winter
and trees stay on me all year. I love being a
mountain and seeing the whole lake. Sometimes
I'm sitting with my best friend the cloud
watching the sunrise.

Chelsea Lothringer
Rowe Elementary School
Las Vegas, NV
Grade 5

The Wonderful Moon

The moon is high in the sky tonight.
Large and bright.
It shines with a bluish-white glow.

Hanging in the sky all alone.
Around it is nothing,
Only black emptiness.
It is all that exists.

Its beauty is mesmerizing.
Warm and magical.
Protective.
When you see it you feel safe.

A smooth, glassy marble.
As wonderful as life itself.

Rickey Ghormley
Laredo Middle School
Aurora, CO
Grade 6

Treasures From the Sea

Sharp, shaped, spiral shell
looking like a stairwell,
slippery castle top,
sea worn and smooth,
little round univalve,
shaped like a hovercraft.
Small ridged shells,
stuck on sparkling sand.
How long have you been
here on Ohope Beach?
What were you doing before
I picked you up?
Why are you shaped like that
Treasure from the sea?

Aaron Gallagher
Montview Elementary School
Aurora, CO
Grade 5

School Lunch

Overdone hamburgers,
   spoiled Mac n' cheese;
please don't serve that,
   I'd rather eat peas.

Mushy broccoli
dipped in tartar sauce —
   it all looks so gross,
it's just as bad as moss.

Taylor Baum
Hurricane Elementary School
Hurricane, UT
Grade 6

Fluffy Pillows

Beautiful, so white
So soft and very fluffy
Up high in the sky.

Krystal Mirabelli
Kearns-St Ann School
Salt Lake City, UT
Grade 6

Cats

Cats are pretty
Cats are fun
Cats are cuddly
Every one.

Monique Egan
Petersen Elementary School
Sunnyside, UT
Grade 5

School Bike

school
fun hard
writing spelling playing
students teachers wheels pedals
riding pedaling tiring
fun fast
bike

Anthony Gilbert
Washington Terrace Elementary School
Ogden, UT
Grade 4

Leaves

As I opened up my eyes,
Something was falling from the skies.
Yellow, orange, and green and red,
I saw these colors from my bed.

As the colors swirled around,
The things were blown up and down.
I went outside to see those sights
For they weren't like birds or flying kites.

As I went to look around,
I saw those flat things on the ground.
I caught one falling from the sky,
It felt like the texture on a tie.

It smelled like garbage in a dump.
The worm on top of it made me jump.
There were many in the trees,
I guess they must be leaves.

Jarom Chung
Challenger School
Sandy, UT
Grade 6

Anger

It's welling up inside you,
Driving you insane.
Beating you to pulp,
Let no feeling be retained.

Your anger is your enemy,
It drives you to the edge.
Makes you do real stupid things,
Puts your feet upon the ledge.

Anger is a feeling,
That you can't control.
It explodes in your mind,
Like the sound from the knoll.

Daniel Blaney
Afflerbach Elementary School
Cheyenne, WY
Grade 6

A New Day

The sun's warmth
Wakes the world
Bright arms
Awaken white clouds

The rooster's call
And birds chirpin'
Start the day

The dew upon flowers
Shimmers and sparkles
Slowly dripping
Only to hit the green, green grass

I wait for the new day
So warm and bright
As the world awakens
From a silent night

Renée Mulcare
Laredo Middle School
Aurora, CO
Grade 6

Pikes Peak

Tall, red,
hiking, walking, driving
a scary drop off edge
screaming, screeching, falling,
big, humongous,
Colorado's peak

Markus Henson
Larkspur Elementary School
Larkspur, CO
Grade 4

Snow Day

As I played in the glistening snow, I built a snowman.
He had a bright smile and two twigs for two arms.
It seemed like he was missing something
I grabbed a chilly scarf
It made him beautiful

I went inside to get some hot chocolate
It unfroze me like a snowman in the summer
I grabbed a dainty shovel
The snow was getting glossy
Then I made a huge snow-covered hill out of snow
Then I went down the huge hill on my sled
I went swiftly down the hill
I went inside, I was freezing
Then I went to my toasty bed

Zach Bumke
Hawthorne Elementary School
Missoula, MT
Grade 5

My Memories of Ben Franklin School

It's almost the end of my fifth grade year
And thoughts of the past bring both a smile and a tear

I remember my first day as the nervous new kid
I was worried about everything I said or did

I had Mrs. Phillips teach me first grade
And I made new friends that I'd never trade

In second grade we had a dinosaur play
Mrs. Santisteven made work fun each and everyday

In third grade we went to Denver on a really cool bus
Mrs. Beren's morning jokes were a favorite for us

Science with Mr. Popp was the greatest, this is true
And his gift making ideas were the best I ever knew

In fifth grade there's been so much to do
Conflict manager, choir, and the school store too

Mrs. Studen's math homework keeps me busy at night
Mrs. Rotolo's class helps me to spell things right

Mrs. Bechina has me first everyday
And sometimes I wish next year I could stay

But my friends and I will meet at Heaton next year
And I'm sure we'll do fine because we learned a lot here

Kristi Vigil
Franklin Elementary School
Pueblo, CO
Grade 5

Let's Go

Let's go,
as I see my friend scamper across the grass.
Let's go, let's go.
We will play board games now!
Come on and play.
Let's read and type, and ride our bike.
Come on let's go outside Lin, and start this day
all over
Again!

Lincoln Jarman
Washington Terrace Elementary School
Ogden, UT
Grade 4

Colors

Blue drips into the ocean,
Into the night pink flows.
Gray leaves without a tear,
While white peacefully snows.

As yellow brightens smiles,
Into people tan soars.
Orange jumps into fruit to make you well,
While black makes you sick with memories of wars.

All these colors create a garden,
As mysterious as a rose.
Weaving and fluttering as they take flight,
With their leaving, the beauty grows.

Laura Munch
McClelland Center School
Pueblo, CO
Grade 5

Butterflies

Butterflies are beautiful
floating through the air
like clouds in the sky
their big wings flapping together
bump
bump
bump
and they have so many different colors like
red
or
green
they land on flowers one by one
when at last
they stop flapping their colorful wings
they close them up not to be seen.

Mandi Morfin
Washington Terrace Elementary School
Ogden, UT
Grade 4

Summer
beach
trees sand
swimming boating tanning
water fun run plate
sliding swinging tagging
bat ball
baseball

Kyle DeYoung
Washington Terrace Elementary School
Ogden, UT
Grade 4

Puppy
Puppy
Soft, Hairy
Running, Playing, Sleeping
Running through the yard
As fast as she can
Dog

Kayla Smith
Ecker Hill Middle School
Park City, UT
Grade 6

I Had a Dream That Sang to Me
I had a dream
That sang of hope
Sang of peace
Sang of trust
Sang of freedom.
It said to find
Within my heart
And my mind
My hope
My trust
My peace
And my freedom
I had a dream that sang to me

Sabrina Thornton
Roy Moore Elementary School
Silt, CO
Grade 5

The Bears
The bears are black
The bears are brown
I see the bears all around
The bears are pink
The bears are white
I really have a fright!

Alexandra Helen Henry-Brown
Peck Elementary School
Arvada, CO
Grade 4

Books
Books can be about anything,
from shoes to ships to kings.

They can be about mystical fairies
or horses with wings.

They can be about poems,
oh, yes they can.

Books can be about
dogs or cats.

I even read a book
on houses and rats.

I only named a few,
there are lots, lots more.

Tons more books for you to adore!

Books

Lauren Waldron
Bonneville Elementary School
Salt Lake City, UT
Grade 4

Riddle
Sticky and furry,
some are the slimiest thing
some have wings
some are tiny
and some are huge
they can have a bunch of legs
what are they?

Answer: bugs

Ali Tawfig
Heatherwood Elementary School
Boulder, CO
Grade 4

Riding Away
I sit on the bull
I put my rope on
I do my wrap
I nod my head
The bull turns back
The whistle blows
I jump off
Success

Miles Schuster
Cherry Valley Elementary School
Franktown, CO
Grade 4

Sleep
Once I close my eyes
I'm in a different world
Free from all my fears.

Marc Pagni
Kearns-St Ann School
Salt Lake City, UT
Grade 6

Dad
My dad goes to work,
so my mom can stay home.
He works really hard,
so he can get paid.

My dad is the best,
you have to meet him.
His name is Larin —

I love him so.

He takes care of the chickens.
He feeds the dog.
He does the garden.
He is the nicest dad ever.

When we have a hurt leg,
he rubs it until it gets better.
When we are scared at night,
he lets us sleep on his floor.

When he goes on a vacation,
he always brings us something.
He is the coolest dad ever.
I love him a lot.

Kristin Cox
Hurricane Elementary School
Hurricane, UT
Grade 6

A Million Years From Now
A million years from now,
You'll remember me.
And I'll remember you,
Wherever you may be.
No matter where we are,
Each other we will see.
I may dance upon a golden bridge,
You may sail upon the sea.
But a million years from now
Together we will be.

Clair Smith
Cortez Middle School
Cortez, CO
Grade 6

I Washed Your Clothes

I washed your favorite clothes in the toilet.
I put your shoes in too.
I even put the soap and everything in.
I know you loved those clothes.
But, when I flushed and opened the lid,
they were gone.
Oh, please, oh please forgive me.
Well, they did look dirty,
but it was funny when you went to school
in your underwear the next day.

Austin Warner
Ecker Hill Middle School
Park City, UT
Grade 6

Whispering Trees

Autumn ...when the leaves begin to fall,
The trees to me begin to call,
Of grinning pumpkins, spooky dampness and short good-byes.
It's scary out there. Quick! Cover my eyes.

As the branches scratch at winter's stare,
They tell me as they shiver bare,
Of families, snowstorms and homemade pie,
Of snowmen, lights and that bearded guy.

In spring, when the buds and bees come out,
The trees tell what it is all about,
That leaves and flowers will no more freeze.
Of pollen that brings on that sneeze, sneeze, sneeze!

In summer, with its shadow of shade,
The trees tell of bare feet and cool lemonade.
Of bee stings, ice cream and willows that weep,
And the breeze through the leaves that lulls me to sleep.

Lindy Stauffer
Willow Valley Middle School
Wellsville, UT
Grade 6

Winter Fun

When I went out to play, I saw the glossy snow.
I got out on my snowboard.
I went down a hill.
I hit a snowman and destroyed it.
I built a snow fort that was glittering in the snow.
I stuck a stick in it and it fell with a crunch.
I went to plow snow and I slipped on the frost.
It was breathtaking.
That's my winter fun.

Kyle Duboise
Hawthorne Elementary School
Missoula, MT
Grade 5

Digger

As the tears streamed down my face,
I could bear it no more.
Of my cat I could find no trace.
No longer meowing, evermore.

If only I could stroke his fur,
Just one last time.
Digger's life seemed like a blur.
He was so sublime.

Though Digger was old,
He didn't lounge about on the floor.
He was worth his weight in gold,
No much, much more.

As I stare blankly at the wall,
I remember his bright blue shimmering eyes,
And his worn-out tennis ball.
I long for comfort, to ease my cries.

Hannah Farris
Challenger School
Sandy, UT
Grade 6

Snow White Tears

On the inside I feel like a bawling dove,
who soars through my body like a hawk.
It sobs so quietly only I can hear.
It moves as graceful as a dolphin,
swimming through the sea.
It lives in my heart at night,
and by day in my brain.
It sees and hears everything
that I see and hear.
Its tears are white as clouds.
When I am weeping it goes into my throat
and chokes me so I can't breathe. Then I stop.
I wish I could have a laughing dove instead.

Kelsi Armijo
First Presbyterian Church Academy
Las Vegas, NV
Grade 6

Whining Willows

I am a willow swaying through the air.
The wind makes me do this though I fear.
It's howling against me, blowing my back,
and then I start whining in your ear.
I wish to be a human animal or even a deadly beast
but I am just a willow swaying through the air.

Wendy Qi
Eisenhower Elementary School
Boulder, CO
Grade 4

Spring!

Spring sings with....
Flowers springing from the ground,
Pools of mud rippling,
Squirrels scurrying up the trees,
Birds chirping,
That is spring,
No season is like it,
So cherish it!

Rachel Chalat
Bergen Valley Elementary
Evergreen, CO
Grade 4

The Move

Tears,
Stinging and burning my eyes.
Watching,
The truck being filled.
Waiting,
For the right time to say good-bye.
Wondering,
When I will see my friends.
Then going,
Leaving,
All that I know and have is gone.
Gone,
To start a new life,
Beyond the horizon.

Jamey Graham
Laredo Middle School
Aurora, CO
Grade 6

April Day

Raindrops fall on an April day
They fall like silver tears
They stop to see
A beautiful rainbow.

Lauren Stanford
Riverdale Elementary School
Denver, CO
Grade 4

Stars

Stars, stars in the sky
I like to watch them way up high
Some are big, some are small
I really like to watch them all
In the morning when I wake
I wish I could have said, "Bye"

Leah Contreras
St Vincent De Paul School
Salt Lake City, UT
Grade 6

Summer Vacation

Summer
Cool breeze
Running, playing, relaxing
A world without winter
Vacation

Kristen Lemmert
Christ Lutheran School
Murray, UT
Grade 5

Babies

Babies
Beautiful children
Drooling, eating, sleeping
Little creatures of nature
Humans

Alicia Brollier
Christ Lutheran School
Murray, UT
Grade 5

Autumn

Red, green, yellow, brown
All these colors swirling 'round
Cool, calm, bare trees now

Samantha Garrigues
Christ Lutheran School
Murray, UT
Grade 5

Albert

Smart
Funny
Strong willed
Trickster

Wishes to gain eyesight back
Dreams of winning the lottery
Wants to crack another joke
Who wonders why people who live in
America buy cars from other places

Who fears losing his eyesight forever
Who likes kids
Who loves all people in his family
Who likes my grandma
Who plans to spoil his kids rotten

Who's kindness and loyalty are
Going to get him to heaven.

Brandi Clay
Franklin Elementary School
Pueblo, CO
Grade 5

Football

Football is a fall sport,
That you sign up to play,
You work very hard,
Each and every day.

You have a bunch of teammates,
Sometimes even your friends,
So when it comes to game time,
The fun never ends.

You play on a grassy field,
Underneath the sun,
You start to get sweaty and hot,
When the game has just begun.

The game is set,
The ball is in play,
The quarterback throws,
Touchdown is on the way.

The game is done,
The whistles are blowing,
The fans have left,
Our smiles are showing.

Matt Meranda
St Vincent De Paul School
Salt Lake City, UT
Grade 6

Parents

Dad
Clean, nice
Walking, talking, helping
Singer, runner, reader, teacher
Loving, learning, planting
Sweet, helpful
Mom

Taylor Kersten-Wines
Jacks Valley Elementary School
Minden, NV
Grade 4

Knife

Knife
blade, handle
shining, cutting, sharpening
metal, wood, bowl, stick
feeding, lifting, shoving
curve, dent
Spoon

Andrew Pierce
Ecker Hill Middle School
Park City, UT
Grade 6

Skate Boarding

The air rushes past my face
As I speed down the sidewalk
On my fresh Rage board,
My wheels clicking in cracks of the sidewalk.
My feet are steady on the deck.
Now I am air born.

Zach Brecht
Cozy Hollow School
Rock River, WY
Grade 6

Wind

Wind
Swirling through the scary woods,
Blowing away baskets of goods,
Making sounds that chill you,
Woo woo woo woo
Wind
Blowing hair in your face,
Blowing away first base,
Woo woo woo
Wind
Blowing the pages of a book,
Blowing the stories of Captain Hook]Woo woo
Wind

Sasha Horsley
Lund Elementary School
Lund, NV
Grade 6

Rainstorm

We don't care what we're told,
We don't care if mommy will scold.

We'll splish and splash through the gutters,
Just don't tell our mothers.

Because today is a great day to play,
The sun can wait another day.

Today is a day to sing and yell,
And what the storm will bring,
Only time can tell.

Whether it will be sun or snow, sleet or hail,
We can always tell the tale
Of the rain...

Because it is not a day to muddle,
The world is our big, fun puddle!

Kate Comeford
Morningside Elementary School
Salt Lake City, UT
Grade 6

Love

Love looks like a big bright present shimmering in
    the sunlight.
Love smells like the scent of apple cake cooling in
    the fresh air.
Love sounds like robins singing a sweet tune.
Love tastes like a sweet cupcake with chocolate
    smeared all over the top.
Love feels like a baby hugging you with it's soft
    cuddly warm skin.
Love is a good warm feeling in your body.

Vanessa Hinojos
Moore Elementary School
Silt, CO
Grade 4

The Cold Snow

I was walking through the frozen snow, then I saw my sister
So I whitewashed her, but she got me back with the frozen snow

We went to glide on the snow, but all we have is slush
So I went inside because I was in a rush

We were going to sled
But no snow
So we went bowling instead
When we were bowling

It started to snow
It was cold because of the frost

That's when I wished I had fur
The snowflakes fell, they were cold

I got to shovel the driveway so my mom could get out
I want to study bobsleds

Steven Richard
Hawthorne Elementary School
Missoula, MT
Grade 5

Learning to Walk Again

I've been trying to walk for 2 months now
Many people have tried to show me how.
I was hoping to be walking by Easter,
But it looks like it's going to be later.
Everybody says to keep trying,
But sometimes after trying to walk,
I feel like crying.
It kind of feels like living as a baby,
I'll be on crutches by summer, maybe.

Jayci Robb
Ecker Hill Middle School
Park City, UT
Grade 6

My Father This, My Father That

My father this, my father that
My father tells me what to do
You must wash the dishes,
Comb your hair, drink your milk.
If only I could do such a thing to him!
I'd make him bow to me, me, Me.
Make him drink milk and no pop
No TV. Go to bed at 8 o'clock.
No later!
I deserve better, I DESERVE BETTER.
... what? What's that you say?
I have to go? Stop writing?
Go to the movies with you?
Sure Dad, you're the best!

Sofia Hernandez Crade
Summit Elementary School
Divide, CO
Grade 4

My Special Mom

I love the way you smile
I love the way you laugh
I love the way you speak
to me in such a gentle voice
but all together
all added up
For you're the special one
Jessica Lancaster
St Ignatius Elementary School
St Ignatius, MT
Grade 5

Opportunity

To opportunity, a welcoming host
You open new doors,
You help me the most,
To see the world.

To opportunity, a pathway to success
You show me new places,
You are the best,
In helping me rise.

But opportunity, if I let you slide by,
I shall be mourning,
For I can't open my eyes,
To all possibilities.

Oh, opportunity, a key in my hand,
I'll take your advice
And with your help,
I can stand.

Lily Fang
Campus Middle School
Englewood, CO
Grade 6

Two Boards Nailed Together

Two boards nailed together for all humanity,
Two boards nailed together for all the world to see.
It isn't the boards that saved us,
Nor the nails that held it tight,
But the blind man that He healed,
And who regained his sight.
It's the hands that stopped the winds and rains on that stormy day,
And the hands pierced with sorrow when He died that Friday.
Its not the stone that they rolled away, nor the tomb itself,
But the man who rose up on the third day, and who bore our sins himself.

Morgan Bird
St Anne School
Las Vegas, NV
Grade 6

At Night I Sit and Wonder

At night I sit and wonder, wonder about the things I hear.
I hear a rabbit and a mouse, and maybe even a bear.
At night I sit and wonder, wonder about the things I hear.

At night I sit and wonder, wonder about the things I hear.
I hear a ladybug and a squirrel, and sometimes I think a deer.
At night I sit and wonder, wonder about the things I hear.

At night I sit and wonder, wonder about the things I hear.
I hear a snowflake falling gently, and a raindrop like a tear.
At night I sit and wonder, wonder about the things I hear.

At night I sit and wonder, wonder about the things I hear.
I hear a leaf and a blueberry, and the pinecone at the rear.
At night I sit and wonder, wonder about the things I hear.

At night I sit and wonder, wonder about the things I hear.
I hear the stars shining brightly, and the moon that acts like a mirror.
At night I sit and wonder, wonder about the things I hear.

Brooke Shell
Farnsworth Elementary School
Salt Lake City, UT
Grade 6

Running

Your heart is beating faster and faster as you stand on the starting line,
like a cheetah chasing its prey on the open prairie.
You hear the gun bang,
like the open shrill of a wolf howling on a cold winter night.
The wind blowing at your face,
like a tornado going through the desert,
the sweat dripping down your face,
like a rainy spring day,
as you cross the finish line you know that you have won.

Wyatt Thurston
Hudson Elementary School
Hudson, WY
Grade 5

School

Going to school makes me crazy,
When I'm there I feel so lazy,
I fall asleep in school cuz it's bad,
The teacher wakes me up AHH!! She's mad,
Geez, someone woke up on the wrong side of the bed,
All day she keeps bumping her head,
Oh no, her face is turning red,
Class is dismissed is what she said,
Tomorrow, Tomorrow is what I dread.

Billy Maxey
Academy Charter School
Castle Rock, CO
Grade 6

Poetry Is

Poetry is life and lament that lingers
But poets take the credit
Poetry is pain and perseverance on paper
But poets take the credit
Poetry is love and loathing in lines
But poets take the credit
Poetry is sadness and sweetness in stanzas
But poets take the credit
Poetry is weakness and wonder in words
But poets take the credit
Poetry is honey and help to the head
But poets take the credit
Poetry is money and miracles to the mind
But poets take the credit
Poetry is the source of life
But poets take the credit

Avery Harrison
Ricks Center for Gifted Children
Denver, CO
Grade 6

Months Poem

January is the month that bites your skin.
February is the month of love.
March is windy,
April is rainy.
May is creeping with flowers.
June is wonderfully mild.
July is swimming like a fish.
August is the most exciting month.
September is the month of which my birthday is placed on.
October is the month of ghosts and goblins.
November is the fattest month of all.
December is the month that Jesus was born,
which is sadly replaced with Santa Claus.

Nichole Dowell
Thompson Falls Elementary School
Thompson Falls, MT
Grade 4

Teddy Bear

I'm sorry I burnt your teddy bear
I was curling my hair with the curling iron;
It slipped out of my hand and fell.
I'm sorry it burnt off his head.
It was a big accident.
I was going to buy you a new one,
but I liked it too much so I kept it.
I could give you my bunny, but his ears fell off.
I could sew them back on.
Well, anyway, I'm sorry I burnt
your teddy bear's head off.

Rebecca Terry
Ecker Hill Middle School
Park City, UT
Grade 6

Fire

Sometimes I wonder why fire exists,
How it is made in its shape,
What brings it to life and what it resists,
How it seems to have a cape,

How some things bring it to life, put it out,
Why sometimes it just appears,
How it can seem to have a spout,
The way it steams when you shed tears.

Sean Stieren
Parmalee Elementary School
Indian Hills, CO
Grade 4

Building a House

Building a house can be very fun,
But if you drop the frame, you'd better run.
This is what I did most of my summer,
But sweeping and cleaning was such a bummer.
I helped with the wall, the cement and the frame,
I went to Home Depot, which was very often lame.
I helped with the boards and stacking drywall.
I climbed through the attic feeling very tall.
Electric, wiring, and of course plumbing too,
Bedrooms and bathrooms, and painting that smells P.U.!
Shingles, windows, carpet, and tile,
In the hot summer the A.C. made me smile.
Finishing this house is what our family needs,
Cold not hot is for what we plead.
Glass and knicks, you'd better be careful,
But the texture on the outside is very beautiful!
Some of these things are only half of what I've done,
But building this house has been very, very fun!

Timminy Haycock
First Presbyterian Church Academy
Las Vegas, NV
Grade 6

Spring

Rejoice
For spring has come
In its delicate way

A cloudless brilliant blue sky
With robins and wrens against it

Animals come out
And peer into the world
Seeing if spring has come

Lush green grass pops out
A stream flowing in the corner
With crystal clear blue water
Running down with a faint rustle

Flowers budding
With that fragrant flower smell

A wonderful
Crisp, cool feeling
A clear clean feeling too
From way deep inside

These things
Will always remind me
Of spring.

Kelsey Chow
Laredo Middle School
Aurora, CO
Grade 6

Mountains

There's a high, high mountain
It's like a huge fountain
It's covered with snow
And you'll never stay low
If you climb up that high, high mountain

It is covered with trees
With a pond at its knees
Where kids can play hockey
It's ridged and rocky
Just look for that high, high mountain

The cliffs are all sharp
Its pond is full of carp
If you like to go fishing
Just walk and keep wishing
That you'll find that high, high mountain.

Nate Halliday
Farmington Elementary School
Farmington, UT
Grade 6

Wildlife

The hawks fly high above the sky,
The deer run free in the wilderness,
The fish swim happily in the river,
The birds sing a lovely song,
The elk bugle in the crisp fall mornings,
The cottontail hop around their holes,

How can people resist wildlife?

Amanda Hanson
Hudson Elementary School
Hudson, WY
Grade 6

Biking-Boarding

Biking
jumps crashes
riding grinding steering
wheels shocks bearings grip tape
falling jumping challenging
fast rolling
boarding

Kevin Gardiner
Washington Terrace Elementary School
Ogden, UT
Grade 4

Shadow

I am the shadow of me today
following the charades
reading my lines
a puppet played by itself

I am a pawn on the chess board today
moved by someone else's will
stationary until thrown away
a player bound by the rules

I am a frightened child today
lonely and confused
lost and alone
a tourist within myself

I am me today
a follower
a leader
a friend

I am many things
but I am always
myself

Jayme Johnson
Ecker Hill Middle School
Park City, UT
Grade 6

Smack

Your muscles twitching
Watching the dancing split ball
Smack! It's gone! Home run!

Kayleb Lassche
Kearns-St Ann School
Salt Lake City, UT
Grade 6

In the Game

When
I enter
the game
most fans
shout my name
even the wind blows
hard. I run on the
grass looking at
players with mass
that run around me in
the rain. I jump for the
ball and then there's
a call, for the ref
called foul....We
won the game
and stopped has
the rain and
what could
be better
than
that?

Brent Johnson
Heatherwood Elementary School
Boulder, CO
Grade 4

Me and Myself

I used to live in Fairfield, CT
but now I live in Utah
I used to be in 5th grade
but now I am in 6th
I used to have one teacher
but now I have 7
I used to walk to school
but now I ride the bus
I used to be 4 feet tall
but now I am 5 feet
I used to wear sweat pants
but now I wear jeans
I used to talk a lot
but now I don't

Zack Fortuna
Ecker Hill Middle School
Park City, UT
Grade 6

Fire In My Glance!

I went walking one day to the Yellowstone playground,
Suddenly, I felt my heart begin to pound.
    For far away I saw in my glance,
Flames of fire doing a dance.
    There was lots and lots of black, curling smoke,
Which really made me want to choke.
    It made me sad, I wanted to cry
To see this beautiful place burn up to the sky.
    But then to its rescue so quickly they came,
I saw firemen working within the flames.
    I saw in their faces, the hot, sweat and fear
As they fought with the fire using all of their gear.
    They worked so hard, they tamed the flames
The fire acted as if it were playing games.
    The firemen kept working, they would not stop,
Until the fire had calmed and the last tree dropped.
    It made me very happy to see the fireman drain,
All the fire that caused so much pain.
    And now I say, "Bless all the firemen who took a chance,
Of putting out the fire I saw in my glance."

Aileen Keliiliki
Mapleton Elementary School
Mapleton, UT
Grade 4

The Clumsy Butterfly

Once there was a butterfly
She flew way up high in the sky.
Bright with color
In the sky she would flutter.

But she was terribly clumsy.
She'd run into tree after tree after tree.
She then thought to herself,
"Gee, I'm so very clumsy!"

"I can't be so clumsy anymore!
Anyway my wing is tore."
"I ripped it on a tree
Oh, can't you see?"

Then one day she took a stand.
"I'm going to be the most graceful butterfly in the land!"
So she fluttered oh so clumsily
Trying to look like a beauty

Then she finally realized,
"I just want to be clumsy old me!"
So she twisted happily
Running into tree after tree after tree.

Jenni Stokes
St Vincent De Paul School
Salt Lake City, UT
Grade 6

The Daisy

From a distance,
        Its long, green stem
        reaches the clouds,

        Its leaves so shiny, so
        crisp, move silently
        in the breeze,

        And the beautiful petals
        catch the eye, such a
        glistening feel they have.

Kathryn E. Nycz
Sacred Heart of Jesus School
Boulder, CO
Grade 5

Spring

Spring sings with the soft melody of the delicate wind,
        casting its soothing song through the trees,
        With the sorrow and sadness of the rain,
        casting its spell,
The beauty of the snow, its brilliant light that shines upon all,
        The freshness of a warm spring day,
        The utter gloom of a dark cloudy day,
        That is the glory of spring.

Matt Sibley
Bergen Valley Elementary
Evergreen, CO
Grade 4

Wyoming Wind

Wyoming is blowing out her candles
        because every day she is a day older.
The wind blows her beautiful hair all around.
        It is like she is combing her hair.
When she sings, her song is very beautiful,
        or very frightening.
        When she cries,
        it rains.
When she rubs the sandman's dust out of her eyes,
        it snows.
And when the sun goes down,
        she turns her light off,
        and if the wind blows,
        she is just saying, "Good night."
In the morning, when the sun rises,
        she turns the light on.
        If the wind blows,
        she is saying,
        "Good Morning!"

Bryttani Scarborough
Crest Hill Elementary School
Casper, WY
Grade 6

So Many Things

So many things,
So many, many
Things to do.
Too many for my little feet
To take me all that way.
Too many for my little hands,
My little eyes
And ears,
But tomorrow
I will start again.
I'm afraid this may
Take years.

Desirae Ramirez
Rowe Elementary School
Las Vegas, NV
Grade 5

Marriage

C'mon hop aboard this train,
It's magical you'll see,
The clouds outside are moving fast,
With your husband/wife you will be.
You love each other very much,
You hold each other tight,
The train is going medium speed,
You will not have a fight.
You'll share your hopes,
You'll share your fears,
You'll never separate,
You'll share your love,
You'll share your secrets,
You'll always have some faith.
This marriage thing will go just fine,
You should know that that's true,
Every day you'll say things like,
"Oh darling I love you!"

Marisa Mostek
Heatherwood Elementary School
Boulder, CO
Grade 4

Spring Fling

Spring has a ring that gives
       you a fling.
A pop of plentiful pleasure.
A blast of beauty blowing you away.
Something happy and hopeful each day.
Spring has a ring that gives you a fling.
Never knowing why.
What a wonderful way of life.

Ariana Brawley
Woodman Elementary School
Lolo, MT
Grade 5

Bees to Yellow Jacket

Bees
Little bugs
Whirling, darting, buzzing
Swirling colors of black and yellow
Yellow jacket

Aaron Loomis
Christ Lutheran School
Murray, UT
Grade 5

A Day at the Beach

The sun is up high,
Giving sweltering heat.
As I dance round and round,
On my burning feet.

The lull of the ocean,
The sand in my toes.
Salt on my lips,
And on my nose.

The sky is a blaze,
In a fire of light.
A rainbow of colors,
Starting the night.

Betsy Buechler
Laredo Middle School
Aurora, CO
Grade 6

The Box

The box was always a mystery.
Just a secret no one knew.
It had a private history.
There wasn't a single clue.

As I peered into the attic
Where the big locked box lay,
I felt like a fanatic,
Wanting to open that box today!

I came so close to looking,
That lock I almost broke.
Mischief was cooking,
But my mind began to choke.

Life just wouldn't be the same,
Without that secret box.
No mystery guessing game.
So in the attic it remains in locks.

Katie Benson
Challenger School
Sandy, UT
Grade 6

The Cat

I have a cat
Who likes to play
He is fat
But also gray

He likes to run
And chase mice around
He likes to have fun
And pee on the ground

He likes to sleep
And climb up the wall
He likes to leap
And pounce on the ball

Once it pops
He runs away
And plays with mops
All night and day

Cody Strietzel
New Life Academy
Durango, CO
Grade 6

Bye!

I'm mailing myself away today,
To Augsburg or Ouray.
My parents will be so sad today,
To hear that I'm away.
They'll weep and cry and sadly say,
"She was so nice and she would play
Games with the kids like Monopoly."
Everyone will be so sad,
To hear me go away today.
But actually I changed my mind,
I think I will just stay.

Isabelle King
Eisenhower Elementary School
Boulder, CO
Grade 4

A Spring Poem

Spring is full of fun and joy;
happiness fills the beautiful air.
Everyone's faces are lit up with joy!
There are beautiful smelling flowers
blooming all around,
and as the pretty day goes by,
everyone goes outside
to see the new spring sky!

Megan Degenfelder
Crest Hill Elementary School
Casper, WY
Grade 5

The House

The parts of a house are very simple,
the windows are how the house breathes,
the kitchen is where the house learns because that's where we do our homework,
the sunroom is where the house nurtures growing plants,
the dining room is where the house feasts,
the entry room is where the house welcomes,
the bathroom is where the house stays out of because of common respect,
the closets are where the house keeps its things,
the halls and the stairs are how the things in the house get to places,
the computer room is where the house watches technology grow,
the basement is where the house is scared because it's dark and cobwebbed,
the garage is where the house mourns for people who are either leaving him or coming to him,
the yard that surrounds the house is where the house watches kids play,
the TV room is where it goes to see movies,
the bedrooms are where the house finally lies down and rests,
but the most important part are the people that live there for they are the heart.

Lindsey Patterson
McClelland Center School
Pueblo, CO
Grade 5

Wyoming

Wyoming makes me feel like a river winding slowly across the meadows.
Like a beaver in his warm lodge in the winter.
Like Old Faithful in Yellowstone bursting with hot water.
Like wildflowers exploding with color in the summer.
Like a bird flying high into the sunset of red, orange, and pink.
Like the Tetons watching over the valley as if it were their destiny.
Wyoming makes me feel like the day ending in a burst of red, yellow, blue, and gold.
Like the nighttime with stars set in a velvet sky while everyone is asleep.
That is what Wyoming makes me feel like.

Oakley Boycott
Hudson Elementary School
Hudson, WY
Grade 5

Green

Green is grass that's cool, and pokey under my feet, and makes a whispy sound in the wind.
Green is the color of eyes that sparkle and glisten in the morning sun,
    that bounce off light and seem to stand out.
Green is the tree tops going back and forth, back and forth making the air seem cleaner.
Green is lettuce crisp and crunchy to my tongue, that seems to have a party when it dances in my mouth.
Green is celery, almost like lettuce, green, and crisp, and crunchy at first.
Green is a nice fresh, crisp, Golden Delicious apple that seems to bounce, and almost like a dance,
    the juice runs down the corner of my mouth that gets your hands all sticky.
Green is a green apple-flavored jolly-rancher.
    Once you pop it in your mouth the flavor goes to work filling your mouth with a sour, zingy taste.
Green is our world. Green paints our world with beautiful, luscious, and gorgeous greens.
That's what green is.

Lindsey Jensen
Manila Elementary School
Pleasant Grove, UT
Grade 6

Animals!

The small, bright, and colorful butterfly,
The talking parrot, colorful and loud,
The bright red fox, swift, quick, sneaky and sly,
The golden lion, standing tall and proud.

The wildly striped zebra, black and white,
The wild monkey, climbing up the trees,
The alligator, with its big bad bite,
The striped, buzzing, and stinging little bees.

The flesh-hungry wolf, with its long, sharp claws,
The big, brown bear, catching fish from the stream,
The yellow tiger, licking its four paws,
The mountain lion, the color of cream.

These animals are all over the place,
And can be found all over the earth's face.

Tim Logan
New Horizons Academy
Las Vegas, NV
Grade 5

Is This Paradise?

Into the glassy stream,
where the silver bass do swim beside the pebbled banks,
among the golden fields
where the air is rich with honey-flowery smells,

Is this paradise?
Or is paradise something more?
Could it be in me,
instead of something I'm waiting for?

I've got a father and a mother
and two sisters bouncing off the walls
When I'm sad, Mom comforts me
and I come whenever she calls.
Dad takes the time to teach me
everything he knows.
(It's when you do good deeds
your kindness really shows.)

So lakes, pine trees and flowers
are what we all want a lot of
But maybe all we really want
is someone else to love.

Kimberly Beswick
Hurricane Elementary School
Hurricane, UT
Grade 6

Spring Winter

Spring
warm green
blossoming playing beginning
flowers daisies snowmobile skiing
snowing snowboarding sledding
white cold
Winter

Alexander Granillo
Washington Terrace Elementary School
Ogden, UT
Grade 4

Easter Egg

Easter
fun warm
playing having meeting
family grandparents chicks
chicken coloring eating boiling
oval white
Egg

Tyler John
Washington Terrace Elementary School
Ogden, UT
Grade 4

Index